CONTROL VALVE HANDBOOK

Second Edition
First Printing

Price $5.00

FISHER CONTROLS COMPANY
Marshalltown, Iowa

Printed in United States of America

Preface to Second Edition

The first edition of this handbook has enjoyed considerable popularity for the last dozen years. As a source of reference material for those in the control valve industry, it has been well received and has been reprinted some eight times. Naturally, during the course of those years, control valve technology has changed and hardware designs have been improved. This edition attempts to document some of those changes, while retaining the general style and usefulness of the original work.

The general scope of this book is unchanged. The subject matter deals only with commonly used automatic control valves, primarily pneumatically operated. Valve accessories, sizing procedures, leakage criteria, fluid velocity, and standard reference tables are included. The industry standards referenced are the latest available at the time of this publication, and the information is presented in a manner intended to represent general practice in the control valve industry. The emphasis on cage-style control valve trim and on rotary-shaft control valves reflects the growing role these constructions are taking in modern industry applications. Also, this edition includes much more metric conversion information than did the first and acknowledges increased industry consciousness of environmental impact with an enlarged section on control valve noise abatement.

We are indebted to the many individuals who contributed to the preparation of this book. Also, we appreciate the cooperation of the Instrument Society of America, publishers of Standard S51.1, *Process Instrumentation Terminology,* and the Crane Company, publishers of Technical Paper No. 410, *Flow of Fluids Through Valves, Fittings, and Pipe,* in permitting us to quote portions of their respective documents.

While we hope this volume is found to be of merit, we welcome suggestions and comments on future additions and improvements. As advancements are made in control valve technology and hardware, further revisions of this book will be forthcoming and will include changes suggested by users of this edition.

Marshalltown, Iowa
October, 1977

Fisher Controls Company

Table of Contents

Table of Contents (Continued)

Table of Contents (Continued)

Section 1

Actuators and Valve Bodies

The following terminology section applies to the physical and operating characteristics of standard sliding-stem control valves with diaphragm or piston actuators. Some of the terms, particularly those pertaining to actuators, are also appropriate for rotary-shaft control valves. Many of the definitions presented are in accordance with ASME Standard 112, *Diaphragm Actuated Control Valve Terminology,* although other popular terms are also included. Additional parenthetical explanation is provided for some of the more complex terms. Component part names are called out on accompanying Figures 1-1 through 1-7. Separate sections follow that define specific rotary-shaft control valve nomenclature, control valve functions and characteristics terminology, and miscellaneous control terminology.

Control Valve Nomenclature

Actuator Spring: A spring, enclosed in the yoke, to move the actuator stem in a direction opposite to that created by diaphragm pressure.

Actuator Stem: A rod-like extension of the diaphragm plate or piston to permit convenient connection to the valve plug stem.

Actuator Stem Extension: An extension of the piston actuator stem to provide a means of transmitting piston motion to the valve positioner. *(See Figure 1-7.)*

Angle Valve: A valve construction having inlet and outlet line connections on different planes, usually perpendicular to each other. *(See also Globe Valve.)*

Bellows Seal Bonnet: A bonnet which uses a bellows for sealing against leakage around the valve plug stem.

Bonnet: The major part of the bonnet assembly, excluding the sealing means. *(This term is often used in referring to the bonnet and its included packing parts. More properly, this group of component parts should be called the Bonnet Assembly.)*

Bonnet Assembly (Commonly *Bonnet,* more properly *Bonnet Assembly*): An assembly including the part through which a valve plug stem moves and a means for sealing against leakage along the stem. It usually provides a means for mounting the actuator.

Bottom Flange: A part which closes a valve body opening opposite the bonnet assembly. In a three-way valve, it may provide an additional flow con-

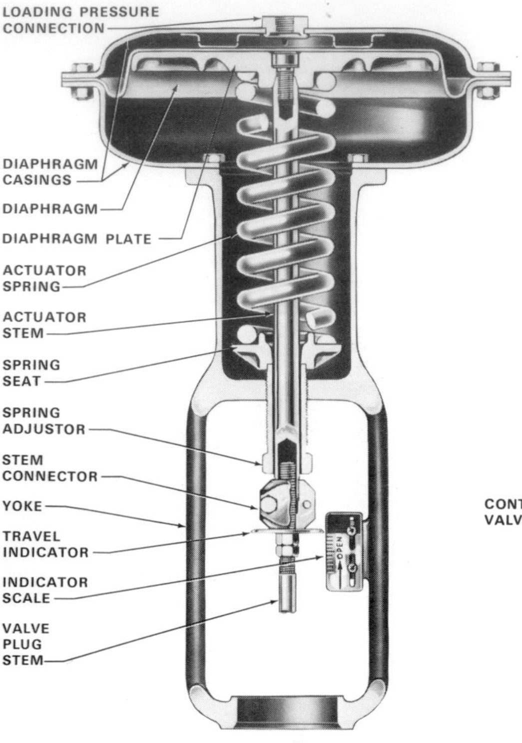

DIRECT-ACTING ACTUATOR

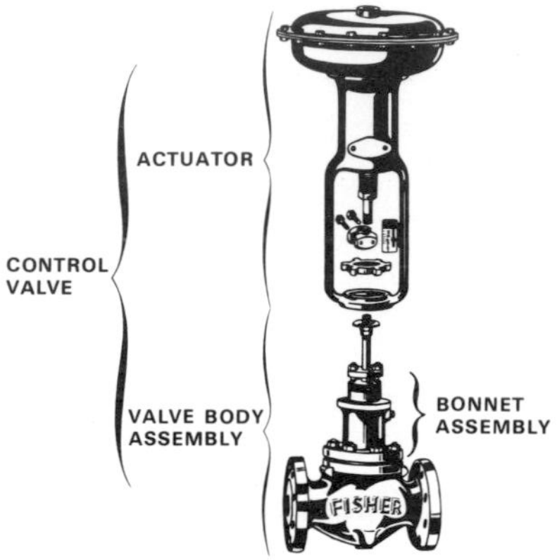

RELATIONSHIP OF MAJOR COMPONENTS

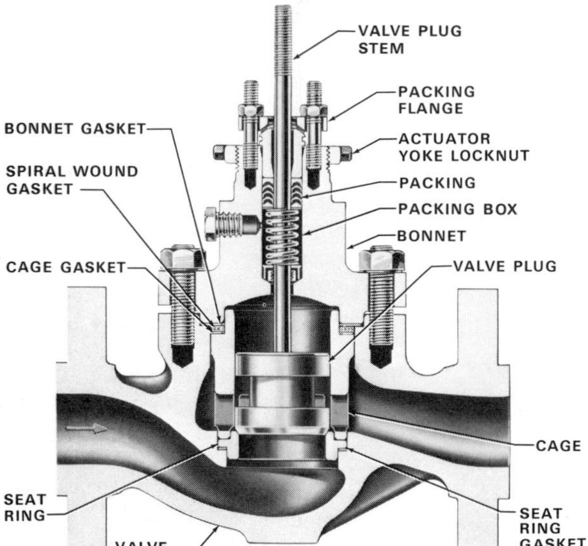

PUSH-DOWN-TO-CLOSE VALVE BODY ASSEMBLY

Figure 1-1. Major Components of Typical Control Valve Assembly

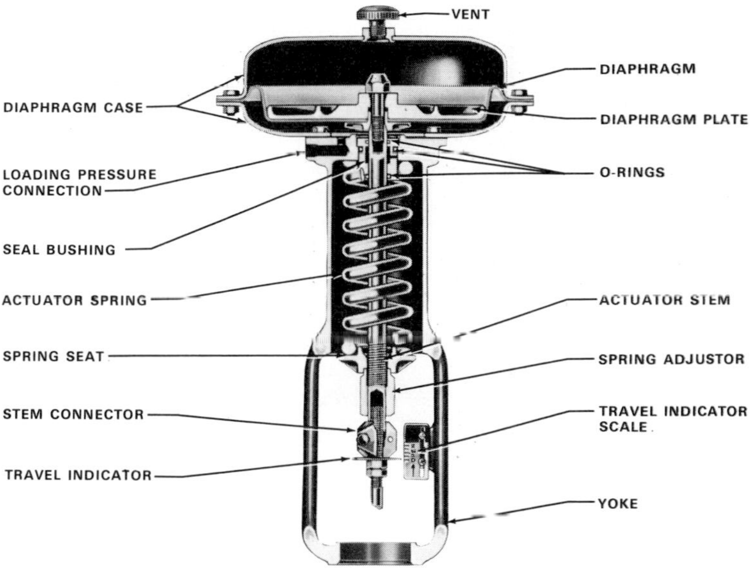

Figure 1-2. Typical Reverse-Acting Diaphragm Actuator

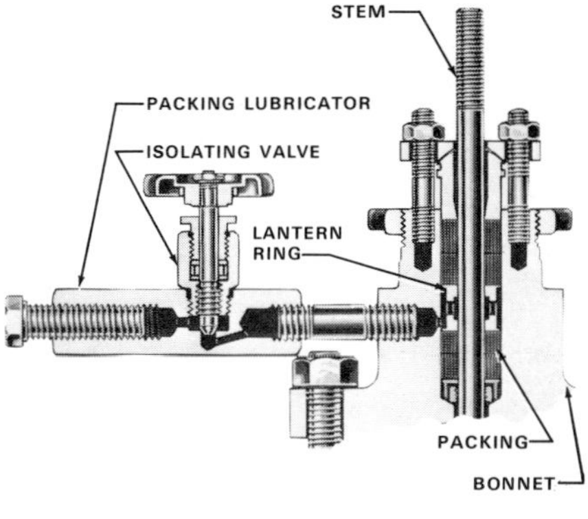

Figure 1-3. Packing Lubricator and Isolating Valve

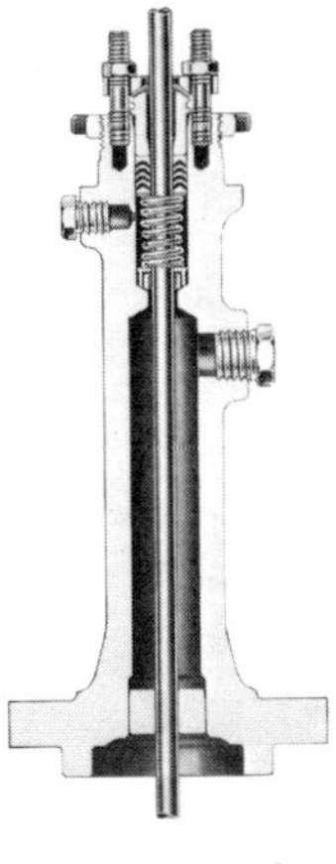

Figure 1-4. Extension Bonnet

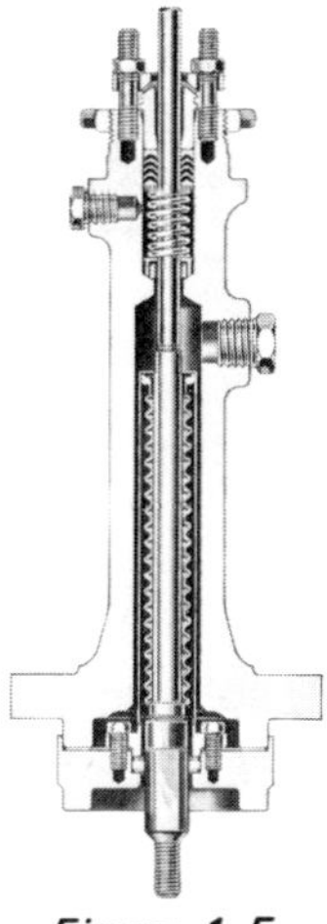

Figure 1-5. Bellows Seal Bonnet

nection. (See typical bottom flange in Figure 1-23.)

Cage: A hollow cylindrical trim element that is a guide to align the movement of a valve plug with a seat ring and/or retains the seat ring in the valve body. *(The walls of the cage contain openings which usually determine the flow characteristic of the control valve. Various cage styles are shown in Figure 1-37.)*

Cylinder: The chamber of a piston actuator in which the piston moves. *(See Figure 1-7.)*

Cylinder Closure Seal: The sealing element at the connection of the piston actuator cylinder to the yoke.

Diaphragm: A flexible pressure responsive element which transmits force to the diaphragm plate and actuator stem.

Diaphragm Actuator: A fluid pressure operated spring opposed or fluid pressure opposed diaphragm assembly for

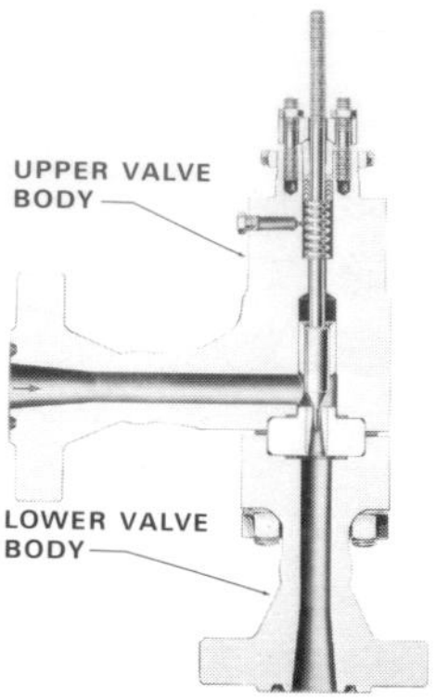

Figure 1-6. Typical Split Valve Body

positioning the actuator stem in relation to the operating fluid pressure or pressures.

Diaphragm Case: A housing, consisting of top and bottom sections, used for supporting a diaphragm and establishing one or two pressure chambers.

Diaphragm Plate: A plate concentric with the diaphragm for transmitting force to the actuator stem.

Direct Actuator: A diaphragm actuator in which the actuator stem extends with increasing diaphragm pressure.

Extension Bonnet: A bonnet with an extension between the packing box and bonnet flange for hot or cold service.

Globe Valve: A valve construction style with a linear motion flow controlling member with one or more ports, normally distinguished by a globular-shaped cavity around the port region. *(Globe valves can be further classified as: Two-way single-ported, Figure 1-16; Two-way double-ported, Figure 1-24; Angle-style, Figure 1-17; Three-way, Figure 1-26; Split-style, Figure 1-6; Unbalanced cage-guided, Figure 1-1; and Balanced cage-guided, Figure 1-21.)*

Guide Bushing: A bushing in a bonnet, bottom flange, or body to align the movement of a valve plug with a seat ring.

Isolating Valve: A hand-operated valve between the packing lubricator and the packing box to shut off the fluid pressure from the lubricator.

Lower Valve Body: A half housing for internal valve parts having one flow connection. *(The seat ring is normally clamped between the upper valve body and the lower valve body in split valve constructions such as that shown in Figure 1-6.)*

Packing Box (Assembly): The part of the bonnet assembly used to seal against leakage around the valve plug stem. Included in the complete packing box assembly are various combinations of some or all of the following component parts: Packing, Packing Follower, Packing Nut, Lantern Ring, Packing Spring, Packing Flange, Packing Flange Studs or Bolts, Packing Flange Nuts, Packing Ring, Packing Wiper Ring, Felt Wiper Ring. *(Individual packing parts are shown in Figure 1-34.)*

Packing Lubricator: An optional part of the bonnet assembly used to inject lubricant into the packing box.

Piston: A movable pressure responsive element which transmits force to the piston actuator stem. *(See Figure 1-7.)*

Piston Actuator: A fluid pressure operated piston and cylinder assembly for positioning the actuator stem in relation to the operating fluid pressure. *(Most piston actuators, such as that shown in Figure 1-7, are double-acting so that full power can be developed in either direction.)*

Port: A fixed opening, normally the inside diameter of a seat ring, through which fluid passes.

Retaining Ring: A split ring that is used to retain a separable flange on a valve body.

Reverse Actuator: A diaphragm actuator in which the actuator stem

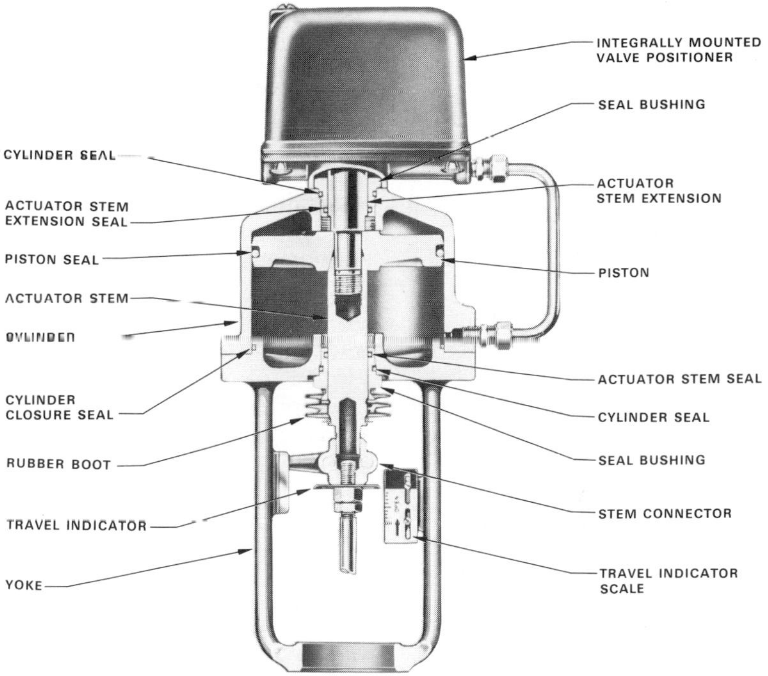

Figure 1-7. Typical Double-Acting Piston Actuator

retracts with increasing diaphragm pressure. *(Reverse actuators have a seal bushing installed in the upper end of the yoke to prevent leakage of the diaphragm pressure along the actuator stem. The seal bushing is shown in Figure 1-2.)*

Rubber Boot: A protective device to prevent entrance of damaging foreign material into the piston actuator.

Seal Bushing: Top and bottom bushings that provide a means of sealing the piston actuator cylinder against leakage. *(Synthetic rubber O-rings are used in the bushings to seal the cylinder, the actuator stem, and the actuator stem extension as shown in Figure 1-7.)*

Seat: That portion of the seat ring or valve body which a valve plug contacts for closure.

Seat Ring: A separate piece inserted in a valve body to form a valve body port.

Separable Flange: A flange which fits over a valve body flow connection. It is generally held in place by means of a retaining ring.

Spring Adjustor: A fitting, usually threaded on the actuator stem or into the yoke, to adjust the spring compression.

Spring Seat: A plate to hold the spring in position and also to provide a flat surface for the spring adjustor to contact.

Stem Connector: A clamp, in two pieces, to connect the actuator stem to the valve plug stem.

Travel Indicator: A pointer, attached near the stem connector, to indicate the travel of the valve plug.

Travel Indicator Scale: A graduated scale attached to the yoke for indication of valve travel.

Trim: The internal parts of a valve which are in flowing contact with the controlled fluid. *(In a globe valve body, trim would typically include valve plug, seat ring, cage, stem, and stem pin.)*

Trim, Soft-seated: Globe valve trim with an elastomer, plastic, or other readily deformable material used as an insert, either in the valve plug or seat ring, to provide very tight shutoff with minimal actuator force.

Upper Valve Body: A half housing for internal valve parts and having one flow connection. *(It usually includes a means for sealing against leakage along the stem and provides a means for mounting the actuator on the split valve body. See Figure 1-6.)*

Valve Body: A housing for internal parts having inlet and outlet flow connections. Among the most common valve body constructions are: a) Single-ported valve bodies having one port and one valve plug, b) Double-ported valve bodies having two ports and one valve plug, c) Two-way valve bodies having two flow connections, one inlet and one outlet, d) Three-way valve bodies having three flow connections, two of which may be inlets with one outlet (for converging or mixing flows), or one inlet and two outlets (for diverging or diverting flows). *(The term* Valve Body, *or even just* Body, *frequently is used in referring to the valve body together with its bonnet assembly and included trim parts. More properly, this group of components should be called the* Valve Body Assembly.*)*

Valve Body Assembly (Commonly *Valve Body* or *Body*, more properly *Valve Body Assembly*): An assembly of a body, bonnet assembly, bottom flange (if used), and trim elements. The trim includes the valve plug which opens, closes, or partially obstructs one or more ports.

Valve Plug: A movable part which provides a variable restriction in a port.

Valve Plug Guide: That portion of a valve plug which aligns its movement in either a seat ring, bonnet, bottom flange, or any two of these.

Valve Plug Stem: A rod extending through the bonnet assembly to permit positioning the valve plug.

Yoke: A structure by which the diaphragm case or cylinder assembly is supported rigidly on the bonnet assembly.

Rotary-Shaft Control Valve Nomenclature

The definitions that follow apply specifically to rotary-shaft control valves. Component part names or installation locations are shown in Figure 1-8.

Actuator Lever: Arm attached to rotary valve shaft to convert linear actuator stem motion to rotary force to position disc or ball of rotary-shaft valve. *(The lever normally is positively connected to the rotary shaft by close tolerance splines or other means to minimize play and lost motion.)*

Ball, Full: The flow-controlling member of rotary-shaft control valves utilizing a complete sphere with a flow passage through it. *(Many varieties use trunnion-mounted, single-piece ball and shaft to reduce torque requirements and lost motion.)(Not illustrated.)*

Ball, V-notch: The flow-controlling member for the most popular styles of throttling ball valves. The V-notch ball includes a polished or plated partial-sphere surface that rotates against the seal ring throughout the travel range. The V-shaped notch in the ball permits wide rangeability and produces an equal percentage flow characteristic.

Note:

The balls mentioned above, and the discs which follow, perform a function comparable to the valve

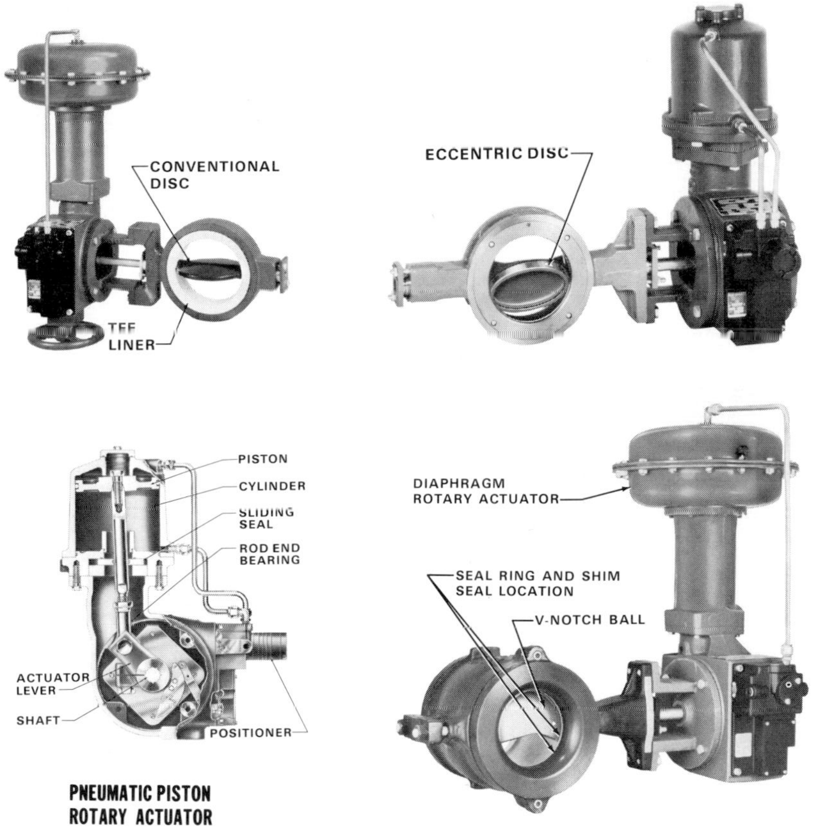

Figure 1-8. Typical Rotary-Shaft Control Valve Constructions

plug in a globe-style control valve. That is, as they rotate they vary the size and shape of the flowstream by opening more or less of the seal area to the flowing fluid.

Disc, Conventional: The flow-controlling member used in the most common varieties of butterfly rotary valves. High dynamic torques normally limit conventional discs to 60 degrees maximum rotating in throttling service.

Disc, Dynamically Designed: A butterfly valve disc *(such as Fisher's patented* **Fishtail®** *disc)* contoured to reduce dynamic torque at large increments of rotation, thereby making it suitable for throttling service with up to 90 degrees of disc rotation.

Disc, Eccentric: Common name for valve design in which the positioning of the valve shaft/disc connections causes the disc to take a slightly eccentric path on opening. *(This allows the disc to be swung out of contact with the seal as soon as it is opened, thereby reducing friction and wear.)*

Flangeless Body: Body style common to rotary-shaft control valves. Flangeless bodies are held between ANSI-class flanges by long through-bolts. *(Sometimes also called wafer-style valve bodies.)*

Flow Ring: Heavy-duty ring used in place of ball seal ring for V-notch rotary valves in severe service applications where some leakage can be tolerated.

Reverse Flow: Flow of fluid in the opposite direction from that normally considered the standard direction. *(Some rotary-shaft control valves, such as conventional-disc butterfly valves, are capable of handling flow equally well in either direction. Other rotary designs may require modification of actuator linkage to handle reverse flow. Capacity and allowable working pressures are often lowered to maintain allowable leakage limits with flow in the reverse direction.)*

Rod End Bearing: The connection often used between actuator stem and actuator lever to facilitate conversion of linear actuator thrust to rotary force with minimum of lost motion. *(Use of a standard reciprocating actuator on a rotary-shaft valve body commonly requires linkage with two rod end bearings; however, selection of an actuator specifically designed for rotary-shaft valve service requires only one such bearing and thereby reduces lost motion.)*

Rotary-Shaft Control Valve: A valve style in which the flow closure member (full ball, partial ball, or disc) is rotated in the flowstream to modify the amount of fluid passing through the valve. *(Typical rotary-shaft control valves are shown in Figure 1-8.)*

Seal Ring: The portion of a rotary-shaft control valve assembly corresponding to the seat ring of a globe valve. Positioning of the disc or ball relative to the seal ring determines the flow area and capacity of the unit at that particular increment of rotational travel. As indicated above, some seal ring designs permit bi-directional flow.

Shaft: The portion of a rotary-shaft control valve assembly corresponding to the valve stem of a globe valve. Rotation of the shaft positions the disc or ball in the flowstream and thereby controls the amount of fluid which can pass through the valve.

Shim Seals: Thin, flat, circular metal gaskets, usually 0.005-inch (0.125 mm) thick, used in varying numbers to adjust seal deflection in V-notch ball rotary control valves. *(Adding more shim seals reduces the amount of seal deflection; reducing the number of shim seals used increases the amount of seal deflection obtained.)*

Sliding Seal: The lower cylinder seal in a pneumatic piston-style actuator designed for rotary valve service. *(This seal permits the actuator stem to move both vertically and laterally without leakage of lower cylinder pressure.)*

Standard Flow: For those rotary-shaft control valves having a separate seal ring or flow ring, the flow direction in which fluid enters the valve body through the pipeline adjacent to the seal ring and exits from the side opposite the seal ring. *(Sometimes called* Forward Flow. *See also* Reverse Flow.)

Trunnion Mounting: A style of mounting the disc or ball on the valve shaft or stub shaft with two bushings diametrically opposed.

Wafer-style Valve Body: A flangeless type of butterfly or gate, short face-to-face, valve body. Also called a flangeless valve body; it is clamped between pipeline flanges.

Zero Deflection: The point at which the addition of one 0.005-inch (0.125 mm) thick shim seal causes contact between the V-notch ball and the ball seal ring to be broken. *(This is the point from which proper ball seal ring deflection is established. All parts must be held tightly together to properly determine the point of zero deflection.)*

Control Valve Functions and Characteristics Terminology

Capacity: Rate of flow through a valve under stated conditions.

Dead Band: The range through which an input can be varied without initiating observable response. *(In a diaphragm-actuated control valve, dead band is the amount the diaphragm pressure can be changed without initiating valve stem movement. It is usually expressed as a percent of diaphragm pressure span.)*

Diaphragm Pressure Span: Difference between the high and low values of the diaphragm pressure range. This may be stated as an inherent or installed characteristic.

Double-Acting Actuator: An actuator including a switching mechanism to permit powered operation in either direction, extending or retracting the actuator stem as dictated by the controller. *See Piston Actuator.*

Dynamic Unbalance: The net force produced on the valve plug in any stated open position by the fluid pressure acting upon it.

Effective Area: In a diaphragm actuator, the effective area is that part of the diaphragm area which is effective in producing a stem force. *(The effective area of a diaphragm may change as it is stroked, usually being a maximum at the start and a minimum at the end of the travel range. Molded diaphragms have less change in effective area than flat sheet diaphragms, and are recommended.)*

Equal Percentage Flow Characteristic: An inherent flow characteristic which for equal increments of rated travel, will ideally give equal percentage changes of the existing flow.

Fail-Closed: A condition wherein the valve port remains closed should the actuating power fail.

Fail-Open: A condition wherein the valve port remains open should the actuating power fail.

Fail-Safe: A characteristic of a particular type of actuator, which upon loss of power supply, will cause the valve plug, ball, or disc to fully close, fully open, or remain in fixed position. *(Fail-safe action may involve the use of auxiliary controls connected to the actuator.)*

Flow Characteristic: Relationship between flow through the valve and percent rated travel as the latter is varied from 0 to 100 percent. This is a special term. It should always be designated as either inherent flow characteristic or installed flow characteristic.

High-Recovery Valve: A valve design that dissipates relatively little flow-stream energy due to streamlined internal contours and minimal flow turbulence. Therefore, pressure downstream of the valve vena contracta recovers to a high percentage of its inlet value. *(Straight-through flow valves, such as rotary-shaft ball valves, are typically high-recovery valves.)*

Inherent Diaphragm Pressure Range: The high and low values of pressure applied to the diaphragm to produce rated valve plug travel with atmospheric pressure in the valve body. *(This range is often referred to as a "bench set" range since it will be the range over which the valve will stroke when it is set on the work bench.)*

Inherent Flow Characteristic: Flow characteristic when constant pressure drop is maintained across the valve.

Inherent Rangeability: Ratio of maximum to minimum flow within which the deviation from the specified inherent flow characteristic does not exceed some stated limit. *(A control valve that still does a good job of controlling when flow increases to 100 times the minimum controllable flow has a rangeability of 100 to 1. Rangeability might also be expressed as the ratio of the maximum to minimum controllable flow coefficients.)*

Installed Diaphragm Pressure Range: The high and low values of pressure applied to the diaphragm to produce rated travel with stated conditions in the valve body. *(It is because of the forces acting on the valve plug that the inherent diaphragm pressure range* *can differ from the installed diaphragm pressure range.)*

Installed Flow Characteristic: Flow characteristic when pressure drop across the valve varies as dictated by flow and related conditions in the system in which the valve is installed.

Leakage: Quantity of fluid passing through an assembled valve when the valve is in the closed position under stated closure forces, with pressure differential and pressure as specified. *(ANSI leakage classifications are outlined on page 50 of this book.)*

Linear Flow Characteristic: An inherent flow characteristic which can be represented ideally by a straight line on a rectangular plot of flow versus percent rated travel. *(Equal increments of travel yield equal increments of flow at a constant pressure drop.)*

Low-Recovery Valve: A valve design that dissipates a considerable amount of flowstream energy due to turbulence created by the contours of the flowpath. Consequently, pressure downstream of the valve vena contracta recovers to a lesser percentage of its inlet value than is the case with a valve having a more streamlined flowpath. *(Although individual designs vary, conventional globe-style valves generally have low pressure recovery capability.)*

Normally Closed Control Valve: One which closes when the diaphragm pressure is reduced to atmospheric.

Normally Open Control Valve: One which opens when the diaphragm pressure is reduced to atmospheric.

Push-Down-to-Close Construction: A globe-style valve construction in which the valve plug is located between the actuator and the seat ring, such that extension of the actuator stem moves the valve plug toward the seat ring, finally closing the valve. *(Also called* Direct Acting. *See Figure 1-1.) (The term may also be applied to rotary-shaft valve constructions where linear extension of the actuator stem moves the ball or disc toward the closed position.)*

Push-Down-to-Open Construction: A globe-style valve construction in which the seat ring is located between the actuator and the valve plug, such that extension of the actuator stem moves the valve plug away from the seat ring, opening the valve. *(Also called* Reverse Acting. *See Figure 1-23.) (The term may also be applied to rotary-shaft valve constructions where linear extension of the actuator stem moves the ball or disc toward the open position.)*

Quick Opening Flow Characteristic: An inherent flow characteristic in which there is maximum flow with minimum travel.

Rated C_v: The value of C_v at the rated full-open position.

Rated Travel: Linear movement of the valve plug from the closed position to the rated full-open position. *(The rated full-open position is the maximum opening recommended by the manufacturer.)*

Seat Load: The contact force between the seat and the valve plug. *(In practice, the selection of an actuator for a given control valve will be based on how much force is required to overcome static, stem, and dynamic unbalance with an allowance made for seat load.)*

Spring Rate: Force change per unit change in length. *(In diaphragm control valves, the spring rate is usually stated in pounds force per inch compression.)*

Static Unbalance: The net force produced on the valve plug in its closed position by the fluid pressure acting upon it.

Stem Unbalance: The net force produced on the valve plug stem in any position by the fluid pressure acting upon it.

Valve Flow Coefficient (C_v): The number of U.S. gallons per minute of 60°F water that will flow through a valve with a one pound per square inch pressure drop.

Vena Contracta: The location where cross-sectional area of the flowstream is at its minimum size, where fluid velocity is at its highest level, and fluid pressure is at its lowest level. *(The vena contracta normally occurs just downstream of the actual physical restriction in a control valve.)*

Miscellaneous Control Terminology

The following terms and definitions are frequently encountered by people associated with control valves and control valve accessories. Some of the terms (indicated with an asterisk) are quoted from the Instrument Society of Amercia standard, *Process Instrumentation Terminology,* ISA 51.1-1976. Others included are also popularly used throughout the control valve industry. Again, parenthetical explanatory notes are included to help in understanding some of the terms.

Actuator Stem Force: The net force from an actuator that is available for actual positioning of the valve plug.

ANSI: Abbreviation for *American National Standards Institute*.

API: Abbreviation for *American Petroleum Institute*.

ASME: Abbreviation for *American Society of Mechanical Engineers*.

ASTM: Abbreviation for *American Society for Testing and Materials*.

Automatic Control System*: A control system which operates without human intervention.

Bode Diagram*: A plot of log amplitude ratio and phase angle values on a log frequency base for a transfer function. *(It is the most common form of graphically presenting frequency response data. See Figure 1-9.)*

Calibration Curve*: A graphical representation of the calibration report. *(Steady state output of a device plotted as a function of its steady state input. The curve is usually shown as percent output span versus percent input span. See Figure 1-9.)*

*Reprinted with permission of the copyright holder: © Instrument Society of America, Standard S51.1, 1976.

Calibration Cycle*: The application of known values of the measured variable and the recording of corresponding values of output readings, over the range of the instrument, in ascending and descending directions. *(A calibration curve obtained by varying the input of a device in both increasing and decreasing directions. It is usually shown as percent output span versus percent input span and provides a measurement of hysteresis. See Figure 1-9.)*

Clearance Flow: That flow below the minimum controllable flow with the valve plug not seated.

Controller*: A device which operates automatically to regulate a controlled variable.

Control Valve*: A final controlling element, through which a fluid passes, which adjusts the size of flow passage as directed by a signal from a controller to modify the rate of flow of the fluid.

Enthalpy: A thermodynamic quantity that is the sum of the internal energy of a body and the product of its volume multiplied by the pressure: $H = U + pV$. *(Also called heat content.)*

Entropy: The theoretical measure of energy which cannot be transformed into mechanical work in a thermodynamic system.

Feedback Signal*: The return signal which results from a measurement of the directly controlled variable. *(For a control valve with a positioner, the return signal is usually a mechanical indication of valve plug stem position which is fed back into the positioner.)*

Frequency Response Characteristic*: The frequency-dependent relation, in both amplitude and phase, between steady-state sinusoidal inputs and the resulting fundamental sinusoidal outputs. *(Output amplitude and phase shift are observed as functions of the input test frequency and used to describe the dynamic behavior of the control device.)*

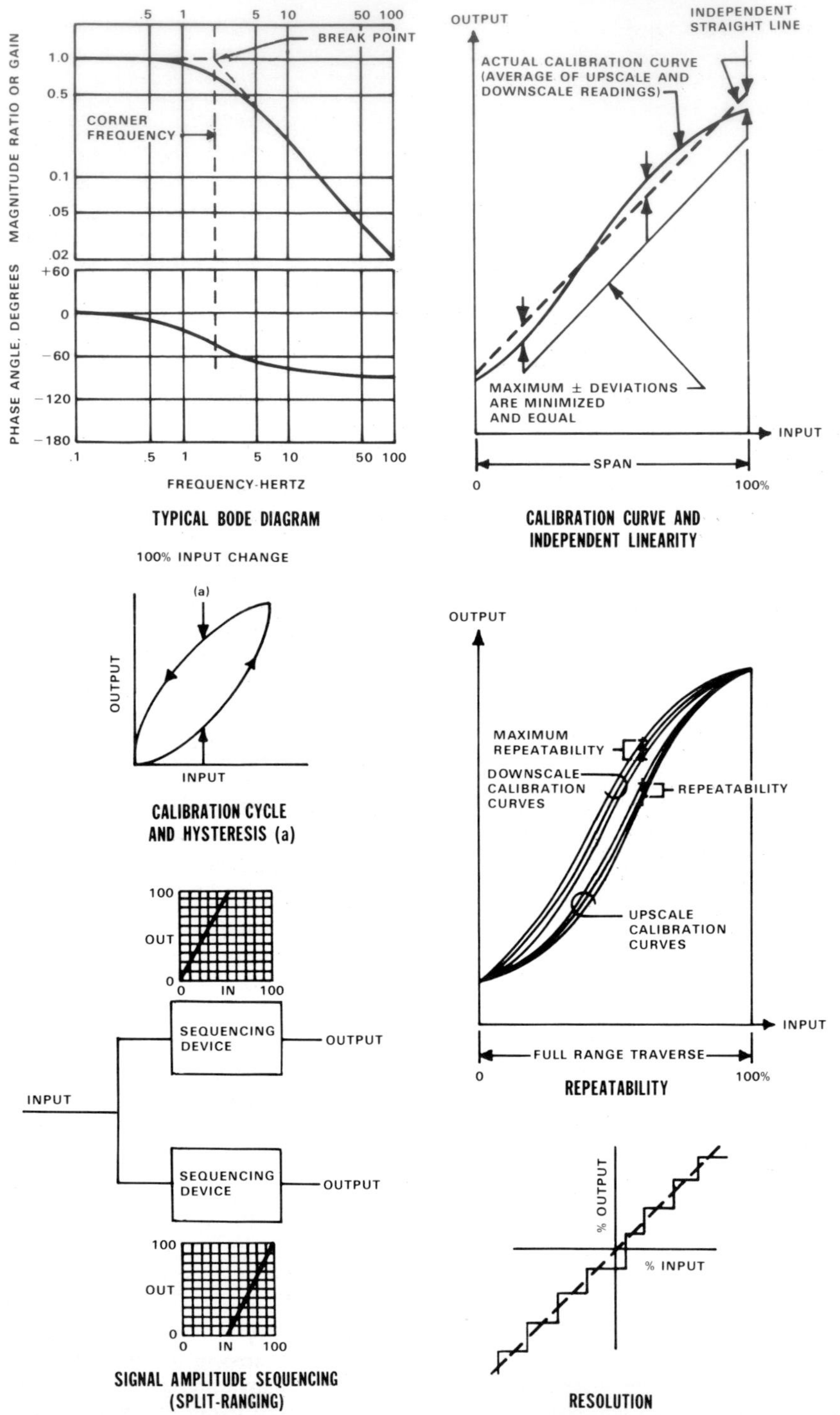

Figure 1-9. Graphic Representation of Various Control Terms

Gain, Closed Loop*: The gain of a closed loop system, expressed as the ratio of the output change to the input change at a specified frequency.

Gain, Dynamic*: The magnitude ratio of the steady-state amplitude of the output signal from an element or system to the amplitude of the input signal to that element or system, for a sinusoidal signal.

Gain, Open Loop: The gain of the loop elements measured by opening the loop. *(The product of all the individual gains in the forward and feedback paths.)*

Gain, Static*: Of gain of an element, or loop gain of a system, the value approached as a limit as frequency approaches zero. *(The ratio of a change in output to a change in input.)*

Hardness: Metallic material hardness is commonly expressed by either a Brinell number or a Rockwell number. *(In either case, the higher the number, the harder the material. For example, a material with a Rockwell "C" hardness of 60 is file hard while a hardness of 20 is fairly soft. Elastomer hardness is determined by a Durometer test.)*

Hunting*: An undesirable oscillation of appreciable magnitude, prolonged after external stimuli disappear. *(Sometimes called* cycling, *hunting is evidence of operation at or near the stability limit. In control valve applications, hunting would appear as an oscillation in the loading pressure to the actuator caused by instability in the control system or the valve positioner.)*

Hysteresis*: That property of an element evidenced by the dependence of the value of the output, for a given excursion of the input, upon the history of prior excursions and the direction of the current traverse. *(Hysteretic error is usually determined by subtracting the value of dead band from the maximum measured separation between upscale going and downscale going indications of the measured variable. Some reversal of output may be expected for any small reversal of input, which distinguishes hysteresis from dead band. See Figure 1-9.)*

ISA: Abbreviation for *Instrument Society of America*.

Independent Linearity*: The maximum deviation of the calibration curve (average of upscale and downscale readings) from a straight line so positioned as to minimize the maximum deviation. *(In control valve operation with a valve positioner, linearity generally means the closeness with which the valve stem position agrees with the instrument pressure input to the positioner. See Figure 1-9.)*

Instrument Pressure: The output pressure from an automatic controller that is used to operate a control valve.

Loading Pressure: The pressure employed to position a pneumatic actuator. *(This is the pressure that actually works on the actuator diaphragm or piston and it may be the "Instrument Pressure" if a valve positioner is not used.)*

NACE: Abbreviation for *National Association of Corrosion Engineers.* (U.S.A.)

OSHA: Abbreviation for *Occupational Safety and Health Act.* (U.S.A.)

Operating Medium: This is the fluid, generally air or gas, used to supply the power for operation of a valve positioner or automatic controller.

Operative Limits*: The range of operating conditions to which a device may be subjected without permanent impairment of operating characteristics.

Range: The region between the limits within which a quantity is measured, received, or transmitted, expressed by stating the lower and upper range values. *(For example: 3 to 15 psi; −40 to +212°F; −40 to +100°C.)*

Repeatability*: The closeness of agreement among a number of consecutive measurements of the output for the same value of the input under the same operating conditions, ap-

* Reprinted with permission of the copyright holder: © Instrument Society of America, Standard S51.1, 1976.

proaching from the same direction, for full range traverses. *(It is usually measured as a non-repeatability and expressed as repeatability in percent of span. It does not include hyesteresis. See Figure 1-9.)*

Resolution* : The least interval between two adjacent discrete details which can be distinguished one from the other. *(Output resolution is the minimum possible output change which a device can produce. Input resolution is the corresponding change required in the input. Resolution is preferably expressed as a percent of span. See Figure 1-9.)*

Sensitivity* : The ratio of the change in output magnitude to the change of the input which causes it after the steady-state has been reached.

Set Point* : An input variable which sets the desired value of the controlled variable. *(Set point should be expressed in the same terms as the controlled variable.)*

Signal* : A physical variable, one or more parameters of which carry information about another variable (which the signal represents).

Signal Amplitude Sequencing (Split Ranging)* : Action in which two or more signals are generated or two or more final controlling elements are actuated by an input signal, each one responding consecutively, with or without overlap, to the magnitude of that input signal. See Figure 1-9.

Span* : The algebraic difference between the upper and lower range-values. *(For example: Range = 0 to 150°F, Span = 150°F; Range = 3 to 15 psig, Span = 12 psig.)*

Speed of Response (Stroking Speed): In control valve operation, this term describes the rate of travel of the actuator.

Supply Pressure* : The pressure at the supply port of a device. *(Common values of control valve supply pressure are 20 psig for a 3 to 15 psig range and 35 psig for a 6 to 30 psig range.)*

Valve Positioner: A control valve accessory which transmits a loading pressure to an actuator to position a valve plug stem exactly as dictated by the instrument pressure signal from an automatic controller.

Zero Error* : Error of a device operating under specified conditions of use, when the input is at the lower range value. *(It is usually expressed as percent of ideal span.)*

Control Valve Actuators

Pneumatically operated control valve actuators are the most popular type in use, but electric, hydraulic, and manual actuators are also widely used. The spring-and-diaphragm pneumatic actuator is most commonly specified, due to its dependability and its simplicity of design. Pneumatically operated piston actuators provide integral positioner capability and high stem force output for demanding service conditions. Adaptations of both spring-and-diaphragm and pneumatic piston actuators are available for direct installation on rotary-shaft control valves.

Electric and electro-hydraulic actuators are more complex and more expensive than pneumatic actuators. They offer advantages where no air supply source is available, where low ambient temperatures could freeze condensed water in pneumatic supply lines, or where unusually large stem forces are needed. A summary follows, discussing the design and characteristics of the popular actuator styles.

Diaphragm Actuators

- Pneumatically operated, using low-pressure air supply from controller, positioner, or other source.

- Various styles include: Direct-acting *(increasing air pressure pushes down diaphragm and extends actuator stem)*; Reverse-acting *(increasing air pressure pushes up diaphragm and retracts actuator stem)*; Reversible *(some small-sized actuators can be assembled for either direct or reverse action)*; Direct-acting unit for rotary valves *(increasing air pressure pushes*

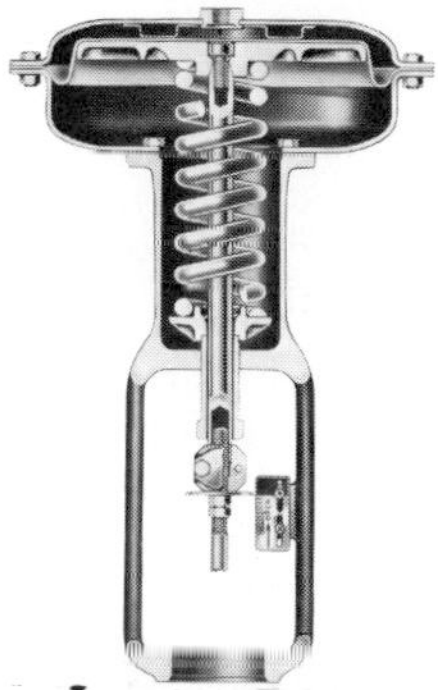

FOR SLIDING-STEM VALVES

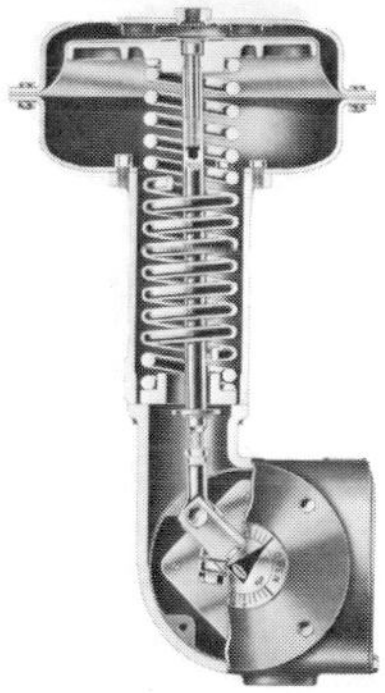

FOR ROTARY-SHAFT VALVES

Figure 1-10. Direct-Acting Diaphragm Actuators
(Actuator stem moves upward with loss of operating air supply pressure. Not reversible.)

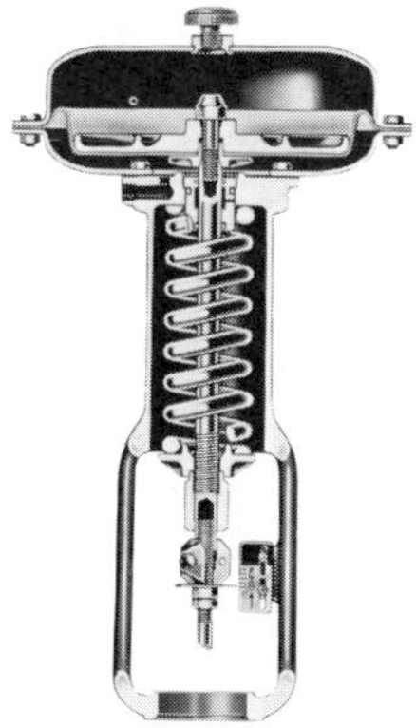

Figure 1-11. Reverse-Acting Diaphragm Actuator
(Actuator stem moves downward with loss of operating air supply pressure. Not reversible.)

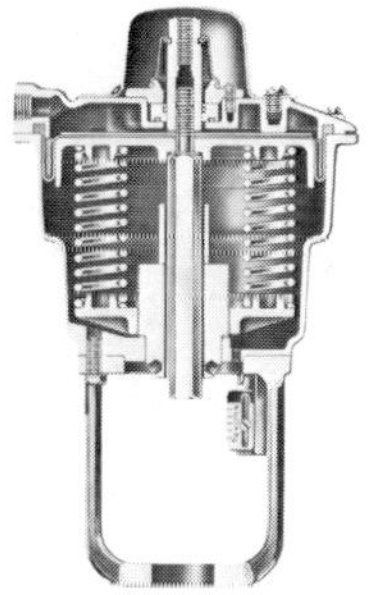

Figure 1-12. Reversible Diaphragm Actuator
(Air pressure may move stem up or down, opposing the springs. Can be assembled to move the actuator stem upward or downward with loss of operating air supply pressure.)

down on diaphragm, which may either open or close the valve, depending on orientation of the actuator lever on the valve shaft).

• Net output thrust is the difference between diaphragm force and opposing spring force.

• Molded diaphragms are used to provide linear performance and increased travels.

• Size is dictated by output thrust required and supply air pressure available.

• Simple, dependable, and economical.

Piston Actuators

• Pneumatically operated using high pressure plant air to 150 psig, often eliminating the need for supply pressure regulator.

• Furnish maximum thrust output and fast response.

• Easily reversible by changing action of the integral valve positioner.

• Best designs are double-acting to give maximum force in both directions.

• Various accessories can be incorporated to position the actuator piston

Figure 1-13. Control Valve with Double-Acting Piston Actuator (Positioner is used for throttling service, but omitted for on/off service.)

Figure 1-14. Control Valve with Double-Acting Electro-Hydraulic Actuator and Handwheel

in the event of supply pressure failure. These include spring-return units, and pneumatic trip valves and lock-up systems.

• Also available are hydraulic snubbers, handwheels, and units without yokes, which can be used to operate butterfly valves, louvers, and similar industrial equipment.

• Other versions for service on rotary-shaft control valves include a sliding seal in the lower end of the cylinder. This permits the actuator stem to move laterally as well as up and down without leakage of cylinder pressure. *(This feature permits direct connection of the actuator stem to the actuator lever mounted on the rotary valve shaft, thereby eliminating much of the lost motion common to jointed leakage.)*

Electro-Hydraulic Actuators

• Require only electrical power to the motor and an electrical input signal from the controller.

• Ideal for isolated locations where pneumatic supply pressure is not available but where precise control of valve plug position is needed.

• Units are normally reversible by making minor adjustments and are usually self-contained, including motor, pump, and double-acting hydraulically operated piston within a weatherproof or explosionproof casing.

Manual Actuators

• Useful where automatic control is not required, but where ease of opera-

FOR ROTARY-SHAFT VALVES

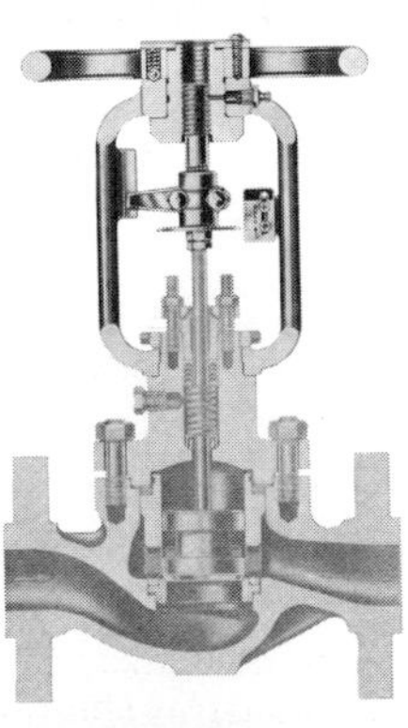

FOR SLIDING-STEM VALVES

Figure 1-15. Typical Manual Actuators

tion and good throttling control is still necessary. Often used to actuate the bypass valve in a three-valve bypass loop around control valves for manual control of the process during maintenance or shutdown of the automatic system.

• Available in various sizes for both globe-style valves and rotary-shaft valves.

• Dial-indicating devices available for some models to permit accurate repositioning of the valve plug or disc.

• Much less expensive than automatic actuators.

Control Valve Bodies

The control valve body regulates the rate of fluid flow as the position of the valve plug or disc is changed by force from the actuator. To do this, the valve body must contain the fluid without external leakage, must have adequate capacity for the intended service, must be capable of withstanding the erosive, corrosive, and temperature influences of the process, and must incorporate appropriate end connections to mate with adjacent pipelines and actuator attachment means to permit transmission of actuator thrust to the valve plug stem or rotary shaft.

Many styles of control valve bodies have been developed through the years. Some have found wide application; others have been designed for meeting specific service conditions and their usage is less frequent. The following summary describes some of the more popular control valve body styles in use today.

Single-Port Valve Bodies

• Most common body style, simple in construction.

• Available in various forms, such as globe, angle, bar stock, forged, and split constructions.

• Generally specified for applications with stringent shutoff requirements. Metal-to-metal seating surfaces or "soft-seating" with nitrile or other elastomeric materials forming the seal, can handle most service requirements.

• Since high-pressure fluid is normally loading the entire area of the port, the unbalance force created must be considered in selecting actuators for single-port control valve bodies.

• Though most popular in the smaller sizes, single-port bodies can often be used in 4-inch to 8-inch sizes with high-thrust actuators.

• Many modern single-seated valve bodies use cage-style construction to retain the seat ring, provide valve plug guiding, and provide a means for establishing a particular flow characteristic. Cage-style trim offers advantages in ease of maintenance and in interchangeability of cages to alter valve flow characteristics.

• Cage-style single-seated valve bodies can also be easily modified by change of trim parts to provide reduced-capacity flow, noise attenuation, or reduction or elimination of cavitation.

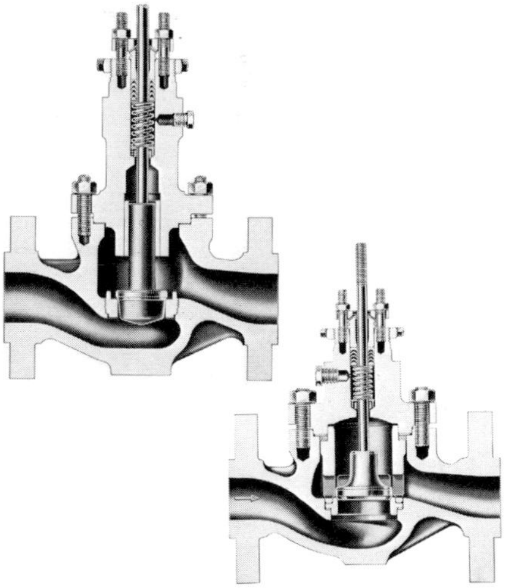

Figure 1-16. Popular Single-Ported Globe-Style Valve Bodies (Valve on left has conventional top-guided trim with screwed-in seat ring; valve on right has cage-guided trim.)

Figure 1-16 on the preceding page shows two of the more popular styles of single-ported or single-seated globe-type control valve bodies. They are widely used in process control applications, particularly in sizes from 1-inch through 3-inch. Normal flow direction is most often up through the seat ring and, in the case of valves with cage-style trim, out through the openings in the cage wall.

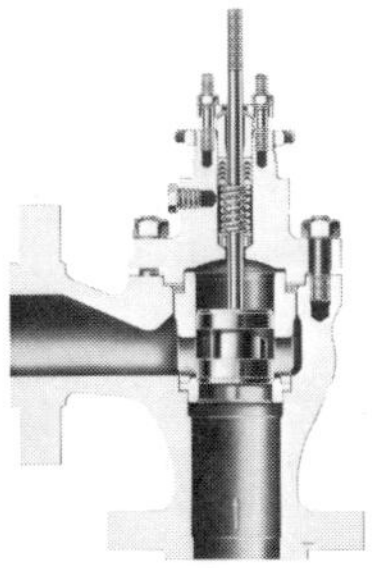

Figure 1-17. Flanged Angle-Style Control Valve Body

Angle valves are nearly always single-ported. They are commonly used in boiler feedwater and heater drain service and in piping schemes where space is at a premium and the valve can also serve as an elbow. The valve shown has cage-style construction. Others may have screwed-in seat rings, expanded outlet connections, restricted trim, and outlet liners for reduction of erosion damage.

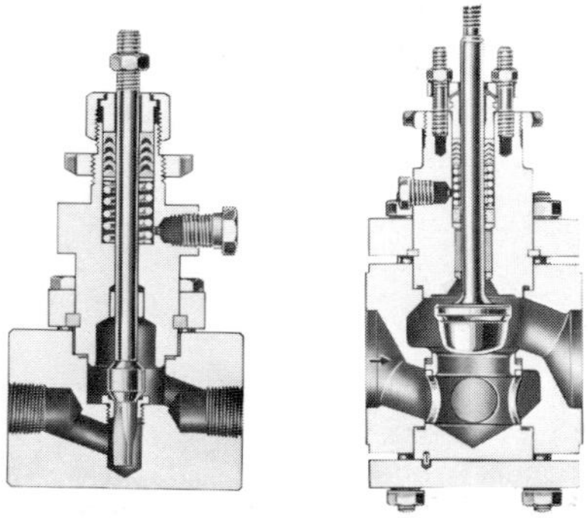

Figure 1-18. Two Popular Varieties of Bar Stock Valve Bodies

Bar stock bodies are often specified for corrosive applications in the chemical industry. They can be machined from any metallic bar stock material and from some plastics. When exotic metal alloys are required for corrosion resistance, a bar stock body is normally less expensive than a body produced from a casting. Some bar stock bodies, available in sizes through 3-inch, have cage-guided trim parts which can be removed for service without removing the body from the pipeline. Others are also available in angle-valve style.

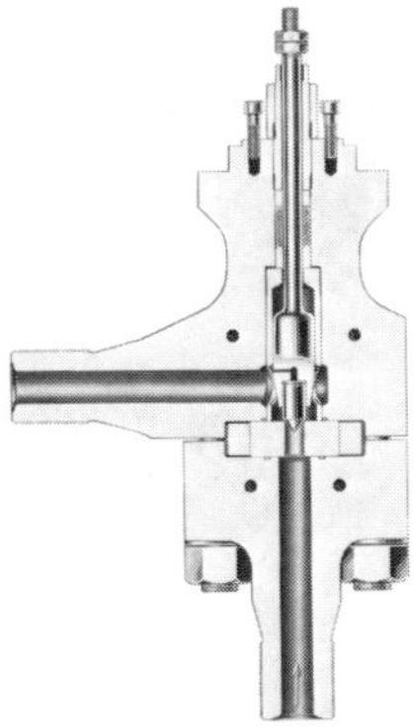

Figure 1-19. Forged High Pressure Control Valve Body

Forged single-ported bodies, generally angle-style, are used for high pressure service. Working pressures to 50,000 psig (3450 bar) are not uncommon in polyethylene production. Port sizes are normally limited to one inch diameter or less for pressures above 10,000 psig (690 bar) due to high unbalance forces involved. Forged bodies are also available with high pressure flanged end connections for less demanding service conditions.

High-pressure single-ported globe bodies are often used in production of gas and oil. Variations available include cage-guided trim, bolted body/bonnet connection, and self-draining angle versions. Flanged versions are available with ratings to ANSI Class 2500.

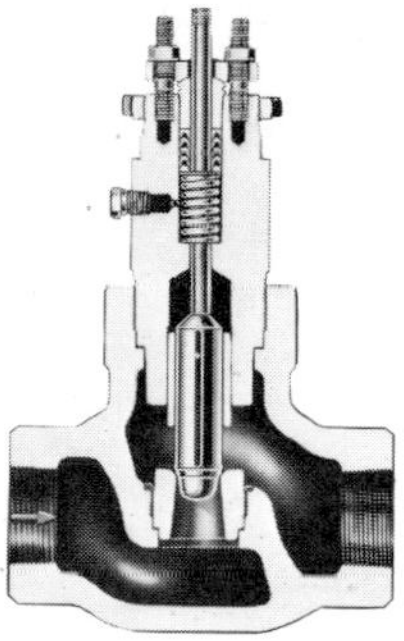

Figure 1-20. High Pressure Globe-Style Control Valve Body

Balanced-Plug Cage-Style Valve Bodies
This popular body style, single-ported in the sense that only one seat ring is used, provides the advantages of a balanced valve plug often associated

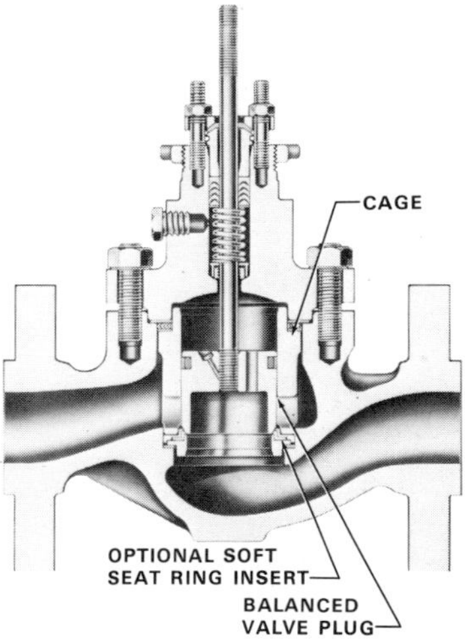

Figure 1-21. Valve Body with Cage-Style Trim, Balanced Valve Plug, and Soft Seat

only with double-ported bodies. Cage-style trim is used to provide valve plug guiding, seat ring retention, and flow characterization. In addition a sliding piston ring-type seal between the upper portion of the valve plug and the wall of the cage cylinder virtually eliminates leakage of the upstream high pressure fluid into the lower pressure downstream system. Downstream pressure acts on both the top and bottom sides of the valve plug, thereby nullifying most of the static unbalance force. Reduced unbalance permits operation of the valve with smaller actuators than those necessary for conventional single-ported bodies. Interchangeability of trim permits choice of several flow characteristics or of noise attenuation or anti-cavitation components. For most available trim designs, the standard direction of flow is in through the cage openings and down through the seat ring. Available in various material combinations, sizes through 16-inch, and pressure ratings to ANSI Class 2500.

High Capacity, Cage-Guided Valve Bodies
This adaptation of the cage-guided bodies mentioned above was designed for noise applications such as high pressure gas reducing stations where sonic gas velocities are often encountered at the outlet of conventional valve bodies. The design incorporates over-

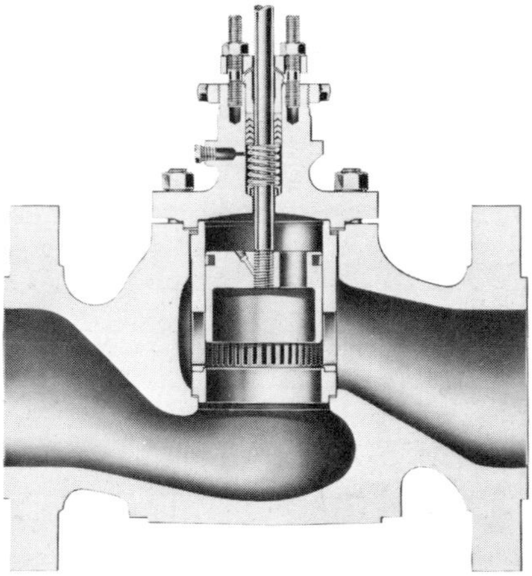

Figure 1-22. High Capacity Valve Body with Cage-Style Noise Abatement Trim

size end connections with a streamlined flow path and the ease of trim maintenance inherent with cage-style constructions. Use of noise abatement trim can reduce overall noise levels by as much as 35 decibels. Also available in cageless versions with screwed-in seat ring, end connection sizes through 12-inch, ANSI Class 600, and versions for liquid service. Flow direction depends on the intended service and trim selection, with unbalanced constructions normally flowing "up" and balanced constructions normally flowing "down".

Reverse-Acting Cage-Guided Valve Bodies

This modification of the cage-guided body permits it to be used when push-down-to-open valve plug action is desired. As shown in Figure 1-23, the body is inverted from its more customary position and a threaded bonnet is installed in the "bottom" of the body.

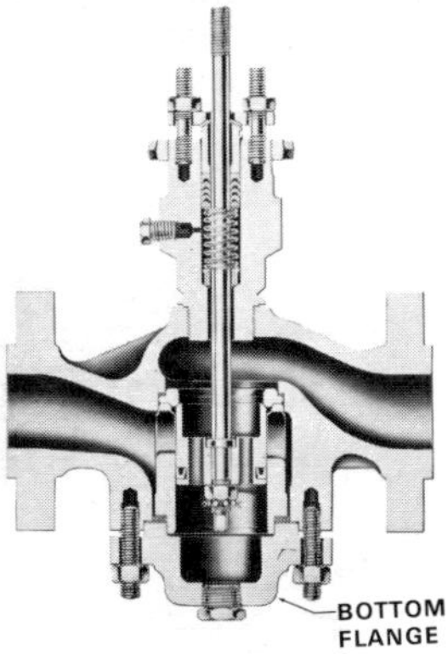

Figure 1-23. Reverse-Acting Valve Body with Balanced, Cage-Guided Valve Plug

A bottom flange provides cage and seat ring alignment and loading. Removal of the bottom flange permits inspection or removal of all trim parts without removing the actuator or taking the body out of the pipeline. Interchangeability of cages can provide flow characteristic variety equal to direct-acting cage-guided valves. Available with metal-to-metal or soft seating, balanced or unbalanced valve plug styles, and a variety of material combinations in sizes through 4-inch ANSI Class 600. In conjunction with a direct-acting diaphragm actuator, this body style provides "Fail-Closed" operation in case of loss of actuator supply pressure.

Double-Ported Valve Bodies

- Dynamic force on plug tends to be balanced as flow tends to open one port and close the other.

- Reduced dynamic forces acting on plug may permit choosing a smaller actuator than would be necessary for a single-ported body with similar capacity.

- Usually furnished only in the larger sizes—6-inch or larger.

- Normally have higher capacity than single-ported valves of the same line size.

- Many double-ported bodies are reversible, so valve plug can be installed as either "push-down-to-open" or "push-down-to-close."

- Metal-to-metal seating usually provides only Class II shutoff capability, although Class III capability is also possible.

- Port-guided valve plugs are often used for on-off or low pressure throttling service. Top-and-bottom-guided valve plugs furnish stable operation for severe service conditions.

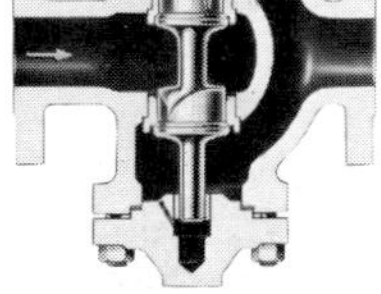

Figure 1-24. Reversible Double-Ported Globe-Style Valve Body

The control valve body shown above is assembled for push-down-to-open valve plug action. The valve plug is essentially balanced and a relatively small amount of actuator force is required to operate the valve. Consequently, this design can often be useful on high-pressure drop applications where dynamic forces on a conventional single-ported valve plug would necessitate use of a very large actuator.

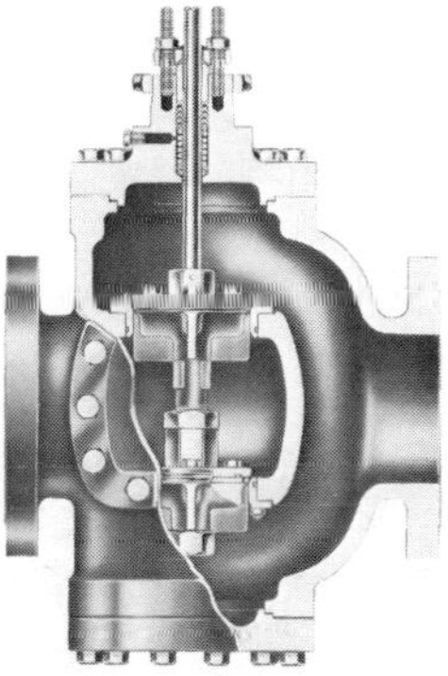

Figure 1-25. Double-Ported Valve Body with Adjustable Soft-Seated Trim

This reversible double-ported control valve body is assembled for push-down-to-close valve plug action. The unit shown has rubber O-ring seating surfaces on the port-guided plug to provide shutoff for stringent leakage requirements. The seat-to-seat distance between the two seats can be adjusted through a handhole plate on the side of the body. This construction is often used in natural gas distribution systems and for process gases and liquids up to 250 psig (17.2 bar) and 150°F (66°C).

Three-Way Valve Bodies

- Three pipeline connections to provide general converging (flow-mixing) or diverging (flow-splitting) service.
- Best designs utilize cage-style trim for positive valve plug guiding and ease of maintenance.
- Variations available with trim materials selected for high temperature service. Standard end connections (flanged, screwed, butt weld, etc.) can be specified to mate with most any piping scheme.

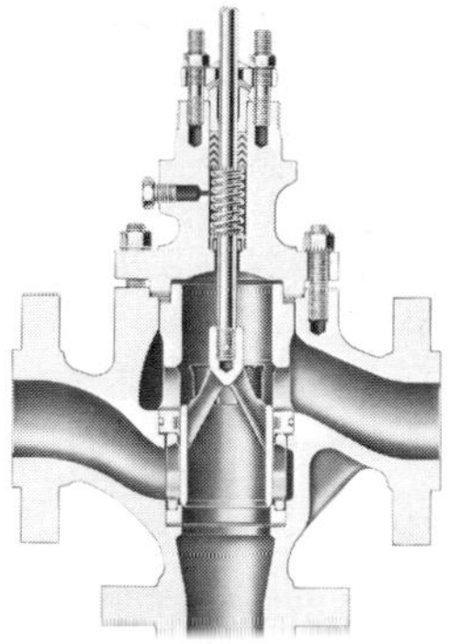

Figure 1-26. Three-Way Valve with Balanced Valve Plug

- Actuator selection demands careful consideration, particularly for constructions with unbalanced valve plug.

Balanced valve plug-style three-way valve body shown with cylindrical valve plug in the "down" postion. This position opens the bottom "common" port to the right-hand port and shuts off the left-hand port. The construction can be used for throttling mid-travel position control of either converging or diverging fluids.

Boot-Style Valve Bodies

- Used on applications handling corrosive chemicals and slurries.
- Elastomer boot provides high rangeability and good shutoff capability.
- Design minimizes number of pressure-retaining and "wetted" parts.

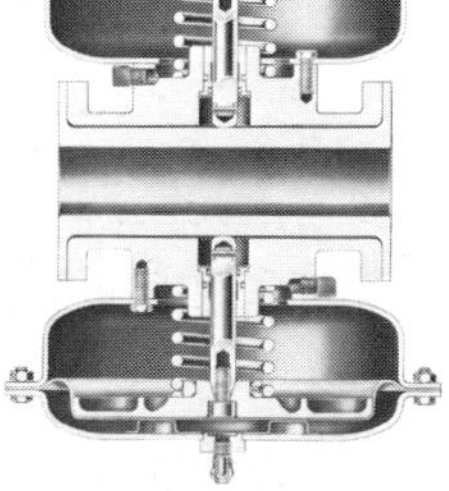

Figure 1-27. Valve Body with Flexible Elastomer Boot

- Operating temperature range limited by capability of boot materials.
- Provides throttling control in either direction up to 100 psig (6.89 bar).
- Alternate design available to provide closure of boot on loss of supply pressure.

Dual-loading of boot by opposed actuators provides throttling control with standard diaphragm actuator loading pressures. Reduced-bore boots are available for best throttling control in installations where normal flow rates are low.

Butterfly Valve Bodies

- Require minimum space for installation.
- Provide high capacity with low pressure loss through the valve.
- Very economical, particularly in larger sizes and in terms of flow capacity per investment dollar.
- Conventional contoured discs provide throttling control for up to 60-degree disc rotation. Patented, dynamically streamlined discs available for applications requiring 90-degree disc rotation.
- Mates with standard raised-face pipeline flanges.
- May require high-output or large actuators if the valve is big or the pressure drop is high, since operating torques may be quite large.
- Units are available for service in nuclear power plant applications with very stringent leakage requirements.
- Standard line can provide good shutoff and corrosion protection with nitrile or TFE liner.

Standard butterfly valves are available in sizes through 72-inch for miscellaneous control valve applications. Smaller sizes can use versions of traditional diaphragm or piston pneumatic actuators, including the modern rotary actuator styles. Larger sizes may require high-output electric or long-stroke pneumatic cylinder actuators.

Figure 1-28. Typical Butterfly Control Valve

Butterfly valves exhibit an approximately equal percentage flow characteristic. They can be used for throttling service or for on-off control. Soft-seat construction can be obtained by the liner method or by including an adjustable soft ring in the body or on the face of the disc.

A dynamically contoured disc, such as the patented **Fishtail®** disc shown, permits control through full 90 degrees of disc rotation, while conventional discs are usually limited to rotation of 60 degrees.

V-Notch Ball Control Valve Bodies

- Straight-through flow design produces little pressure drop.
- Suited to control of erosive or viscous fluids, paper stock, or other slurries containing entrained solids or fibers.
- Uses standard diaphragm or piston rotary actuators, or conventional lineal-travel actuators with minor modifications.
- Ball remains in contact with seal during rotation, which produces a

shearing effect as the ball closes and minimizes clogging.

• Available with either metal or heavy-duty TFE-filled composition ball seal ring to provide excellent rangeability in excess of 300:1.

• Bolts between ANSI Class flanges with long through-bolts.

Figure 1-29. Rotary-Shaft Control Valve with V-Notch Ball

This construction is similar to a conventional ball valve, but with patented, contoured V-notch in the ball. The V-notch produces an equal percentage flow characteristic. **Vee-Ball®** control valves have good rangeability, control, and shutoff capability. They are widely used in the paper industry, chemical plants, sewage treatment plants, the power industry, and petroleum refineries.

Eccentric-Disc Control Valve Bodies

• Effective throttling control for pressure drops up to 740 psig (51 bar).

• Provides linear flow characteristic through 90 degrees of disc rotation.

• Eccentric mounting of disc pulls it away from seal after it begins to open, minimizing seal wear.

• Available in sizes through 24-inch compatible with standard ANSI flanges.

• Uses standard pneumatic diaphragm or piston rotary actuators.

• Standard flow direction is into the concave side of the disc; reverse flow results in reduced capacity.

Figure 1-30. Eccentric-Disc Rotary-Shaft Control Valve

The unit shown is easily field-reversible between push-down-to-open and push-down-to-close operation. Eccentric-disc rotary shaft control valves can handle a wide range of control valve applications at temperatures to 1000°F (540°C). Splined shaft-actuator lever connection prevents lost motion and improper positioning of disc. This design is typical of the rotary-shaft styles of control valves that are rapidly gaining in popularity among control valve users. Generally speaking, the modern high-performance rotary-shaft control valves are proving themselves adaptable to many control requirements and are usually less costly than conventional globe-style valves of equal capability.

Control Valve End Connections

The three common methods of installing control valves in pipelines are by means of screwed pipe threads, bolted gasketed flanges, and welded end connections.

Screwed Pipe Threads

Screwed end connections are quite popular in small control valves and are more economical than flanged ends.

The threads usually specified are tapered female NPT (National Pipe Thread) on the valve body. They form a metal-to-metal seal by wedging over the mating male threads on the pipeline ends. This connection style is usually limited to valves not larger than 2-inch and is not recommended for elevated temperature service. Valve maintenance may be complicated by screwed end connections if it is necessary to take the body out of the pipeline, since the valve cannot be removed without breaking a flanged joint or union connection to permit unscrewing the valve body from the pipeline.

Bolted Gasketed Flanges

Flanged end valves are easily removed from the piping and are suitable for use through the range of working pressures for which most control valves are manufactured. Flanged end connections can be used in a temperature range from absolute zero to approximately 1500°F (815°C). They are used on all valve sizes. The most common flanged end connections are flat face, raised face, and ring type joint.

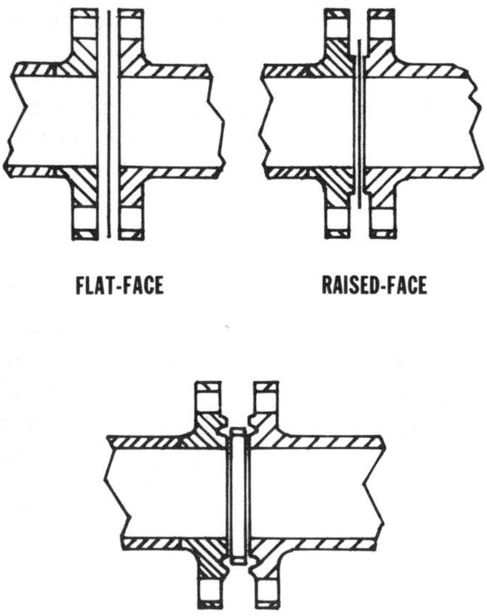

Figure 1-31. Popular Varieties of Bolted Flange Connections

The flat face variety allows the matching flanges to be in full face contact with the gasket clamped between them. This construction is commonly used in low pressure, cast iron and brass valves and has the advantage of minimizing flange stresses caused by initial bolting up force.

The raised face flange has a circular raised face with inside diameter the same as the valve opening and with the outside diameter something less than the bolt circle diameter. The raised face is finished with concentric circular grooves for good sealing and resistance to gasket blowout. This kind of flange is used with a variety of gasket materials and flange materials for pressures through the 6000 psig (414 bar) pressure range and for temperatures through 1500°F (815°C). This style of flanging is normally standard on ANSI Class 250 cast iron bodies and all steel and alloy steel bodies.

The ring-type joint flange is similar in appearance to the raised face flange except that a U-shaped groove is cut in the raised face concentric with the valve opening. The gasket consists of a metal ring with either an eliptical or octagonal cross section. When the flange bolts are tightened, the gasket is wedged into the groove of the mating flange and a tight seal is made. The gasket is generally soft iron or Monel* but is available in almost any metal. This is an excellent joint at high pressure and is used up to 15,000 psig (1034 bar), but is generally not used at high temperatures. It is furnished only on steel and alloy valve bodies when specified.

Welding End Connections

Welding ends on control valves have the advantage of being leak-tight at all pressures and temperatures and are economical in first cost. Welding end valves are more difficult to take from the line and they are obviously limited to weldable materials. Welding ends are manufactured in two styles, socket and butt.

*Trademark of International Nickel Co.

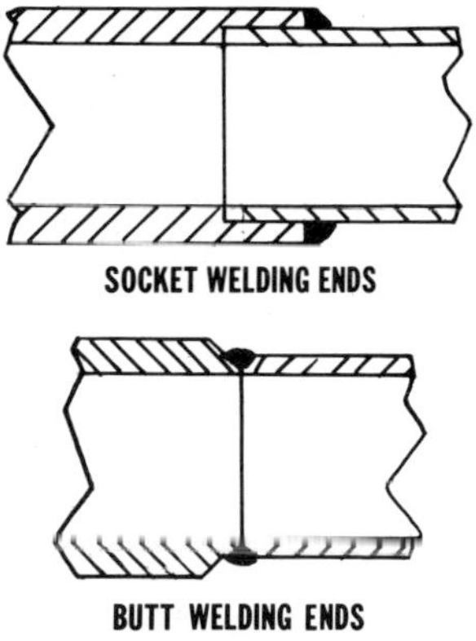

Figure 1-32. Common Welded End Connections

The socket welding ends are prepared by boring in each end of the valve a socket with an inside diameter just slightly larger than the pipe outside diameter. The pipe is slipped into the socket where it butts against a shoulder and is then joined to the valve with a fillet weld. Socket welding ends in a given size are dimensionally the same regardless of pipe schedule. They are usually furnished in small sizes through 2-inch.

The butt welding ends are prepared by bevelling each end of the valve to match a similar bevel on the pipe. The two ends are then butted to the pipeline and joined with a fillet weld. This style of joint is used on all valve styles and the end preparation must be different for each schedule of pipe. Generally furnished for control valves in sizes 2-1/2-inch and larger.

Valve Body Bonnets

The bonnet of a control valve is that part of the body assembly through which the valve plug stem or rotary shaft moves. On globe or angle bodies, it is the pressure retaining component for one end of the valve body. The bonnet normally provides a means of mounting the actuator to the body and houses the packing box. (On some rotary-shaft valves, the packing is housed within an extension of the body itself, or the packing box is a separate component bolted between the body and bonnet.)

On a typical globe-style control valve body, the bonnet is made of the same material as the body, since it is a pressure-containing member, and since it is subject to the same temperature and corrosion effects as the body. In the figures shown on earlier pages of this chapter several styles of body-to-bonnet connections can be seen. The most common is the bolted flange type shown in several figures including Figure 1-1 showing a bonnet with an integral flange and Figure 1-18 showing a bonnet with a separable, slip-on flange held in place with a split ring. Figure 1-19 shows an angle-style valve with an integral bonnet. The bonnet used on the high pressure globe body in Figure 1-20 is screwed into the body, as is the bonnet for the reverse-acting cage-guided body shown in Figure 1-23. Figure 1-8 is typical of rotary-shaft control valves where the packing is housed within the body and a bonnet, per se, is not used. (The actuator linkage housing is not a pressure-containing part and, though it performs as a bonnet in connecting the actuator cylinder to the body, it is usually made from cast aluminum to minimize control valve weight.)

On control valve bodies with cage-style trim, the bonnet furnishes loading force to prevent leakage between the bonnet flange and the body and also between the seat ring and the body. The tightening of the body-bonnet bolting compresses a flat sheet gasket to seal the body-bonnet joint, compresses a spiral-wound gasket on top of the cage, and compresses another flat sheet gasket below the seat ring to provide the seat ring-body seal. The bonnet also provides alignment for the cage (which in turn guides the valve plug) to ensure proper valve plug-seat ring alignment.

As mentioned, the conventional bonnet on a globe-type control valve houses the packing. As shown in Figure 1-1, the packing is most often retained by a packing follower held in place by a flange on the yoke boss area of the bonnet. An alternate packing retention means is shown in Figure 1-18, where the packing follower is held in place by a screwed gland. This alternate is compact, so it is often used on small control valves, but it has a disadvantage in that the user cannot always be sure of thread engagement. Therefore, caution should be used in adjusting packing compression when the control valve is in service.

Standard bolted-flange bonnets have an opening in the side of the packing box. This opening is closed with a standard pipe plug unless: (1) a lubricator or lubricator/isolating valve is required to lubricate the valve stem packing, in which case the lubricator is nipple-mounted to the bonnet opening; (2) it is necessary to purge the valve body and bonnet of process fluid, in which case the opening can be used as a purge connection; or (3) the bonnet opening is being used as a vent connection in conjunction with a bellows seal bonnet, in which case leakage out the vent would indicate that the bellows seal was broken.

Extension Bonnets

Extension bonnets are used for either high or low temperature service to protect valve stem packing from the extreme temperatures. Standard TFE valve stem packing is generally useful for most applications up to 450°F (232°C). However, it is susceptible to damage at low process temperatures if frost forms on the valve stem. The frost crystals can cut grooves in the TFE, forming leakage paths for process fluid along the stem. Extension bonnets can remove the packing box of the bonnet far enough from the extreme temperature of the process that the packing temperature remains within the recommended range.

Extension bonnets are either cast (Figure 1-4) or fabricated (Figure 1-33). Cast extensions are better for high temperature service because of greater

Figure 1-33. Valve Body with Fabricated Extension Bonnet

heat emissivity which provides better cooling effect. Conversely, smooth surfaces, such as can be fabricated from stainless steel tubing, are preferred for cold service since heat influx is normally the major concern. In either case, extension wall thickness should be minimized to cut down heat transfer. Stainless steel is usually preferable to carbon steel because of its lower coefficient of thermal conductivity. On cold service applications, insulation can be added around the extension to protect further against heat influx.

Bellows Seal Bonnets

Bellows seal bonnets (Figure 1-5) are used when no leakage along the stem can be tolerated. They are often used when the process fluid is toxic, volatile, radioactive, or highly expensive. This special bonnet construction protects both the stem and the valve packing from contact with the process fluid. Standard packing box construction above the bellows seal unit will prevent catastrophic failure in the event of rupture or failure of the bellows.

Due to the severity of the service conditions in which they normally operate, control valves with bellows seal bonnets are usually rated at only 300 psig (20.7 bar) at 70°F (21°C). As with other control valve pressure/temperature limitations, these pressure ratings decrease with increasing temperature. Selection of a bellows seal bonnet should be carefully considered, and particular attention should be paid to proper inspection and maintenance after installation.

Control Valve Packing

Most control valves use packing boxes with the packing retained and adjusted by a flange and stud bolts (Figure 1-1). Several packing materials are available that can be used depending on the service conditions to be encountered. Brief descriptions and service condition guidelines follow for several of the more popular materials and typical packing material arrangements are shown in Figure 1-34.

TFE V-Ring

- Plastic material with inherent ability to minimize friction.

- Molded in V-shaped rings which are spring loaded and self-adjusting in the packing box. Packing lubrication is not required.

- Resistant to most known chemicals except molten alkali metals.

- Requires extremely smooth (2 to 4 micro-inches RMS) stem finish to seal properly. Will leak if stem or packing surface is damaged.

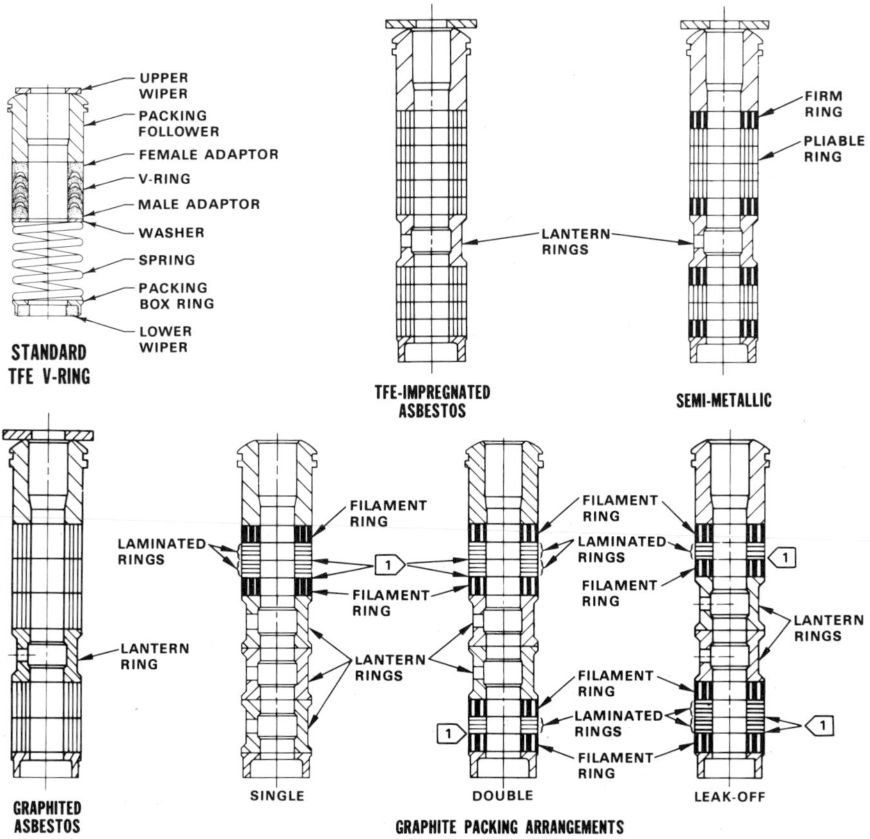

1 LOCATION OF SACRIFICIAL ZINC WASHER, IF USED.

Figure 1-34. Comparative Packing Material Arrangements for Globe-Style Valve Bodies with 1/2-Inch Diameter Stems

- Recommended temperature limits: −40 to +450°F (−40 to +232°C)

- Not suitable for nuclear service, since TFE is easily destroyed by radiation.

TFE-Impregnated Asbestos

- Composed of braided asbestos fibers impregnated with TFE. Molded into rings with square cross-section.

- Has much of the ability of TFE to minimize friction, but can be tightened to stop leakage caused by minor stem damage or imperfection.

- Suggested service temperature limits: −100 to +450°F (−73 to +232°C).

- Packing lubrication is suggested, except when used in oxygen service.

Graphited Asbestos

- Formed ring packing composed of asbestos fiber, lead wool, flake graphite, metal particles, and a small amount of neoprene as a binder.

- Useful on petroleum distillate, steam, oil, and air service to 450°F (232°C).

- Can be adjusted to stop leakage, but provides more friction than TFE packings.

- Packing box lubrication is recommended to reduce friction and improve sealing.

Laminated and Filament Graphite

- Suitable for high temperature nuclear service or where low chloride content is desirable (Grade GTN).

- Provides leak-free operation, high thermal conductivity, and long service life, but produces high stem friction and resultant hysteresis.

- Impervious to most hard-to-handle fluids and high radiation.

- Suitable temperature range: Cryogenic temperatures to 1200°F (649°C).

- Lubrication is not required, but an extension bonnet or steel yoke should be used when packing box temperature exceeds 800°F (427°C).

Semi-Metallic

- Packing rings have asbestos core covered with shredded or braided aluminum foil.

- Used for high temperature and pressure applications where stem surface may not be perfect. Stem should be hardened or chrome plated to reduce wear.

- Suitable for service temperatures up to 900°F (482°C).

- Lubrication is recommended, and an extension bonnet or steel yoke should be used when packing box temperatures exceed 800°F (427°C).

Valve Stem Packing Lubrication

Lubrication is recommended for several of the popular packing materials mentioned above. The preferred lubricant is silicone grease, which provides improved valve stem action and reduces friction at temperatures up to 500°F (260°C). At higher temperatures this lubricant may oxidize and cause a problem in obtaining a tight packing seal. For temperatues within the service limits of the lubricant, performance of graphited asbestos, TFE-impregnated asbestos, and semi-metallic packings can be improved by routine injection of a small amount of silicone grease into the packing box. This is accomplished by means of a lubricator assembly such as that shown in Figure 1-3. By turning the screw of the lubricator, grease is forced into the packing box of the valve. An isolating valve is included with the lubricator on all high-pressure control valves. The isolating valve is closed at all times except when actually lubricating the packing.

Packing should not be lubricated for control valves in oxygen service, since many lubricants, particularly petroleum-base lubricants, are hazardous because of their high heat of combustion and high rate of reaction.

Conventional Characterized Valve Plugs

The valve plug is the movable part of a globe-style control valve assembly which provides a variable restriction to fluid flow. Several valve plug styles are available, each designed to provide a specific flow characteristic, permit a specified manner of guiding or alignment with the seat ring, or have a particular shutoff or damage-resistance capability.

Valve plugs are designed for either two-position or throttling control. In two-position applications, the valve plug is positioned by the actuator at either of two points within the travel range of the assembly. In throttling control, the valve plug may be positioned at any point within the travel range as dictated by the process requirements. Although some valve plugs are reversible, most are designed for either "push-down-to-open" or "push-down-to-close" action. Selection of proper valve plug action must take into consideration the type of actuator being used, the required "fail-safe" position the valve plug should assume in the event of actuator supply pressure failure, and whether fluid pressure tends to open the valve in normal operation or tends to close the valve.

The contour of the valve plug surface adjacent to the seat ring is instrumental in determining the inherent flow characteristic of a conventional globe-style control valve. As the valve plug is moved through its travel range by the actuator, the unobstructed flow area changes in size and shape dependent on the contour of the valve plug. When a constant pressure differential is maintained across the valve, the changing relationship between percentage of maximum flow capacity and percentage of total travel range can be portrayed, as in Figure 1-35, and is designated as the inherent flow characteristic of the valve.

Commonly specified inherent flow characteristics include:

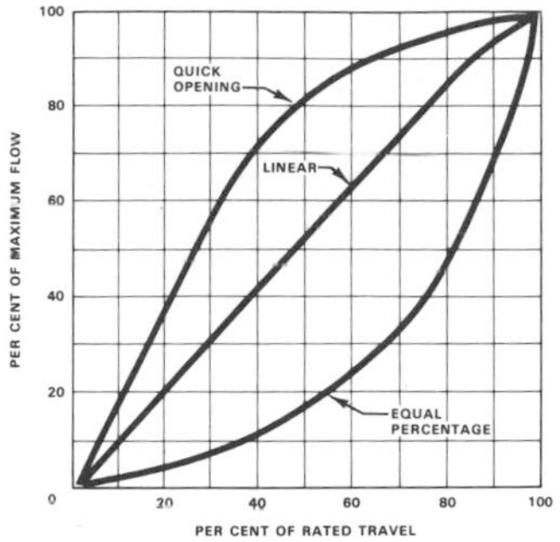

Figure 1-35. Inherent Flow Characteristic Curves

Linear Flow Characteristic— A valve with an ideally linear inherent flow characteristic produces flow rate directly proportional to the amount of valve plug travel, throughout the travel range. For instance, at 50 percent of rated travel, flow rate is 50 percent of maximum flow; at 80 percent of rated travel, flow rate is 80 percent of maximum; etc. Change of flow rate is constant with respect to valve plug travel. Valves with a linear characteristic are often specified for liquid level control and for flow control applications requiring constant gain.

Equal Percentage Flow Characteristic—Ideally, for equal increments of valve plug travel, the change in flow rate with respect to travel may be expressed as a constant percent of the flow rate at the time of the change. The change in flow rate observed with respect to travel will be relatively small when the valve plug is near its seat and relatively high when the valve plug is nearly wide open. Therefore, a valve with an inherent equal percentage flow characteristic provides precise throttling control through the lower portion of the travel range and rapidly increasing capacity as the valve plug nears the wide-open position. Valves with equal percentage flow characteristics are used on pressure control applications, on applications where a large percentage of the pressure drop is normally absorbed by the system itself with only a relatively small percentage available at the control valve, and on applications where highly varying pressure drop conditions can be expected.

Quick-Opening Flow Characteristic—A valve with a quick opening flow characteristic provides a maximum change in flow rate at low travels. The curve is basically linear through the first 40 percent of valve plug travel, then flattens out noticeably to indicate little increase in flow rate as travel approaches the wide open position. Control valves with quick-opening flow characteristics are often used for on/off applications where significant flow

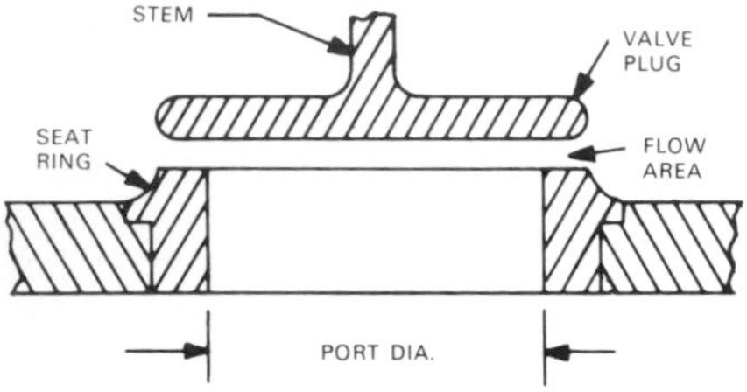

Figure 1-36. Typical Construction to Provide Quick-Opening Flow Characteristic

rate must be established quickly as the valve begins to open. Consequently, they are often used in relief valve applications. (Quick-opening valves can also be selected for many of the same applications for which linear flow characteristics are recommended, since the quick-opening characteristic is linear up to about 70 percent of maximum flow rate. Linearity decreases sharply after flow area generated by valve plug travel equals the flow area of the port. For a typical quick-opening valve, such as that shown in Figure 1-36, this occurs when valve plug travel equals one-fourth of port diameter.)

Characterization of Cage-Guided Valve Bodies

In valve bodies with cage-guided trim, flow characterization is determined by the shape of the flow openings or "windows" in the wall of the cylindrical cage. As the valve plug is moved away from the seat ring, the cage windows are "opened" to permit flow through the valve. Standard cages have been designed to produce linear, equal percentage, and quick opening inherent flow characteristics. Note the differences in the shapes of the cage windows shown in Figure 1-37. The flow rate/travel relationship provided by valves using these cages is equivalent to the linear, quick opening, and equal percentage curves shown for contoured valve plugs in Figure 1-35.

Cage-guided trim in a control valve provides a distinct advantage over conventional valve body assemblies in that maintenance and replacement of internal parts is much simplified. The inherent flow characteristic of the valve can be easily changed by installing a different cage. Interchange of cages to provide a different inherent

QUICK OPENING **LINEAR** **EQUAL PERCENTAGE**

Figure 1-37. Characterized Cages for Globe-Style Valve Bodies

flow characteristic does not require changing valve plug or seat ring. The standard cages shown can be used with either balanced or unbalanced trim constructions. Soft-seating, when required, is available in the form of a retained insert in the seat ring and is independent of cage or valve plug selection. (Cage interchangeability can be extended to specialized cage designs which provide noise attenuation or combat cavitation. These cages furnish a modified linear inherent flow characteristic, but require flow to be in a specific direction through the cage openings. Therefore, it could be necessary to reverse the valve body in the pipeline to obtain proper flow direction.)

Valve Plug Guiding

Accurate guiding of the valve plug is necessary for proper alignment with the seat ring and efficient control of the process fluid. The common methods used are listed below and their names are generally self-descriptive.

- **Top-and-Bottom Guiding**: Valve plug is aligned by guide bushings in the bonnet and bottom flange in the manner shown in Figure 1-24.

- **Cage Guiding**: The outside diameter of the valve plug is in close proximity to the inside wall surface of the cylindrical cage throughout the travel range. Since bonnet, cage, and seat ring are self-aligning on assembly, correct valve plug/seat ring alignment is assured when valve closes. Figure 1-1 illustrates cage guiding.

- **Top Guiding**: Valve plug is aligned by a single guide bushing in the bonnet or valve body, as shown in Figure 1-20.

- **Top-and-Port Guiding**: Valve plug is aligned by a guide bushing in the bonnet or body and also by the valve body port. This construction is typical for control valves using small-diameter valve plugs with fluted skirt projections to control low flow rates. (See Figure 1-18, left view.)

- **Stem Guiding**: Valve plug is aligned with the seat ring by a guide bushing in the bonnet that acts on the valve plug stem. (See Figure 1-18, right view.)

Restricted-Capacity Control Valve Trim

Most control valve manufacturers can provide valves with reduced or restricted-capacity trim parts. The reduced flow rate may be desirable for any of the following reasons: (1) Restricted capacity trim may make it possible to select a valve body large enough for increased future flow requirements, but with trim capacity properly sized for present needs; (2) Valves can be selected for adequate structural strength, yet retain reasonable travel/capacity relationship; (3) Large bodies with restricted capacity trim can be used to reduce inlet and outlet fluid velocities; (4) Purchase of expensive pipeline reducers can be avoided; (5) Over-sizing errors may be corrected by use of restricted capacity trim parts.

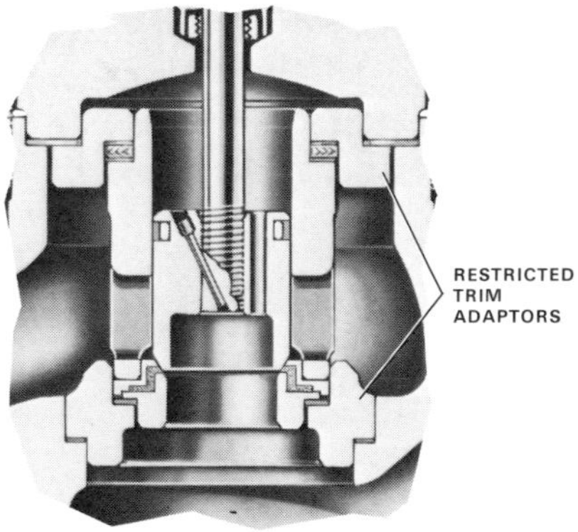

Figure 1-38. Adaptor Method for Providing Reduced Flow Capacity

Conventional globe-style valve bodies can be fitted with seat rings with smaller port-size than normal and valve plugs sized to fit those smaller ports. Valves with cage-guided trim often achieve the reduced capacity effect by utilizing valve plug, cage, and seat ring parts from a smaller valve size of similar construction and adaptor pieces above the cage and below the seat ring to mate those smaller parts with the valve body, as shown in Figure 1-38. Since reduced capacity service is not at all unusual, leading manufacturers provide readily available trim part combinations to perform the required function. Many restricted capacity trim combinations are designed to furnish approximately 40 percent of full-size trim capacity.

Section 2

Valve Positioners, Boosters, and Other Accessories

The Old Guidelines

The selection of the proper equipment for acceptable performance of a control system requires an analysis of the static and dynamic characteristics of each available component in relation to the process being controlled. In the forty years or so since the first availability of pneumatic valve positioners, many manufacturers have adopted "rules of thumb" regarding positioner application. These "rules" dictated positioner usage to counteract such factors as packing box friction, valve plug unbalance, and spring and diaphragm hysteresis. The "rules" suggested that use of a valve positioner was the best way to ensure maintaining a valve plug position proportional to the instrument signal from the controller.

Toward that end, many valve positioners have been developed and are presently available. In function, they are alike, although there are various shapes, styles, and operating principles. Positioners are generally mounted on the side of diaphragm actuators and on the top of piston actuators. They are connected mechanically to the valve stem or piston so that stem position can be compared with the position dictated by the controller. Schematic drawings are shown in Figures 2-1 and 2-2 for two styles of commonly used positioners.

Extensive Fisher Controls Company research on application of positioners has produced some interesting and surprising results in terms of the "rules of thumb" mentioned above. The research included analog computer simulation of a variety of process control loops, an experimental testing program to verify the conclusions drawn from the computer simulation, and an analytical study of the non-linearity of valve plug travel due to packing friction. Several varieties of positioners were considered in the research.

The analog simulations of fast control systems indicated that greater packing friction made the use of a positioner *less* desirable and that the better the positioner accuracy and response, the *poorer* the system control. Intentionally degrading positioner performance by reducing positioner-actuator loop gain provided progressively more stability, allowed tighter controller settings, and provided better process control for fast systems. Including a pneumatic isolating amplifier (volume booster) in the system provided still better performance. The booster, such as that shown

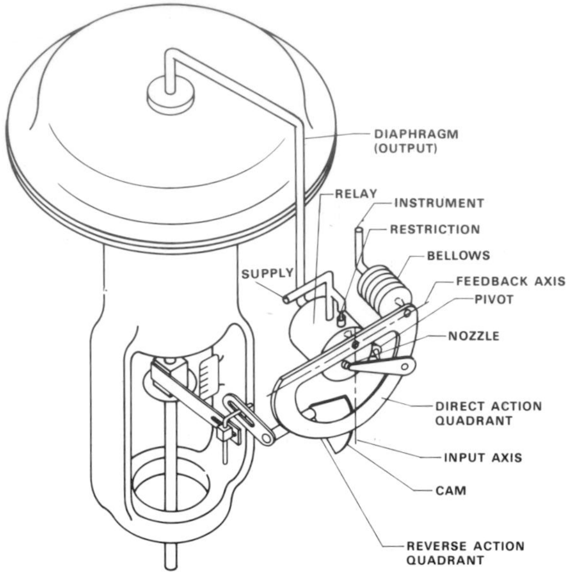

Figure 2-1. Positioner Schematic for Diaphragm Actuator

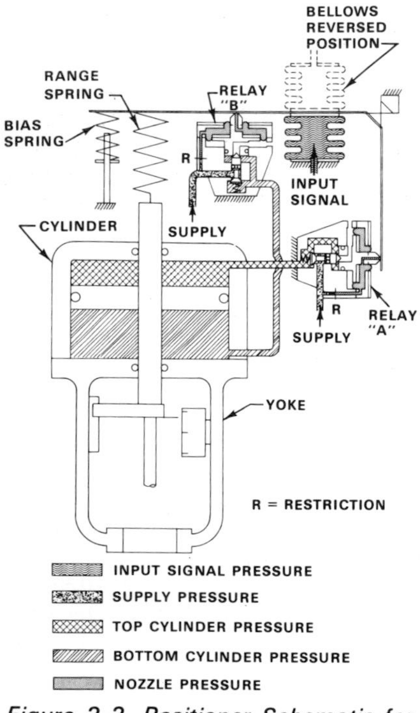

Figure 2-2. Positioner Schematic for Piston Actuator

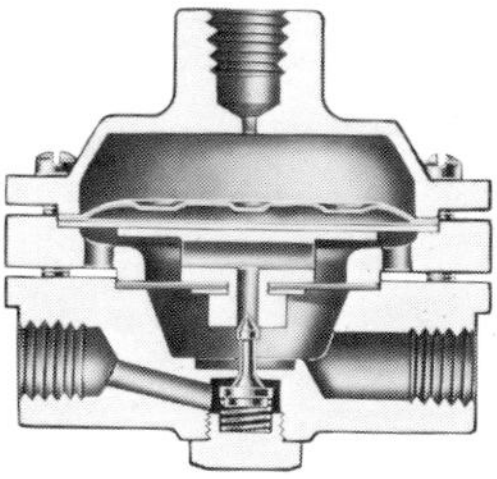

Figure 2-3. Typical Booster

in Figure 2-3, was representative of a positioner with the poorest possible positioning accuracy. Since the stroking speed of the actuator was not affected, the improved performance apparently resulted from the ability of the booster to isolate the controller from the large capacitive load of the actuator.

The computer study indicated that use of positioners is clearly beneficial on relatively slow systems and clearly detrimental on relatively fast systems. The need for using or not using a positioner is completely independent of the old "rules of thumb" with one exception. If stem friction or stickiness is unusually high, it becomes increasingly important to ignore the old "rules" and follow fast system/slow system principle for positioner application.

The experimental verification phase of the research program bore out the conclusions reached in the computer simulation phase. Liquid pressure control systems were used to evaluate conclusions relating to fast systems and liquid level control systems were used to evaluate slow system conclusions. Theoretical analysis of packing friction non-linearity again reinforced the new guidelines.

The New Guidelines

The testing program and analysis lead to the following conclusions and guidelines for application of auxiliary positioners or boosters for control systems.

A. Previous "rules" based on actuator loading, valve unbalance, and stem friction should be discarded.

B. In many control systems, a properly sized spring-and-diaphragm actuator will do an excellent job without the use of either a positioner or a booster.

C. An auxiliary positioner or booster should be considered for systems where it is necessary to:

1. Split-range the controller output to more than one valve.

2. Amplify the controller output signal pressure above the standard range in order to provide increased actuator thrust or stiffness.

3. Provide the best possible control with minimum overshoot and fastest possible recovery following a disturbance or load change where long controller instrument lines are involved.

Determination of which auxiliary device (positioner or booster) to use for the above situations is dependent on the speed of system response. If the system is relatively fast, such as is typical of liquid pressure control loops, some gas pressure control loops, and most flow control loops, the proper choice is a booster. If the system is relatively slow, such as is typical of liquid level, blending, temperature, and some reactor control loops, the proper choice is a positioner. Fortunately, for those in-between cases when it is difficult to determine if a system is fast or slow, the choice has little effect on performance.

Springless piston actuators are used to operate valves when high forces are needed. They require the use of positioners since no inherent restoring mechanism is provided. For slow loops where positioners are normally beneficial, this presents no problem. For fast systems, where positioners should be avoided but thrust requirements necessitate spring-less actuators, there may be no alternative but to operate with relatively loose controller settings.

Motion transmitters are available for use with pneumatically actuated control valves. They are used in conjunction with indicating or recording instruments for remote indication of valve stem position. A pneumatic output pressure signal is transmitted that is directly proportional to valve stem position.

Other Control Valve Accessories

Handwheels and Manual Operators

Figure 2-4. Side-Mounted Handwheel for Diaphragm Actuators

Used with either direct-acting or reverse-acting actuators, this unit acts as an adjustable travel stop to limit either full opening or full closing of the valve or to position the valve manually.

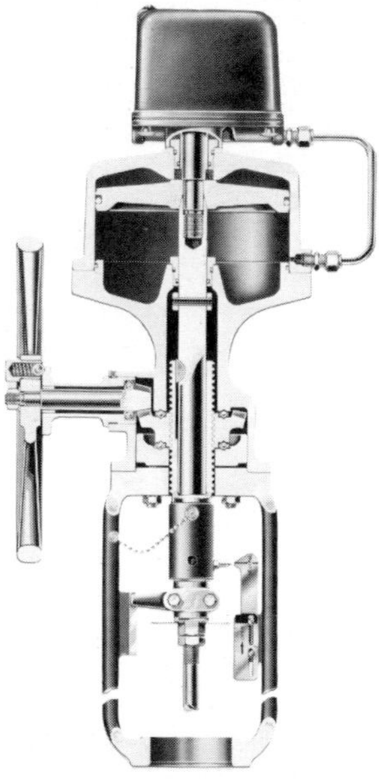

Figure 2-5. Side-Mounted Handwheel for Piston Actuators

Used to manually position the valve, this unit also acts as an adjustable travel stop to limit either full opening or full closing of the valve.

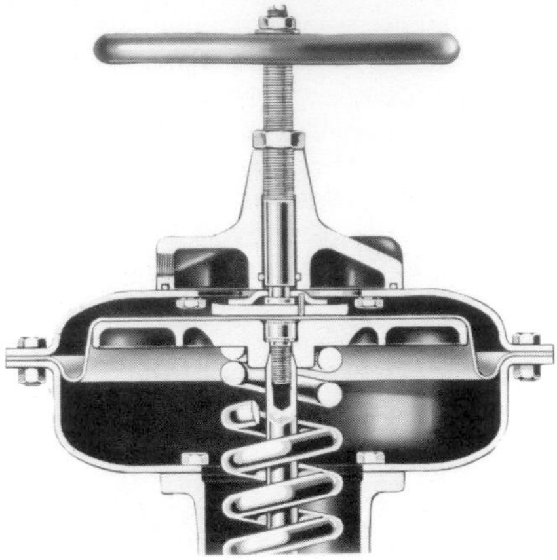

Figure 2-6. Top-Mounted Handwheel for Direct-Acting Diaphragm Actuator

This unit can be used as an adjustable travel stop to limit travel in the upward direction or to manually close push-down-to-close valves.

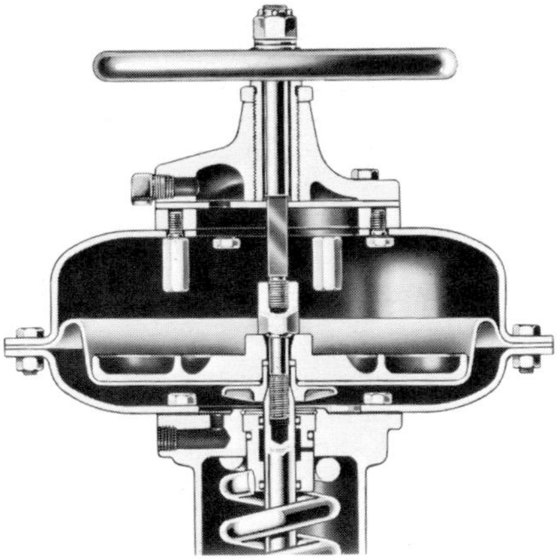

Figure 2-7. Top-Mounted Handwheel for Reverse-Acting Diaphragm Actuator

This unit can be used as an adjustable travel stop to limit travel in the downward direction or to manually close push-down-to-open valves.

Hydraulic Snubber

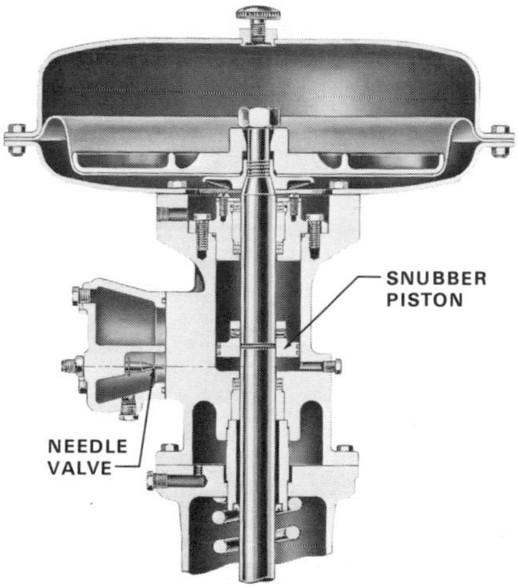

Figure 2-8. Hydraulic Snubber Installed on Reverse-Acting Diaphragm Actuator

Dampens vertical instability of the valve plug on severe control valve applications. Piston moving in an oil-filled cylinder provides the damping action, which is adjustable by changing needle valve position in the oil flow passage. Similar units are also available for use on direct-acting diaphragm actuators and for piston actuators.

Limit Switches

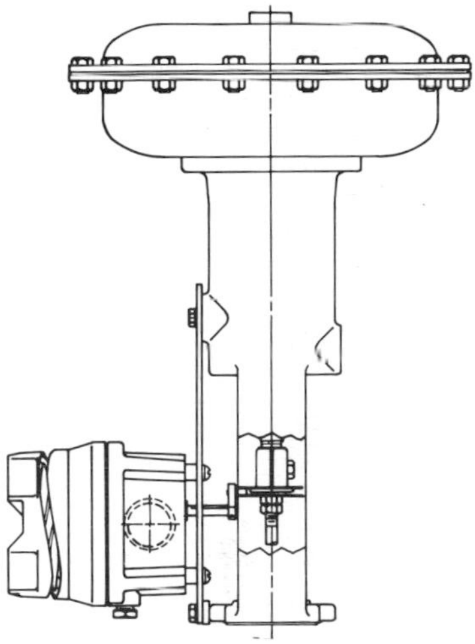

Figure 2-9. Cam-Operated Limit Switches

Limit switches are used to operate signal lights, small solenoid valves, electric relays, or alarms. The cam-operated type shown is available with from two to six individual switches operated by movement of the valve stem. The switches are housed in an assembly that mounts on the side of the actuator. Each switch is individually adjustable and can be supplied for either alternating current or direct current systems. Other styles of valve-mounted limit switches are also available for service where electrical specifications exceed the capabilities of the cam-operated design.

Solenoid Valve Manifold

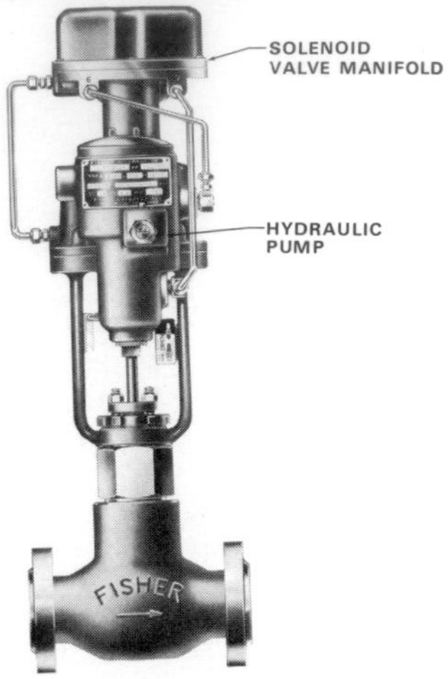

Figure 2-10. Solenoid Valve Manifold

A solenoid valve manifold can be used on a double-acting piston actuator to permit hydraulic operation of the actuator. The manifold mounts on top of the actuator cylinder and, by means of the making or breaking of an electric current signal, switches output of a connected hydraulic pump to either above or below the actuator piston. Precise control of valve plug position can be achieved with a unit such as that shown above.

Supply Pressure Regulator

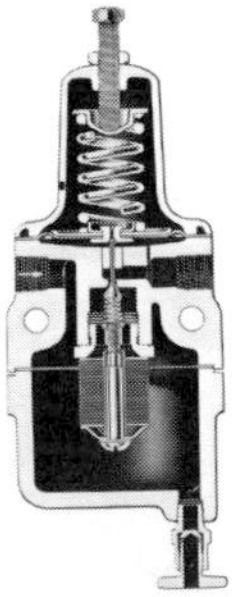

Figure 2-11. Supply Pressure Regulator with Filter and Moisture Trap

Supply pressure regulators are used to reduce plant air supply to valve positioners and other control equipment. Common reduced air supply pressures are 20 and 35 psi. The regulator can be nipple-mounted or bolted to the actuator.

Pneumatic Lock-Up Systems

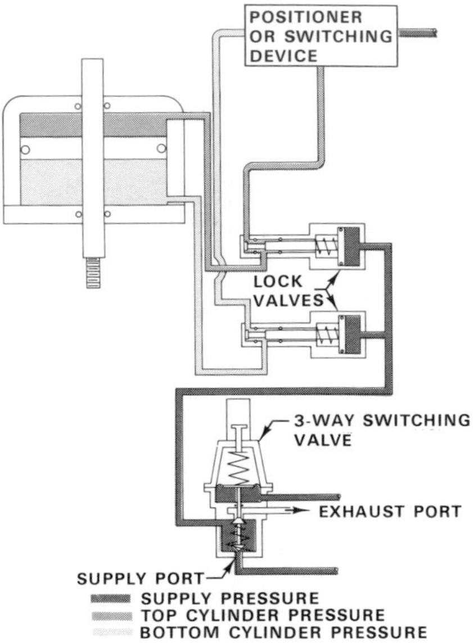

Figure 2-12. Lock-Up System Schematic for Piston Actuator

Pneumatic lock-up systems are used with control valves to lock in existing actuator loading pressure in the event of supply pressure failure. Normal operation resumes automatically when supply pressure is restored. Functionally similar arrangements are available for control valves using diaphragm actuators.

Fail-Safe Systems for Piston Actuators

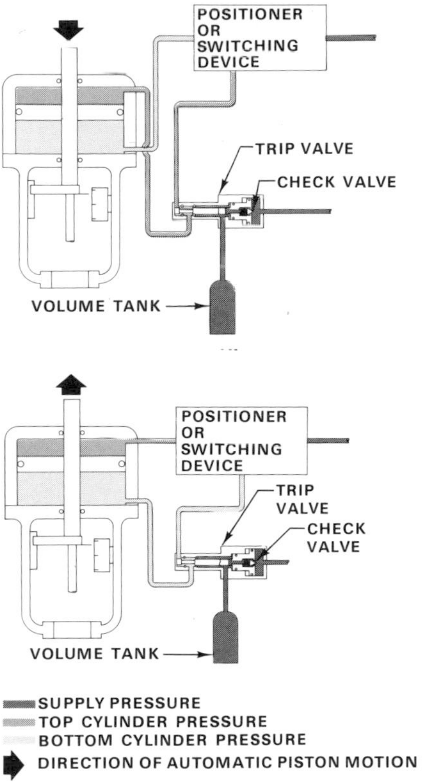

Figure 2-13. Schematics of "Fail-Safe" Systems

In these "fail-safe" systems, the actuator piston is moved to the top or bottom of the cylinder when supply pressure falls below a pre-determined value. The volume tank, which is charged with supply pressure, provides loading pressure for the actuator piston when supply pressure fails, thus moving the piston to the desired position. Automatic operation resumes, and the volume tank is recharged, when supply pressure is restored to normal.

Electro-Pneumatic Transducers

Figure 2-14. Electro-Pneumatic Transducer with Supply Regulator for Operation of Diaphragm-Actuated Control Valve

The transducer receives a direct current input signal and uses a torque motor, nozzle-flapper, and pneumatic relay to convert the electric signal to a proportional pneumatic output signal. Nozzle pressure operates the relay and is piped to the torque motor feedback bellows to provide a comparison between input signal and nozzle pressure. As shown, the transducer can be mounted directly on a control valve and operate the valve without need for additional boosters or relays. On/off electro-pneumatic transducers are also available and are commonly used to replace solenoid valves in intrinsically safe systems.

Electro-Pneumatic Valve Positioners

Figure 2-15. Electro-Pneumatic Positioner on Diaphragm Actuator

Electro-pneumatic positioners are used in electronic control loops to operate pneumatic diaphragm control valve actuators. The positioner receives a direct current input signal, and uses a torque motor, nozzle-flapper, and pneumatic relay to convert the input signal to a pneumatic output signal. The output signal is applied directly to the actuator diaphragm, producing a valve plug position that is proportional to the input signal. Valve plug position is mechanically fed back to the torque motor to provide for error correction by comparison of plug position and input signal. Split-range operation capability can provide full travel of the actuator with only a portion of the input signal range.

Section 3

Control Valve Selection

Considerations Required

Control valves are called on to handle all kinds of fluids at temperatures from the cryogenic range to well over 1000°F *(538°C)*. So selection of a control valve body assembly requires particular consideration to provide the best available combination of valve body style, material, and trim construction design for the intended service. Capacity requirements and system operating pressure ranges must also be considered in selecting a control valve to insure satisfactory operation without undue initial expense.

Reputable control valve manufacturers and their representatives are dedicated to helping the customer select the control valve most appropriate for the existing service conditions. Since there are frequently several possible "correct" choices for an application, it is important that all the following information be provided by the customer:

- Type of fluid to be controlled
- Temperature of fluid
- Viscosity of fluid
- Specific gravity of fluid
- Flow capacity required (Maximum and Minimum)
- Inlet pressure at valve (Maximum and Minimum)
- Outlet pressure (Maximum and Minimum)
- Pressure drop during normal flowing conditions
- Pressure drop at shutoff
- Maximum permissible noise level, if pertinent, and the measurement reference point
- Degrees of superheat or existence of flashing, if known
- Inlet and outlet pipeline size and schedule

Typical ordering specifications should also include the following information relating to the control valve:

- Item number
- Valve type number
- Quantity required
- Valve size
- Special tagging information required
- Valve body construction (angle, double-port, butterfly, etc.)

- Body material (ASTM A126 Class B cast iron, ASTM A216 Grade WCB, etc.)
- End connections and rating (screwed, ANSI Class 600 RF flanged, ANSI Class 1500 RTJ flanges, etc.)
- Valve plug or disc style (quick opening, **ēdisc™**, **Micro-Flute™**, **Fishtail®**, etc.)
- Valve plug guiding (cage-style, port-guided, etc.)
- Valve plug action (push down to close or push down to open)
- Port size (full or restricted)
- Valve trim materials required
- Action desired on air failure (valve to open, close, or retain last controlled position)
- Flow action (flow tends to open valve or flow tends to close valve)
- Actuator size required
- Instrument air supply available
- Bonnet style (plain, extension, etc.)
- Packing material (TFE V-ring, laminated graphite, etc.)
- Accessories required (positioner, handwheel, etc.)
- Instrument signal (3 to 15 psi, 4 to 20 mA, etc.)

From the foregoing list, it's easy to see there are quite a few things to specify in ordering a control valve. Some of the options have been discussed in previous chapters of this book and others will be explored in this and following chapters.

Valve Body Materials

Body material selection is usually based on the pressure, temperature, corrosive properties, and erosive properties of the flow media. Sometimes a compromise must be reached in selecting a material. For instance, a material with good erosion resistance may not be satisfactory because of poor corrosion resistance when handling a particular fluid.

Some service conditions require use of exotic alloys and metals to withstand particular corrosive properties of the flowing fluid. Naturally these materials are much more expensive than more common metals and so economy may also be a factor in material selection. Fortunately, the majority of control valve applications handle relatively non-corrosive fluids at reasonable pressures and temperatures. Therefore, cast iron and cast carbon steel are the most commonly used valve body materials and can provide satisfactory service at much lower cost than the exotic alloy materials.

The following thumbnail descriptions will provide some basic information on various popular castable materials used for control valve bodies. ASTM material designations are included. Use of proper ASTM designations is considered good practice and is encouraged in specifying materials, particularly for pressure-containing parts. Additional engineering data on these and other materials appears on pages 123 through 129.

Cast carbon steel (ASTM A216 Grade WCB)—Most popular steel material is used for valve bodies in moderate services such as control of air, saturated or superheated steam, non-corrosive liquids and gases. Casting cost per pound is roughly four times that of cast iron, but WCB is useful at much higher pressures and temperatures than cast iron, as is shown in Figures 3-1 and 3-6. (Check applicable codes for suitability of WCB for prolonged usage at temperatures above 775°F (413°C), as carbon phase may be converted to graphite.) Can be welded without heat treatment unless nominal thickness exceeds 1-1/4 inches (32 mm).

Cast chrome-moly steel (ASTM A217 Grade WC9)—Addition of chromium and molybdenum provide corrosion and creep resistance. Rough castings may be 1-1/2 times as costly as WCB, but can be used to 1050°F (566°C). WC9 requires pre-heating before welding and heat treatment after welding. See Figures 3-2 and 3-6 for pressure-temperature rating curve.

Cast chrome-moly steel (ASTM A217 Grade C5)—Popular steel alloy for use up to 1100°F (593°C) on high pressure steam, oils, gases, petroleum vapors, sea water, and other mildly corrosive fluids. Also resistant to erosion at high temperature and to creep. Weldable, with heat treatment. Figures 3-3 and 3-6 provide pressure-temperature rating. Casting cost normally somewhat higher than WCB.

Cast Type 304 stainless steel (ASTM A351 Grade CF8)—Heat treated stainless material for valves controlling oxidizing or very corrosive fluids. Frequently used above 1000°F (538°C) and below minus 150°F (−101°C). Rough casting cost is approximately 2-1/2 times that of WCB. Pressure-temperature ratings are shown in Figures 3-4 and 3-6. Type 304 is readily weldable without heat treatment.

Cast Type 316 stainless steel (ASTM A351 Grade CF8M)—Useful for many of same services as Type 304, but addition of molybdenum gives Type 316 greater resistance to corrosion pitting, creep, and oxidizing fluids. Raw material is heat-treated to provide maximum corrosion resistance. Castings are slightly more expensive than Type 304, but provide greater strength than 304. Pressure-temperature ratings appear in Figures 3-5 and 3-6.

Cast iron (ASTM A126)—Inexpensive, non-ductile material used for valve bodies controlling steam, water, gas, and non-corrosive fluids. See Figure 3-7 for pressure-temperature ratings.

Cast bronze (ASTM B61 and ASTM B62)—B62 is the "standard" valve body bronze and is slightly less expensive than B61 in the rough state. B61 is more frequently used for valve trim parts. Both materials are satisfactory for steam, air, water, oil, non-corrosive gas, and some dilute acid services. Good resistance to some types of corrosion, and suitable for cryogenic temperatures. ANSI pressure-temperature rating curves shown in Figure 3-8.

Pressure-Temperature Ratings for Standard Class Valves
(In accordance with ANSI B16.34-1977)

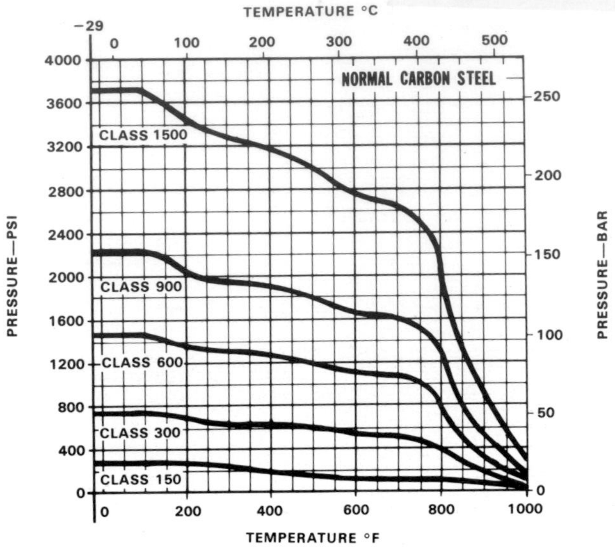

Figure 3-1. Ratings for Normal Carbon Steel Valves

[Fisher Controls Company recommends limiting ASTM A216 Grade WCB valves to 800°F (427°C).]

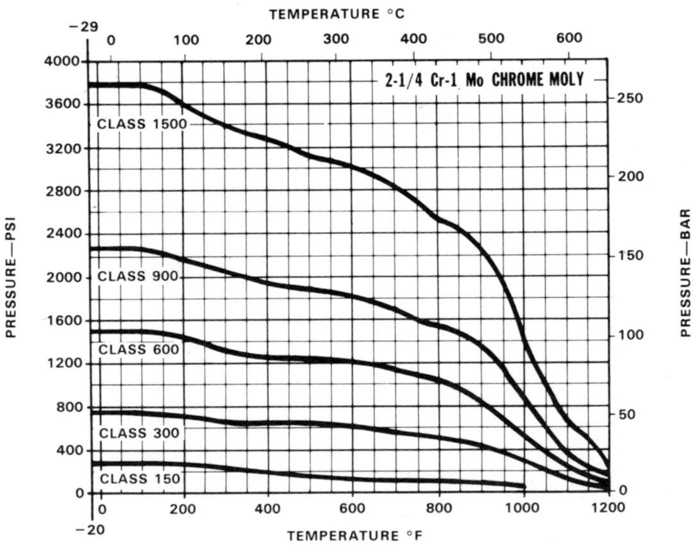

Figure 3-2. Ratings for 2 1/4 Cr-1 Mo Chrome Moly Alloy Steel Valves

[ASTM A217 WC9 valves should be limited to 1050°F (566°C).]

Pressure-Temperature Ratings for Standard Class Valves
(In accordance with ANSI B16.34-1977)

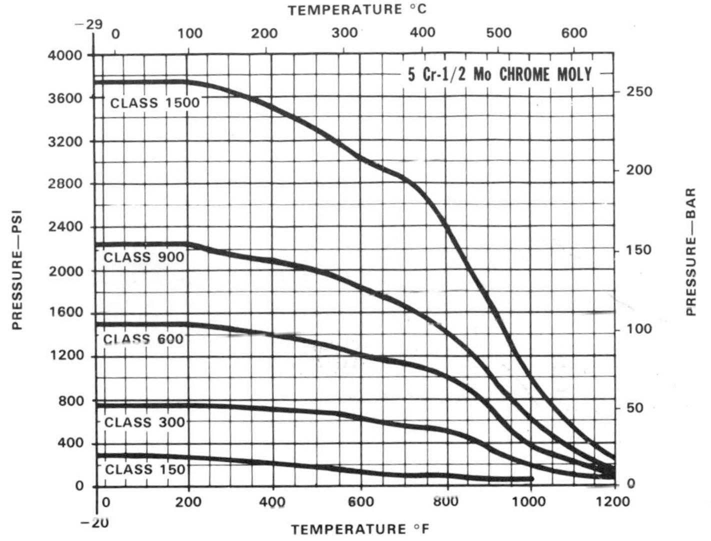

Figure 3-3. Ratings for 5 Cr-1/2 Mo Chrome Moly Alloy Steel Valves
[ASTM A217 Grade C5 valves should be limited to 1100°F (593°C).]

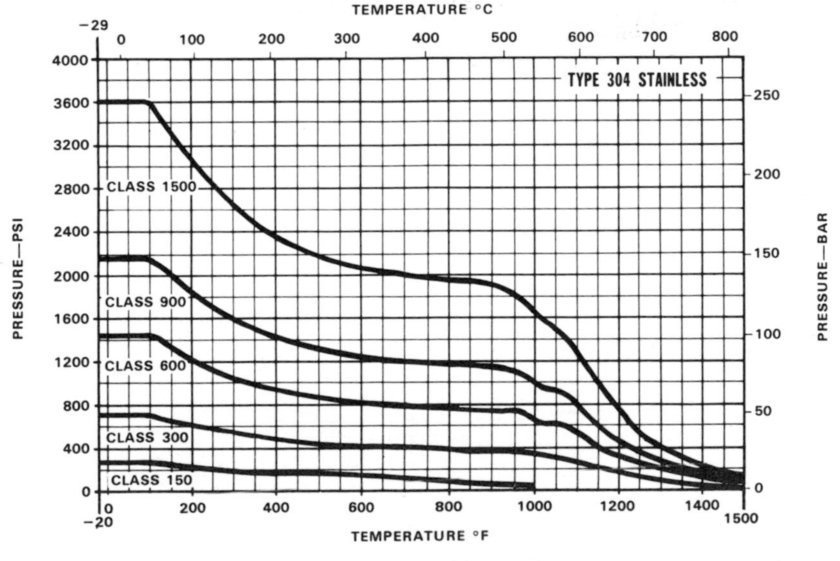

Figure 3-4. Ratings for Type 304 Stainless Steel Valves

Pressure-Temperature Ratings for Standard Class Valves
(In accordance with ANSI B16.34-1977)

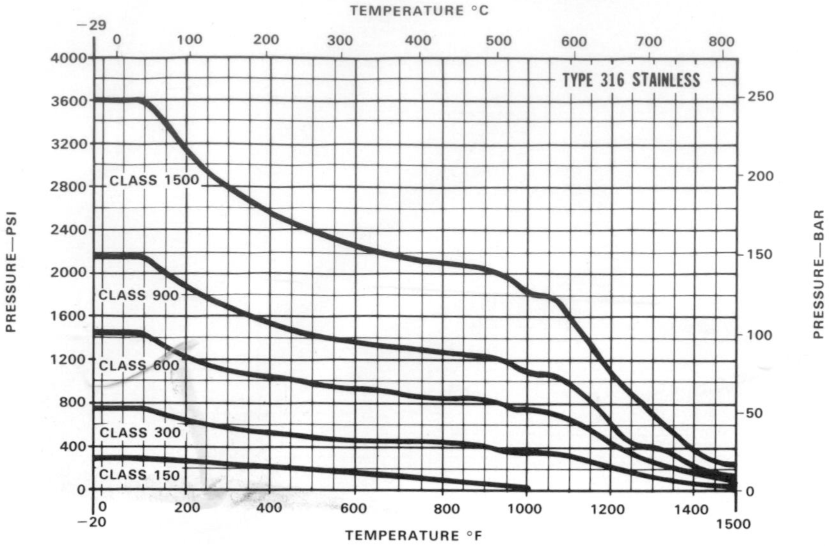

Figure 3-5. Ratings for Type 316 Stainless Steel Valves

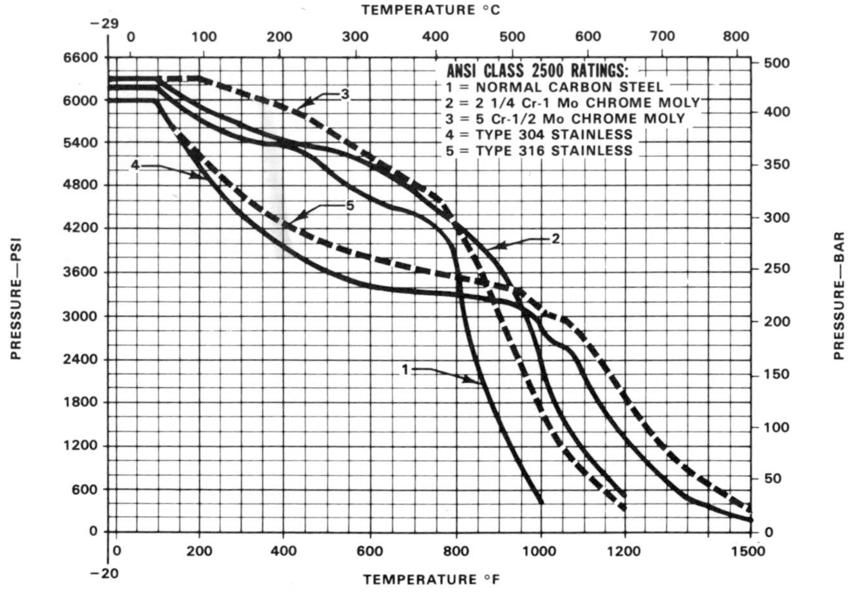

Figure 3-6. Ratings for Standard ANSI Class 2500 Valves

[Fisher Controls Company recommends limiting Curve 1 to 800°F (427°C) for ASTM A216 Grade WCB, Curve 2 to 1050°F (566°C) for ASTM A217 WC9, and Curve 3 to 1100°F (593°C) for ASTM A217 Grade C5.]

Pressure-Temperature Ratings ASTM A126 Cast Iron Valves

(In accordance with ANSI B16.1-1975.)

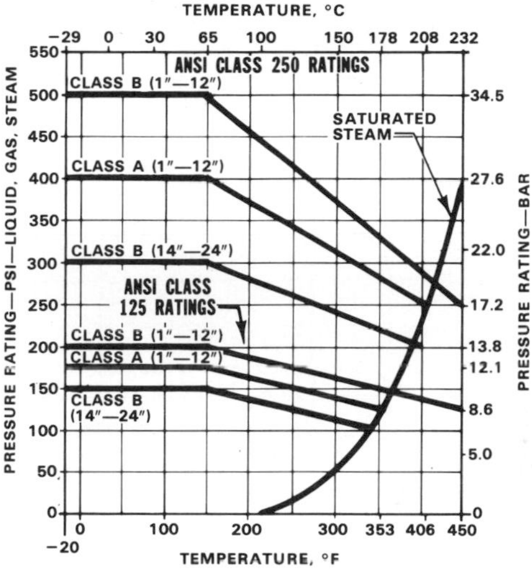

Figure 3-7. Ratings for ASTM A126 Cast Iron Valves

ASTM B61 and B62 Cast Bronze Valves

(In accordance with ANSI B16.24-1971.)

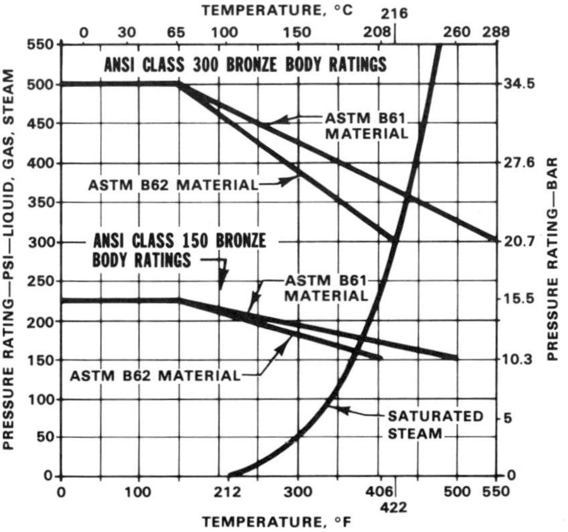

Figure 3-8. Ratings for ASTM B61 and B62 Cast Bronze Valves

Face-To-Face Dimensions for Flanged, Globe-Style Control Valves

(Inch Dimensions are in accordance with ISA S4.01.1-1977.)

BODY SIZE (INCHES)	ANSI CLASS AND END CONNECTIONS											
	125 FF (CI) 150 RF (Steel)		250 RF (CI) 300 RF (Steel)		150 RTJ (Steel)		300 RTJ (Steel)		600 RF (Steel)		600 RTJ (Steel)	
	In.	mm	In.	mm	In.	mm	In.	mm	In.	mm	In.	mm
1	7.25	184	7.75	197	7.75	197	8.25	210	8.25	210	8.25	210
1-1/4	7.88	200	8.38	213	8.38	213	8.88	225	9.00	229	9.00	229
1-1/2	8.75	223	9.25	235	9.25	235	9.75	248	9.88	251	9.88	251
2	10.00	254	10.50	267	10.50	267	11.12	283	11.25	286	11.38	289
2-1/2	10.88	276	11.50	292	11.38	289	12.12	308	12.25	311	12.38	314
3	11.75	299	12.50	318	12.25	311	13.12	333	13.25	337	13.38	340
4	13.88	352	14.50	368	14.38	365	15.12	384	15.50	394	15.62	397
6	17.75	451	18.62	473	18.25	464	19.25	489	20.00	508	20.12	511
8	21.38	543	22.38	568	21.88	556	23.00	584	24.00	610	24.12	613
10	26.50	673	27.88	708	27.00	686	28.50	724	29.62	752	29.75	756
12	29.00	737	30.50	775	29.50	749	31.12	790	32.25	819	32.38	822
16	40.00	1016	41.62	1057	40.50	1029	42.25	1073	43.62	1108	43.75	1111

Abbreviations used above: FF—Flat Face; RF—Raised Face; RTJ—Ring-Type Joint; CI—Cast Iron

Face-to-Face Dimensions for Single Flange and Flangeless Wafer-Style Butterfly Control Valves

(In accordance with MSS-SP67-1976)

BODY SIZE (INCHES)	NARROW VALVE BODY INSTALLED FACE-TO-FACE DIMENSIONS*			
	†		‡	
	In.	mm	In.	mm
1-1/2	1.31	33.3	1.38	35.1
2	1.69	42.9	1.75	44.5
2-1/2	1.81	46.0	1.88	47.8
3	1.81	46.0	1.88	47.8
4	2.06	52.3	2.12	53.8
6	2.19	55.6	2.25	57.2
8	2.38	60.5	2.50	63.5
10	2.69	68.3	2.81	71.4
12	3.06	77.7	3.19	81.0
14	3.06	77.7	3.19	81.0
16	3.12	79.2	3.25	82.6
18	4.00	101.6	4.12	104.6
20	4.38	111.2	4.50	114.3

*Bodies compatible with ANSI Class 125 or 250 cast iron flanges or ANSI Class 150 or 300 steel flanges through 12-inch size; dimensions shown for 14-inch and larger sizes apply to Class 150 or lower pressure class only.

† Those valves having sleeves or liners which extend over the body face and/or auxiliary seals contained in the body faces; when the body is bolted between flanges, the sleeve, liner, or auxiliary seals are compressed and act as a flange gasket.

‡ Those valves not having sleeves or liners which extend over the body faces. This type valve may or may not have auxiliary seals in the body faces and may require separate flange gaskets. If separate gaskets are required, the thickness of the gaskets used must be added to the dimensions shown to determine the installed length.

Face-to-Face Dimensions for Flangeless, Partial-Ball Valves*
(In accordance with ISA S4.01.2-1977)

BODY SIZE (INCHES)	FACE-TO-FACE	
	In.	mm
3/4	3.00	76
1	4.00	102
1-1/2	4.50	114
2	4.88	124
3	6.50	165
4	7.62	194
6	9.00	229
8	9.50	243
10	11.69	297
12	13.31	338
16	15.75	400

*ANSI Classes 150 through 600.

Wear & Galling Resistance Chart Of Material Combinations

	304 SST	316 SST	Bronze	Inconel	Monel	Hastelloy B	Hastelloy C	Titanium 75A	Nickel	Alloy 20	Type 416 Hard	Type 440 Hard	17-4PH	Alloy 6 (co-cr)	ENC*	Cr Plate	Al Bronze
304 SST	P	P	F	P	P	P	F	P	P	P	F	F	F	F	F	F	F
316 SST	P	P	F	P	P	P	F	P	P	P	F	F	F	F	F	F	F
Bronze	F	F	S	S	S	S	S	S	S	S	F	F	F	F	F	F	F
Inconel	P	P	S	P	P	P	F	P	F	F	F	F	F	F	F	F	S
Monel	P	P	S	P	P	P	F	F	F	F	F	F	F	S	F	F	S
Hastelloy B	P	P	S	P	P	P	F	F	S	F	F	F	F	S	F	S	S
Hastelloy C	F	F	S	F	F	F	F	F	F	F	F	F	F	S	F	S	S
Titanium 75A	P	P	S	P	F	F	F	P	F	F	F	F	F	S	F	F	S
Nickel	P	P	S	F	F	S	F	F	P	P	F	F	F	S	F	F	S
Alloy 20	P	P	S	F	F	F	F	F	P	P	F	F	F	S	F	F	S
Type 416 Hard	F	F	F	F	F	F	F	F	F	F	F	F	F	S	S	S	S
Type 440 Hard	F	F	F	F	F	F	F	F	F	F	S	F	S	S	S	S	S
17-4 PH	F	F	F	F	F	F	F	F	F	F	F	S	P	S	S	S	S
Alloy 6 (co-cr)	F	F	F	F	S	S	S	S	S	S	S	S	S	F	S	S	S
ENC*	F	F	F	F	F	F	F	F	F	F	S	S	S	S	P	S	S
Cr Plate	F	F	F	F	F	S	S	F	F	F	S	S	S	S	S	P	S
Al Bronze	F	F	F	S	S	S	S	S	S	S	S	S	S	S	S	S	P

*Electroless nickel coating.
S—Satisfactory
F—Fair
P—Poor

Control Valve Seat Leakage Classifications
(In accordance with ANSI B16.104-1976)

Leakage Class Designation	Maximum Leakage Allowable	Test Medium	Test Pressures	Testing Procedures Required for Establishing Rating
I	. . .	. . .	. . .	No test required provided user and supplier so agree.
II	0.5% of rated capacity	Air or water at 50-125°F (10-52°C)	45-60 psig or max. operating differential, whichever is lower	Pressure applied to valve inlet, with outlet open to atmosphere or connected to a low head loss measuring device, full normal closing thrust provided by actuator.
III	0.1% of rated capacity	As above	As above	As above
IV	0.01% of rated capacity	As above	As above	As above
V	0.0005 ml per minute of water per inch of port diameter per psi differential	Water at 50-125°F (10-52°C)	Max. service pressure drop across valve plug, not to exceed ANSI body rating. (100 psi pressure drop minimum)	Pressure applied to valve inlet after filling entire body cavity and connected piping with water and stroking valve plug closed. Use net specified max. actuator thrust, but no more, even if available during test. Allow time for leakage flow to stabilizer.
VI	Not to exceed amounts shown in following table based on port diameter	Air or Nitrogen at 50-125°F (10-52°C)	50 psig or max. rated differential pressure across valve plug, whichever is lower.	Actuator should be adjusted to operating conditions specified with full normal closing thrust applied to valve plug seat. Allow time for leakage flow to stabilize and use suitable measuring device.

Class VI Seat Leakage Allowable
(In accordance with ANSI B16.104-1976)

NOMINAL PORT DIAMETER		LEAK RATE	
Inches	Millimeters	ml Per Minute	Bubbles Per Minute*
1	25	0.15	1
1-1/2	38	0.30	2
2	51	0.45	3
2-1/2	64	0.60	4
3	76	0.90	6
4	102	1.70	11
6	152	4.00	27
8	203	6.75	45

*Bubbles per minute as tabulated are an easily measured suggested alternative based on a suitable calibrated measuring device such as a 1/4-inch O.D. x 0.032-inch wall tube submerged in water to a depth of 1/8-inch to 1/4-inch. The tube end shall be cut square and smooth with no chamfers or burrs and the tube axis shall be perpendicular to the surface of the water. Other apparatus may be constructed and the number of bubbles per minute may vary from these shown, as long as they correctly indicate the flow in ml per minute.

Valve Trim Material Temperature Limits

MATERIAL	LOWER		UPPER	
	°F	°C	°F	°C
Type 304 Stainless Steel	−450	−268	600	316
Type 316 Stainless Steel	−450	−268	600	316
Bronze	−460	−273	450	232
Inconel[1]	−400	−240	1200	649
K Monel[1]	−400	−240	900	482
Monel	−400	−240	900	482
Hastelloy B[2]			700	371
Hastelloy C[2]			1000	538
Titanium			600	316
Nickel	−325	−198	600	316
Alloy 20	50	46	600	316
Type 416 Stainless Steel 40RC	−20	−29	800	427
CA-6NM	−20	−29	800	427
Nitronic 50[3]	−325	−198	1000	538
Type 440 Stainless Steel 60RC	−20	−29	800	427
17-4 PH (CB-7CU)	−40	−40	800	427
Alloy 6 (co-cr)	−460	−273	1500	816
Electroless Nickel Plating	−450	−268	800	427
Chrome Plating	−450	−268	1100	593
Aluminum Bronze	−460	−273	600	316
Nitrile	−40	−40	200	93
Fluoroelastomer (Viton[4] and Fluorel[5])	−10	−23	400	204
TFE	−450	−268	450	232
Nylon	−100	−73	200	93
Polyethylene	−100	−73	200	93
Neoprene	−40	−40	180	82

1. Trademark of International Nickel Co.
2. Trademark of Stellite Div., Cabot Corp.
3. Trademark of Armco Steel Corp.
4. Trademark of E.I. DuPont Co.
5. Trademark of 3M Co.

Corrosion Information

This corrosion table is intended to give only a general indication of how various materials will react when in contact with certain fluids. The recommendations cannot be absolute because concentration, temperature, pressure, and other conditions may alter the suitability of a particular material. There are also economic considerations that may influence material selection. Use this table as a guide only.

FLUID	MATERIAL													
	Carbon Steel	Cast Iron	302 or 304 Stainless Steel	316 Stainless Steel	Bronze	Monel*	Hastelloy† B	Hatelloy† C	Durimet‡ 20	Titanium	Cobalt-Base Alloy 6	416 Stainless Steel	440C Hard Stainless Steel	17-4PH Hard Stainless Steel
Acetaldehyde	A	A	A	A	A	A	I.L.	A	A	I.L.	I.L.	A	A	A
Acetic Acid, Air Free	C	C	B	B	B	B	A	A	A	A	A	C	C	B
Acetic Acid, Aerated	C	C	A	A	A	A	A	A	A	A	A	C	C	B
Acetic Acid Vapors	C	C	A	A	B	B	I.L.	A	B	A	A	C	C	B
Acetone	A	A	A	A	A	A	A	A	A	A	A	A	A	A
Acetylene	A	A	A	A	I.L.	A	A	A	A	I.L.	A	A	A	A
Alcohols	A	A	A	A	A	A	A	A	A	A	A	A	A	A
Aluminum Sulfate	C	C	A	A	B	B	A	A	A	A	I.L.	C	C	I.L.
Ammonia	A	A	A	A	C	A	A	A	A	A	A	A	A	I.L.
Ammonium Chloride	C	C	B	B	B	B	A	A	A	A	B	C	C	I.L.
Ammonium Nitrate	A	C	A	A	C	C	A	A	A	A	A	C	B	I.L.
Ammonium Phosphate (Mono-Basic)	C	C	A	A	B	B	A	A	B	A	A	B	B	I.L.
Ammonium Sulfate	C	C	B	A	B	A	A	A	A	A	A	C	C	I.L.
Ammonium Sulfite	C	C	A	A	C	C	I.L.	A	A	A	A	B	B	I.L.
Aniline	C	C	A	A	C	B	A	A	A	A	A	C	C	I.L.
Asphalt	A	A	A	A	A	A	A	A	A	I.L.	A	A	A	A
Beer	B	B	A	A	B	A	A	A	A	A	A	B	B	A
Benzene (Benzol)	A	A	A	A	A	A	A	A	A	A	A	A	A	A
Benzoic Acid	C	C	A	A	A	A	I.L.	A	A	A	I.L.	A	A	A
Boric Acid	C	C	A	A	A	A	A	A	A	A	A	B	B	I.L.

Butane	A	A	A	A	A	A	A	A	A	I.L.	A	A	A	A
Calcium Chloride (Alkaline)	B	B	C	B	C	A	A	A	A	A	I.L.	C	C	I.L.
Calcium Hypochlorite	C	C	B	B	B	B	C	A	A	A	I.L.	C	C	I.L.
Carbolic Acid	B	B	A	A	A	A	A	A	A	A	A	I.L.	I.L.	I.L.
Carbon Dioxide, Dry	A	A	A	A	A	A	A	A	A	A	A	A	A	A
Carbon Dioxide, Wet	C	C	A	A	B	A	A	A	A	A	A	A	A	A
Carbon Disulfide	A	A	A	A	C	B	A	A	A	A	A	B	B	I.L.
Carbon Tetrachloride	B	B	B	B	A	A	B	A	A	A	I.L.	C	A	I.L.
Carbonic Acid	C	C	B	B	B	A	A	A	A	I.L.	I.L.	A	A	A
Chlorine Gas, Dry	A	A	B	B	B	A	A	A	A	C	B	C	C	C
Chlorine Gas, Wet	C	C	C	C	C	C	C	B	C	A	B	C	C	C
Chlorine, Liquid	C	C	C	C	B	C	C	A	B	C	B	C	C	C
Chromic Acid	C	C	C	B	C	A	C	A	C	A	B	C	C	C
Citric Acid	I.L.	C	B	A	A	B	A	A	A	A	I.L.	B	B	B
Coke Oven Gas	A	A	A	A	B	B	A	A	A	A	A	A	A	A
Copper Sulfate	C	C	B	B	B	C	I.L.	A	A	A	I.L.	A	A	A
Cottonseed Oil	A	A	A	A	A	A	A	A	A	A	A	A	A	A
Creosote	A	A	A	A	C	A	A	A	A	I.L.	A	A	A	A
Ethane	A	A	A	A	A	A	A	A	A	A	A	A	A	A
Ether	B	B	A	A	A	A	A	A	A	A	A	A	A	A
Ethyl Chloride	C	C	A	A	A	A	A	A	A	A	A	B	B	I.L.
Ethylene	A	A	A	A	A	A	A	A	A	A	A	A	A	A
Ethylene Glycol	A	A	A	A	A	A	I.L.	I.L.	A	I.L.	A	A	A	A
Ferric Chloride	C	C	C	C	C	C	C	B	C	A	B	C	C	I.L.
Formaldehyde	B	B	A	A	A	A	A	A	A	A	A	A	A	A
Formic Acid	I.L.	C	B	B	A	A	A	A	A	C	B	C	C	B
Freon, Wet	B	B	B	A	A	A	A	A	A	A	A	I.L.	I.L.	I.L.
Freon, Dry	B	B	A	A	A	A	A	A	A	A	A	I.L.	I.L.	I.L.
Furfural	A	A	A	A	A	A	A	A	A	A	A	B	B	I.L.
Gasoline, Refined	A	A	A	A	A	A	A	A	A	A	A	A	A	A

*Trademark of International Nickel Co.
†Trademark of Stellite Division, Cabot Corp.
‡Trademark of Duriron Co.
A—Recommended.
B—Minor to moderate effect, proceed with caution.
C—Unsatisfactory.
I.L.—Information lacking.

- Continued -

FLUID	MATERIAL													
	Carbon Steel	Cast Iron	302 or 304 Stainless Steel	316 Stainless Steel	Bronze	Monel*	Hastelloy† B	Hatelloy† C	Durimet‡ 20	Titanium	Cobalt-Base Alloy 6	416 Stainless Steel	440C Hard Stainless Steel	17-4PH Hard Stainless Steel
Glucose	A	A	A	A	A	A	A	A	A	A	A	A	A	A
Hydrochloric Acid (Aerated)	C	C	C	C	C	C	A	B	C	C	B	C	C	C
Hydrochloric Acid (Air Free)	C	C	C	C	C	C	A	B	C	C	B	C	C	C
Hydrofluoric Acid (Aerated)	B	C	C	B	C	C	A	A	B	C	B	C	C	C
Hydrofluoric Acid (Air Free)	A	C	C	B	C	A	A	A	B	C	I.L.	C	C	I.L.
Hydrogen	A	A	A	A	A	A	A	A	A	A	A	A	A	A
Hydrogen Peroxide	I.L.	A	A	A	C	A	B	B	A	A	I.L.	B	B	I.L.
Hydrogen Sulfide, Liquid	C	C	A	A	C	C	A	A	B	A	A	C	C	I.L.
Magnesium Hydroxide	A	A	A	A	B	A	A	A	A	A	A	A	A	I.L.
Mercury	A	A	A	A	C	B	A	A	A	A	A	A	A	B
Methanol	A	A	A	A	A	A	A	A	A	A	A	A	B	A
Methyl Ethyl Ketone	A	A	A	A	A	A	A	A	A	I.L.	A	A	A	A
Milk	C	C	A	A	A	A	A	A	A	A	A	C	C	C
Natural Gas	A	A	A	A	A	A	A	A	A	A	A	A	A	A
Nitric Acid	C	C	A	B	C	C	C	B	A	A	C	C	C	B
Oleic Acid	C	C	A	A	B	A	A	A	A	A	A	A	A	I.L.
Oxalic Acid	C	C	B	B	B	B	A	A	A	B	B	B	B	I.L.
Oxygen	A	A	A	A	A	A	A	A	A	A	A	A	A	A
Petroleum Oils, Refined	A	A	A	A	A	A	A	A	A	A	A	A	A	A
Phosphoric Acid (Aerated)	C	C	A	A	C	C	A	A	A	B	A	C	C	I.L.
Phosphoric Acid (Air Free)	C	C	A	A	C	B	A	A	A	B	A	C	C	I.L.
Phosphoric Acid Vapors	C	C	B	B	C	C	A	I.L.	A	B	C	C	C	I.L.
Picric Acid	C	C	A	A	C	C	A	A	A	I.L.	I.L.	B	B	I.L.
Potassium Chloride	B	B	A	A	B	B	A	A	A	A	I.L.	C	C	I.L.
Potassium Hydroxide	B	B	A	A	B	A	A	A	A	A	I.L.	B	B	I.L.

Propane	A	A	A	A	A	A	A	A	A	A	A	A	A	A
Rosin	B	B	A	A	A	A	A	A	A	I.L.	A	A	A	A
Silver Nitrate	C	C	A	A	C	C	A	A	A	A	B	B	B	I.L.
Sodium Acetate	A	A	B	A	A	A	A	A	A	A	A	A	A	A
Sodium Carbonate	A	A	A	A	A	A	A	A	A	A	A	B	B	A
Sodium Chloride	C	C	B	B	A	A	A	A	A	A	A	B	B	B
Sodium Chromate	A	A	A	A	A	A	A	A	A	A	A	A	A	A
Sodium Hydroxide	A	A	A	A	C	A	A	A	A	A	A	B	B	A
Sodium Hypochloride	C	C	C	C	B-C	B-C	C	A	B	A	I.L.	C	C	I.L.
Sodium Thiosulfate	C	C	A	A	C	C	A	A	A	A	I.L.	B	B	I.L.
Stannous Chloride	B	B	C	A	C	B	A	A	A	A	I.L.	C	C	I.L.
Stearic Acid	A	C	A	A	B	B	A	A	A	A	B	B	B	I.L.
Sulfate Liquor (Black)	A	A	A	A	C	A	A	A	A	A	A	I.L.	IL.	I.L.
Sulfur	A	A	A	A	C	A	A	A	A	A	A	A	A	A
Sulfur Dioxide, Dry	A	A	A	A	A	A	B	A	A	A	A	B	B	I.L.
Sulfur Trioxide, Dry	A	A	A	A	A	A	B	A	A	A	A	B	B	I.L.
Sulfuric Acid (Aerated)	C	C	C	C	C	C	A	A	A	B	B	C	C	C
Sulfuric Acid (Air Free)	C	C	C	C	B	B	A	A	A	B	B	C	C	C
Sulfurous Acid	C	C	B	B	B	C	A	A	A	A	B	C	C	I.L.
Tar	A	A	A	A	A	A	A	A	A	A	A	A	A	A
Trichloroethylene	B	B	B	A	A	A	A	A	A	A	A	B	B	I.L.
Turpentine	B	B	A	A	A	B	A	A	A	A	A	A	A	A
Vinegar	C	C	A	A	B	A	A	A	A	I.L.	A	C	C	A
Water, Boiler Feed	B	C	A	A	C	A	A	A	A	A	A	B	A	A
Water, Distilled	A	A	A	A	A	A	A	A	A	A	A	B	B	I.L.
Water, Sea	B	B	B	B	A	A	A	A	A	A	A	C	C	A
Whiskey and Wines	C	C	A	A	A	B	A	A	A	A	A	C	C	I.L.
Zinc Chloride	C	C	C	C	C	C	A	A	A	A	B	C	C	I.L.
Zinc Sulfate	C	C	A	A	B	A	A	A	A	A	A	B	B	I.L.

*Trademark of International Nickel Co.
†Trademark of Stellite Division, Cabot Corp.
‡Trademark of Duriron Co.
A—Recommended.
B—Minor to moderate effect, proceed with caution.
C—Unsatisfactory.
I.L.—Information lacking.

Elastomer Information

Elastomer Selection

Selection of a suitable elastomer material for use in control valve applications requires knowledge of the service conditions in which the material will be used, as well as knowledge of the general properties of the material itself. Service temperature, pressure conditions, rate of flow, type of valve action (throttling or on-off), and chemical composition of the flowing fluid should all be known. Usage ratings listed below (Good, Fair, etc.) should be used as a guide only. Specific compounds within any one material may vary, which could change the usage rating.

General Properties

Property		Natural Rubber	Buna-S	Nitrile	Neoprene	Butyl	Thiokol[1]	Silicone	Hypalon[2]	Viton[2,3,4]	Polyurethane[4]	Polyacrylic[3]	Ethylene Propylene[5]
Tensile Strength, Psi (Bar)	Pure Gum	3000 (207)	400 (28)	600 (41)	3500 (241)	3000 (207)	300 (21)	200-450 (14-31)	4000 (276)	. . .	. . .	100 (7)	. . .
	Reinforced	4500 (310)	3000 (207)	4000 (276)	3500 (241)	3000 (207)	1500 (103)	1100 (76)	4400 (303)	2300 (159)	6500 (448)	1800 (124)	2500 (172)
Tear Resistance		Excellent	Poor-Fair	Fair	Good	Good	Fair	Poor-Fair	Excellent	Good	Excellent	Fair	Poor
Abrasion Resistance		Excellent	Good	Good	Excellent	Fair	Poor	Poor	Excellent	Very Good	Excellent	Good	Good
Aging: Sunlight		Poor	Poor	Poor	Excellent	Excellent	Good	Good	Excellent	Excellent	Excellent	Excellent	Excellent
Aging: Oxidation		Good	Fair	Fair	Good	Good	Good	Very Good	Very Good	Excellent	Excellent	Excellent	Good
Heat (Max. Temp.)		200°F (93°C)	200°F (93°C)	250°F (121°C)	200°F (93°C)	200°F (93°C)	140°F (60°C)	450°F (232°C)	300°F (149°C)	400°F (204°C)	200°F (93°C)	350°F (177°C)	350°F (177°C)
Static (Shelf)		Good	Good	Good	Very Good	Good	Fair	Good	Good	. . .	. . .	Good	Good
Flex Cracking Resistance		Excellent	Good	Good	Excellent	Excellent	Fair	Fair	Excellent	. . .	Excellent	Good	. . .
Compression Set Resistance		Good	Good	Very Good	Excellent	Fair	Poor	Good	Poor	Poor	Good	Good	Fair

Solvent Resistance:												
Aliphatic Hydrocarbon	Very Poor	Very Poor	Good	Fair	Poor	Excellent	Poor	Fair	Excellent	Very Good	Good	Poor
Aromatic Hydrocarbon	Very Poor	Very Poor	Fair	Poor	Very Poor	Good	Very Poor	Poor	Very Good	Fair	Poor	Fair
Oxygenated Solvent	Good	Good	Poor	Fair	Good	Fair	Poor	Poor	Good	Poor	Poor	. . .
Halogenated Solvent	Very Poor	Very Poor	Very Poor	Very Poor	Poor	Poor	Very Poor	Very Poor	. . .	. . .	Poor	Poor
Oil Resistance:												
Low Aniline Mineral Oil	Very Poor	Very Poor	Excellent	Fair	Very Poor	Excellent	Poor	Fair	Excellent	. . .	Excellent	Poor
High Aniline Mineral Oil	Very Poor	Very Poor	Excellent	Good	Very Poor	Excellent	Good	Good	Excellent	. . .	Excellent	Poor
Synthetic Lubricants	Very Poor	Very Poor	Fair	Very Poor	Poor	Poor	Fair	Poor	. .	. . .	Fair	Poor
Organic Phosphates	Very Poor	Very Poor	Very Poor	Very Poor	Good	Poor	Poor	Poor	Poor	Poor	Poor	Very Good
Gasoline Resistance:												
Aromatic	Very Poor	Very Poor	Good	Poor	Very Poor	Excellent	Poor	Poor	Good	Fair	Fair	Fair
Non-Aromatic	Very Poor	Very Poor	Excellent	Good	Very Poor	Excellent	Good	Fair	Very Good	Good	Poor	Poor
Acid Resistance:												
Diluted (Under 10%)	Good	Good	Good	Fair	Good	Poor	Fair	Good	Excellent	Fair	Poor	Very Good
Concentrated[6]	Fair	Poor	Poor	Fair	Fair	Very Poor	Poor	Good	Very Good	Poor	Poor	Good
Low Temperature Flexibility (Max.)	−65°F (−54°C)	−50°F (−46°C)	−40°F (−40°C)	−40°F (−40°C)	−40°F (−40°C)	−40°F (−40°C)	−100°F (−73°C)	−20°F (−29°C)	−30°F (−34°C)	−40°F (−40°C)	−10°F (−23°C)	−50°F (−45°C)
Permeability to Gases	Fair	Fair	Fair	Very Good	Very Good	Good	Fair	Very Good	Good	Good	Good	Good
Water Resistance	Good	Very Good	Very Good	Fair	Very Good	Fair	Fair	Fair	Excellent	Fair	Fair	Very Good
Alkali Resistance:												
Diluted (under 10%)	Good	Good	Good	Good	Very Good	Poor	Fair	Good	Excellent	Fair	Poor	Excellent
Concentrated	Fair	Fair	Fair	Good	Very Good	Poor	Poor	Good	Very Good	Poor	Poor	Good
Resilience	Very Good	Fair	Fair	Very Good	Very Good	Poor	Good	Good	Good	Fair	Very Poor	Very Good
Elongation (Max.)	700%	500%	500%	500%	700%	400%	300%	300%	425%	625%	200%	500%

1. Trademark of Thiokol Chemical Co.
2. Trademark of E.I. DuPont Co.
3. Do not use with steam.
4. Do not use with ammonia.
5. Do not use with petroleum base fluids. Use with ester base non-flammable hydraulic oils and low pressure steam applications to 300°F (149°C).
6. Except for nitric and sulfuric acid.

Fluid Compatibility

The following table rates and compares the compatibility of elastomer material with specific fluids. Note that this information should be used as a guide only. An elastomer which is compatible with a fluid may not be suitable over the entire range of its temperature capability. In general, chemical compatibility decreases with an increase in service temperature.

Fluid	Natural Rubber	Neoprene	Nitrile	EPT	Poly-urethane	Viton*	Hypalon*	Butyl	Silicone
Acetic Acid (30%)	B	C	B	A+	C	B	B	A	A
Acetone	B	B	C	A	C	C	B	A	B
Air, Ambient	B	A	A	A	A	A	A	A	A
Air, Hot (200°F) (93°C)	C	C	A	A	B	A	A	A	C
Air, Hot (400°F) (204°C)	C	C	C	C	C	B	C	C	C
Alcohol, Ethyl	A	A	A	A	B	B	A	A	A
Alcohol, Methyl	A	A+	A	A	C	C	A	A	A
Ammonia, Anhydrous	C	A	C	A	C	C	B	A	C
Ammonia, Gas (Hot)	C	B	C	B	C	C	B	C	B
Beer (Beverage)	A	A	B	A	C	A	A	A	A
Benzene	C	C	C	C	C	A	C	C	C
Black Liquor	B	B	A	B	C	A+	C	C	C
Blast Furnace Gas	C	C	B	C	C	A	C	C	A
Brine (Calcium Chloride)	A	A	A	A	A	B	A	A	A
Butadiene Gas	C	B	C	C	C	B	B	C	C
Butane, Gas	C	A	A+	C	B	A	A	C	C
Butane, Liquid	C	B	A	C	C	A	C	C	C
Carbon Tetrachloride	C	C	C	C	C	A	C	C	C
Chlorine, Dry	C	C	C	C	C	A	C	B	C
Chlorine, Wet	C	C	C	C	C	A	C	C	C
Coke Oven Gas	C	C	B	C	C	A+	B	C	B
Dowtherm† A	C	C	C	C	C	A	C	C	C
Ethyl Acetate	C	C	C	B	C	C	C	B	B
Ethylene Glycol	A	A	A	A+	B	A	A	A	A
Freon 11	C	B	A	C	C	A+	A	C	C
Freon 12	B	A+	A	B	A	B	A	B	C
Freon 22	C	A+	C	A	C	C	A	A	C

Freon 114	A	A	A	A	A	B	B	A	C
Gasoline	C	B	A+	C	B	A	B	C	C
Hydrogen Gas	B	A	A	A	A	A	A	A	C
Hydrogen Sulfide (Dry)	B	A	C	A+	B	C	A	A	C
Hydrogen Sulfide (Wet)	C	B	C	A+	C	C	C	A	C
Jet Fuel (JP-4)	C	C	A	C	B	A	C	C	C
Methylene Chloride	C	C	C	C	C	B	C	C	C
Milk	A	A	A+	A	C	A	A	A	A
Natural Gas	C	A	A+	C	B	A	A	C	C
Natural Gas + H_2S (Sour Gas)	C	A	B	C	B	C	A	C	C
Natural Gas, Sour + Ammonia	C	B	B	C	C	C	B	C	C
Naphthalene	C	C	C	C	B	A	C	C	C
Nitric Acid (10%)	C	B	C	B	C	A	B	B	B
Nitric Acid (50 to 100%)	C	C	C	C	C	A	C	C	C
Nitric Acid Vapor	C	B	C	B	C	A	B	B	C
Nitrogen	A	A	A	A	A	A	A	A	A
Oil (Fuel)	C	B	A+	C	C	A	A	C	C
Ozone	C	B	C	A	A	A	A	B	A
Paper Stock	C	B	B	B	C	A	B	B	C
Propane	C	A	A	C	B	A	A	C	C
Sea Water	B	B	A	A	B	A	B	A	B
Sea Water + Sulfuric Acid	C	B	C	B	B	A	B	B	C
Soap Solutions	B	A	A	A	A	A	A	A	A
Steam	C	C	C	B	C	C	C	B	C
Sulfur Dioxide	C	A	C	A+	B	A	C	B	A
Sulfuric Acid (to 50%)	C	B	C	B	B	A	B	B	C
Sulfuric Acid (50 to 100%)	C	C	C	B	C	A	C	B	C
Water (Ambient)	A	A	A	A	A	A	A	A	A
Water (200°F) (93°C)	C	C	B	A+	C	B	B	B	C
Water (300°F) (149°C)	C	C	C	B	C	C	C	B	C
Water (De-ionized)	A	A	A	A	A	A	A	A	A
Water, White	B	B	A	A	B	A	B	A	B

*Trademark of E.I. DuPont Co.
†Trademark of Dow Chemical Co.
A+—Best possible selection.

A—Recommended.
B—Minor to moderate effect. Proceed with caution.
C—Unsatisfactory.

Service Temperature Limitations

Material	Low Limit		High Limit	
	°F	°C	°F	°C
Natural Rubber	−60	−51	160	71
Neoprene	−40	−40	175	79
Nitrile	−20	−29	200	93
Polyurethane	−40	−40	200	93
Hypalon*	0	−18	225	107
Butyl	−20	−29	300	149
Ethylene Propylene (EPT)	−40	−40	300	149
Viton*	0	−18	400	204
Silicone	−65	−54	400	204

*Trademark of E.I. DuPont Co.

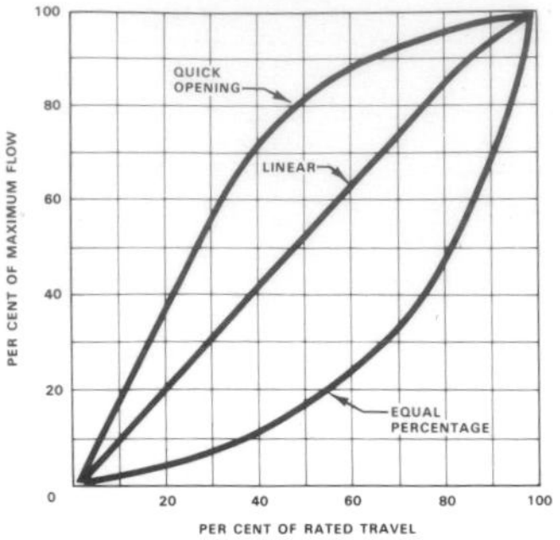

Figure 3-9. Typical Flow Characteristic Curves

Service Temperature Limitations for Elastomers

Temperature ranges indicated in the table above suggest limits within which the materials will function adequately. Temperatures shown are not necessarily inherent temperature limits. Dynamic forces imposed on the materials are also considered. Frequently, tear strength and other physical properties decrease rapidly as service temperature increases.

Control Valve Flow Characteristics

Introduction

The flow characteristic of a control valve is the relationship between the flow rate through the valve and the valve travel as the travel is varied from 0 to 100%. "Inherent flow characteristic" refers to the characteristic observed with a constant pressure drop across the valve. By "installed flow characteristic", we mean the one obtained in service where the pressure drop varies with flow and other changes in the system.

The purpose of characterizing control valves is to provide for a relatively uniform control loop stability over the expected range of system operating conditions. To establish the flow characteristic needed to "match" a given system requires a dynamic analysis of the control loop. Analysis of the more common processes have been performed, however, so we can establish some useful guidelines for the selection of the proper flow characteristic. But first, let's look briefly at the flow characteristics in use today.

Discussion of Flow Characteristics

Figure 3-9 illustrates typical flow characteristic curves. The quick opening flow characteristic provides for maximum change in flow rate at low valve travels with a fairly linear relationship. Additional increases in valve travel give sharply reduced changes in flow rate, and when the valve plug nears the wide open position, the change in flow rate approaches zero. In a control valve, the quick opening valve plug is used primarily for on-off service; but it is also suitable for many applications where a linear valve plug would normally be specified.

The linear flow characteristic curve shows that the flow rate is directly proportional to the valve travel. This proportional relationship produces a characteristic with a constant slope so that with constant pressure drop, the valve gain will be the same at all flows. (Valve gain is the ratio of an incremental change in flow rate to an incremental change in valve plug position. Gain is a function of valve size and configuration, system operating conditions and valve plug characteristic.) The linear valve plug is commonly specified for liquid level control and for certain flow control applications requiring constant gain.

In the equal percentage flow characteristic, equal increments of valve travel produce equal percentage changes in the existing flow. The change in flow rate is always proportional to the flow rate just before the change in valve plug, disc, or ball position is made. When the valve plug, disc, or ball is near its seat and the flow is small, the change in flow rate will be small; with a large flow, the change in flow rate will be large. Valves with an equal percentage flow characteristic are generally used on pressure control applications, and on other applications where a large percentage of the pressure drop is normally absorbed by the system itself, with only a relatively small percentage available at the control valve. Valves with an equal percentage characteristic should also be considered where highly varying pressure drop conditions can be expected. Fisher **Micro-Form,**™ **Micro-Flute**™, **V-Pup**®, and equal percentage valve plugs and cages all exhibit an equal percentage flow characteristic. Fisher rotary stem **Vee-Ball**®, **Hi-Ball**® and butterfly valves have flow characteristics which are approximately equal percentage.

Selection of Flow Characteristic

Here are some guidelines that will help in the selection of the proper flow characteristic. Remember, however, that there will be occasional exceptions to most of these "rules of thumb", and that a positive recommendation is possible only by means of a complete dynamic analysis. It should also be noted that where a linear characteristic is recommended, a quick opening valve plug could be used, and while the controller will have to operate on a wider proportional band setting, the same degree of control accuracy may be expected.

Liquid Level Systems

Control Valve Pressure Drop	Best Inherent Characteristic
Constant ΔP	Linear
Decreasing ΔP with Increasing Load, ΔP at Maximum Load $>$ 20% of Minimum Load ΔP	Linear
Decreasing ΔP with Increasing Load, ΔP at Maximum Load $<$ 20% of Minimum Load ΔP	Equal Percentage
Increasing ΔP with Increasing Load, ΔP at Maximum Load $<$ 200% of Minimum Load ΔP	Linear
Increasing ΔP with Increasing Load, ΔP at Maximum Load $>$ 200% of Minimum Load ΔP	Quick Opening

Flow Control Processes

FLOW MEASUREMENT SIGNAL TO CONTROLLER	LOCATION OF CONTROL VALVE IN RELATION TO MEASURING ELEMENT	BEST INHERENT CHARACTERISTIC	
		Wide Range of Flow Set Point	Small Range of Flow but Large ΔP Change at Valve with Increasing Load
Proportional To Flow	In Series	Linear	Equal Percentage
	In Bypass*	Linear	Equal Percentage
Proportional To Flow Squared	In Series	Linear	Equal Percentage
	In Bypass*	Equal Percentage	Equal Percentage

*When control valve closes, flow rate increases in measuring element.

Pressure Control Systems

Application	Best Inherent Characteristic
Liquid Process	Equal Percentage
Gas Process, Small Volume, Less Than 10 ft. (3 meters) of Pipe Between Control Valve and Load Valve	Equal Percentage
Gas Process, Large Volume [Process has a Receiver, Distribution System or Transmission Line Exceeding 100 ft. (30.5 meters) of Nominal Pipe Volume] Decreasing ΔP with Increasing Load, ΔP at Maximum Load > 20% of Minimum Load ΔP	Linear
Gas Process, Large Volume, Decreasing ΔP with Increasing Load, ΔP at Maximum Load < 20% of Minimum Load ΔP	Equal Percentage

Valve Sizing

While selection of appropriate control valve materials and pressure-temperature ratings warrant careful considerations, choosing the correct valve size is no doubt equally important. Simply specifying a valve size to match an existing pipeline size leaves much to chance and will likely create an impractical situation in terms of initial investment and adequacy of control. Obviously, a valve too small will not pass the required amount of flow. A valve too large will be unnecessarily expensive and may well create instability problems as it attempts to control at very low increments of travel. Naturally, knowledge of the process conditions mentioned earlier in this chapter is necessary to determine proper valve size.

Sizing for Liquid Service

Using the principle of conservation of energy, Daniel Bernoulli discovered that as a liquid flows through an orifice, the square of the fluid velocity is directly proportional to the pressure differential across the orifice and inversely proportional to the specific gravity of the fluid. Therefore, the greater the pressure differential, the higher the velocity; the greater the density, the lower the velocity. Logically, the volume flow rate for liquids can be calculated by multiplying the fluid velocity times the flow area.

By taking into account units of measurement, the proportionality relationship previously mentioned, energy losses due to friction and turbulence, and varying discharge coefficients for various types of orifices (or valve bodies), a basic liquid sizing equation can be written as follows:

$$Q = C_v\sqrt{\Delta P/G} \qquad (1)$$

where:

Q = Capacity in gallons per minute

C_v = Valve sizing coefficient determined experimentally for each style and size of valve, using water at standard conditions as the test fluid

ΔP = Pressure differential in psi

G = Specific gravity of fluid (water at 60°F = 1.0000)

Thus, C_v is numerically equal to the number of U.S. gallons of water at 60°F that will flow through the valve in one minute when the pressure differential across the valve is one pound per square inch. C_v varies with both size and style of valve, but provides an index for comparing liquid capacities of different valves under a standard set of conditions.

To aid in establishing uniform measurement of liquid flow capacity coefficients (C_v) among valve manufactures, the Fluid Controls Institute (FCI)

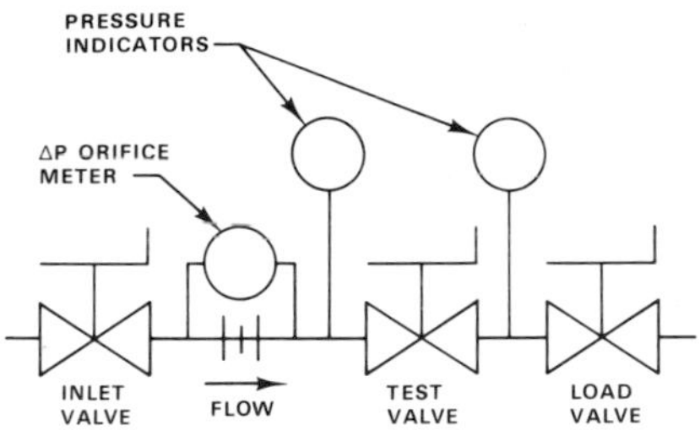

Figure 3-10. Standard FCI Test Piping for C_v Measurement

has developed a standard test piping arrangement, as shown in Figure 3-10. Using such a piping arrangement, most valve manufacturers develop and publish C_v information for their respective products, making it relatively easy to compare capacities of competitive products.

To calculate the expected C_v for a valve controlling water or other liquids that behave like water, the basic liquid sizing equation above can be re-written as follows:

$$C_v = Q\sqrt{\frac{G}{\Delta P}} \qquad (2)$$

Viscosity Corrections

Viscous conditions can result in significant sizing errors in using the basic liquid sizing equation, since published C_v values are based on test data using water as the flow medium. Although the majority of valve applications will involve fluids where viscosity corrections can be ignored, or where the corrections are relatively small, fluid viscosity should be considered in each valve selection.

Fisher Controls Company has developed a nomograph and procedure (Figure 3-11) that provides a viscosity correction factor (F_v). It can be applied to the standard C_v coefficient to determine a corrected coefficient (C_{vr}) for viscous applications.

Finding Valve Size

Using the C_v determined by the basic liquid sizing equation and the flow and viscosity conditions of the proposed installation, a fluid Reynolds number can be found by using the nomograph and procedure shown on the next page. The graph of Reynolds number vs. viscosity correction factor (F_v) is used to determine the correction factor needed. (If the Reynolds number is greater than 3500, the correction will be ten percent or less.) The actual required C_v (C_{vr}) is found by the equation:

$$C_{vr} = F_v C_v \qquad (3)$$

From the valve manufacturer's published liquid capacity information, select a valve having a C_v equal to or higher than the required coefficient (C_{vr}) found by the equation above.

Predicting Flow Rate

Select the required liquid sizing coefficient (C_{vr}) from the manufacturer's published liquid sizing coefficients (C_v) for the style and size valve being considered. Calculate the maximum flow rate (Q_{max}) in gallons per minute (assuming no viscosity correction required) using the following adaptation of the basic liquid sizing equation:

$$Q_{max} = C_{vr}\sqrt{\Delta P/G} \quad . \qquad (4)$$

Then incorporate viscosity correction by determining the fluid Reynolds number and correction factor F_v from the viscosity correction nomograph and the procedure included on it.

Calculate the predicted flow rate (Q_{pred}) using the formula:

$$Q_{pred} = \frac{Q_{max}}{F_v} \quad . \qquad (5)$$

Predicting Pressure Drop

Select the required liquid sizing coefficient (C_{vr}) from the manufacturer's published liquid sizing coefficients (C_v) for the valve style and size being considered. Determine the Reynolds number and correct factor F_v from the nomograph and the procedure on it. Calculate the sizing coefficient (C_{vc}) using the formula:

$$C_{vc} = \frac{C_{vr}}{F_v} \qquad (6)$$

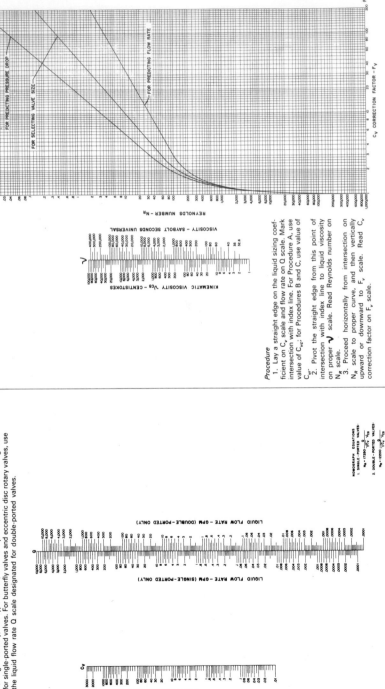

Nomograph Instructions

Use this nomograph in liquid sizing to correct for the effects of viscosity. When assembling data, all units must correspond to those shown on the nomograph. For high-recovery, ball-type valves, use the liquid flow rate Q scale designated for single-ported valves. For butterfly valves and eccentric disc rotary valves, use the liquid flow rate Q scale designated for double-ported valves.

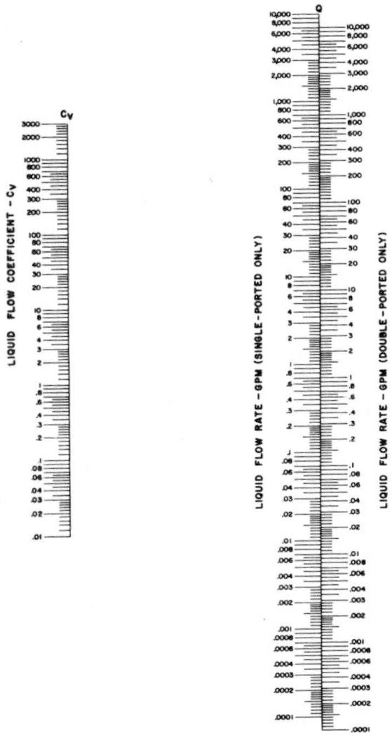

INDEX

NOMOGRAPH EQUATIONS

1. SINGLE-PORTED VALVES: $N_R = 17250 \frac{Q}{\sqrt{C_V}\, \nu_{cs}}$
2. DOUBLE-PORTED VALVES: $N_R = 12200 \frac{Q}{\sqrt{C_V}\, \nu_{cs}}$

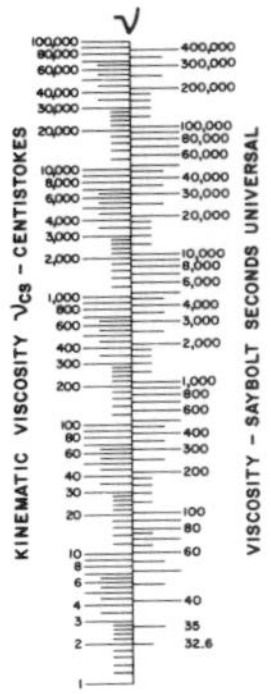

Procedure

1. Lay a straight edge on the liquid sizing coefficient on C_v scale and flow rate on Q scale. Mark intersection with index line. For Procedure A, use value of C_{vc}; for Procedures B and C, use value of C_{vr}.
2. Pivot the straight edge from this point of intersection with index line to liquid viscosity on proper ν scale. Read Reynolds number on N_R scale.
3. Proceed horizontally from intersection on N_R scale to proper curve, and then vertically upward or downward to F_v scale. Read C_v correction factor on F_v scale.

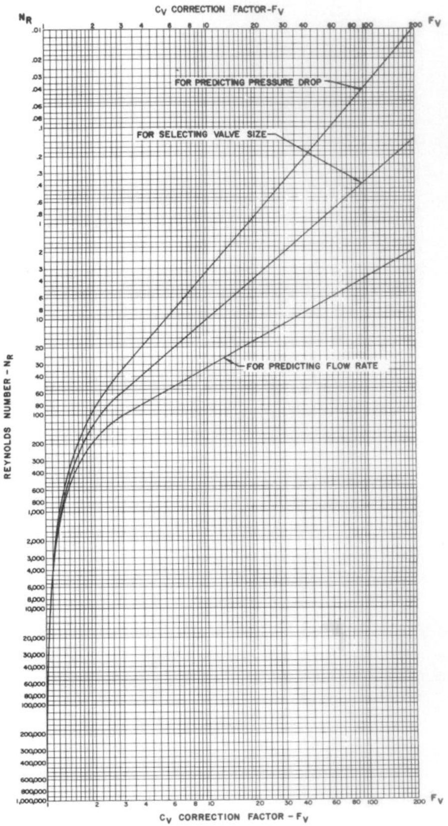

Figure 3-11. Nomograph for Determining Viscosity Correction

Calculate the predicted pressure drop (ΔP_{pred}) using the formula:

$$\Delta \mathbf{P}_{pred} = \mathbf{G}\ (\mathbf{Q}/\mathbf{C}_{vc})^2 \qquad (7)$$

Flashing & Cavitation
The occurrence of either flashing or cavitation within a control valve can have a significant effect on the valve sizing procedure. These two related physical phenomena tend to limit flow through the control valve in many common applications and must, therefore, be taken into account in order to accurately size a valve. Structural damage to the valve and adjacent piping may also result. Knowledge of what is actually happening within the valve may permit selection of a size or style of valve which can reduce, or compensate for, the undesirable effects of flashing or cavitation.

The "physical phenomena" label is used to describe flashing and cavitation because these conditions represent actual changes in the form of the fluid media. The change is from the liquid state to the vapor state and results from the increase in fluid velocity at or just downstream of the greatest flow restriction, normally the valve port. As liquid flow passes through the restriction, there is a necking down, or contraction, of the flow stream. The minimum cross-sectional area of the flow stream occurs just downstream of the actual physical restriction at a point called the vena contracta, as shown in Figure 3-12.

To maintain a steady flow of liquid through the valve, the velocity must be greatest at the vena contracta, where cross sectional area is the least. The increase in velocity (or kinetic energy) is accompanied by a substantial decrease in pressure (or potential energy) at the vena contracta. Further downstream, as the fluid stream expands into a larger area, velocity decreases and pressure increases. But, of course, downstream pressure never recovers completely to equal the pressure that existed upstream of the valve. The pressure differential (ΔP) that exists

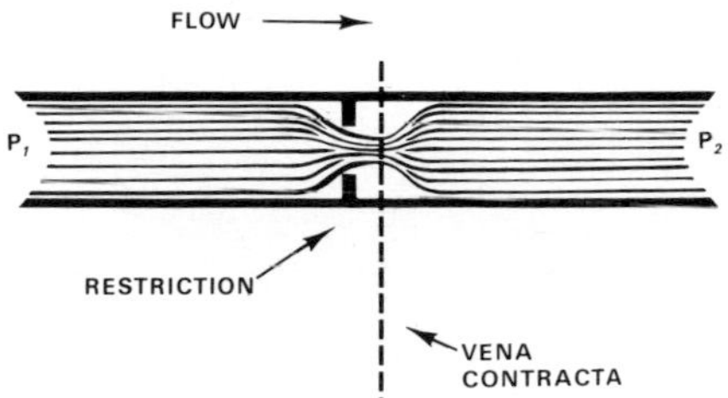

Figure 3-12. Vena Contracta Illustration

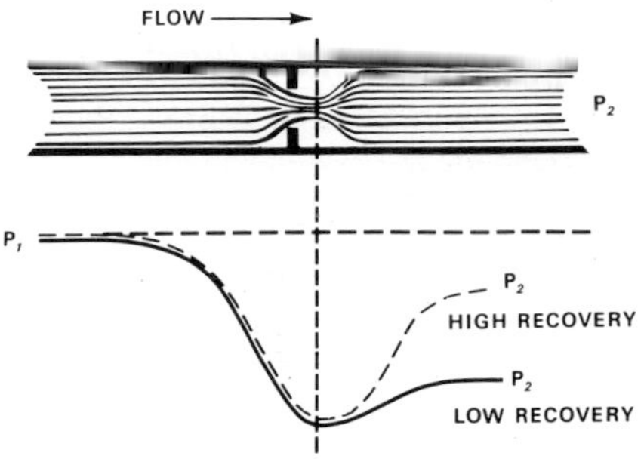

Figure 3-13. Comparison of Pressure Profiles for High and Low Recovery Valves

across the valve is a measure of the amount of energy that was dissipated in the valve. Figure 3-13 provides a pressure profile explaining the differing performance of a streamlined high recovery valve, such as a ball valve, and a valve with lower recovery capabilities due to greater internal turbulence and dissipation of energy.

Regardless of the recovery characteristics of the valve, the pressure differential of interest pertaining to flashing and cavitation is the differential between the valve inlet and the vena contracta. If pressure at the vena contracta should drop below the vapor pressure of the fluid (due to increased fluid velocity at this point) bubbles will form in the flow stream. Formation of bubbles will increase greatly as vena contracta pressure drops further below the vapor pressure of the liquid. At this stage, there is no difference between flashing and cavitation, but the potential for structural damage to the valve definitely exists.

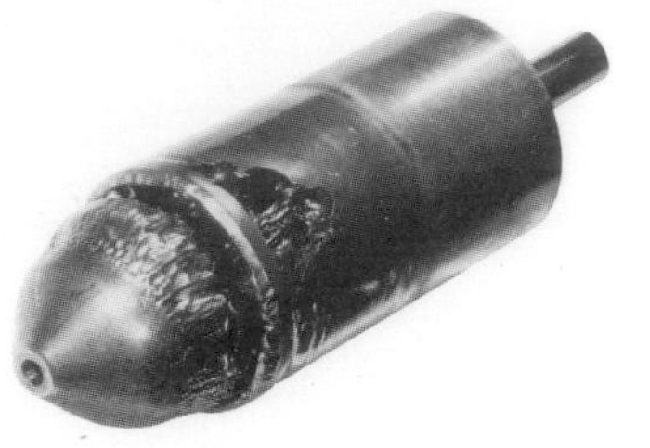

Figure 3-14. Typical Appearance Of Flashing Damage

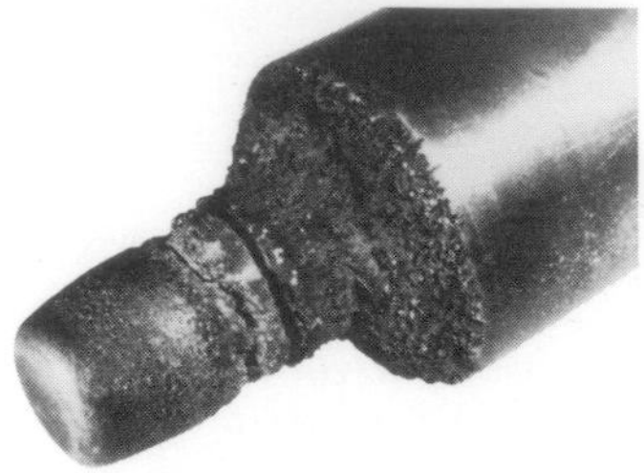

Figure 3-15. Typical Appearance of Cavitation Damage

If pressure at the valve outlet remains below the vapor pressure of the liquid, the bubbles will remain in the downstream system and the process is said to have "flashed." Flashing can produce serious erosion damage to the valve trim parts and is characterized by a smooth, polished appearance of the eroded surface, as shown in Figure 3-14. Flashing damage is normally greatest at the point of highest velocity, which is usually at or near the seat line of the valve plug and seat ring.

On the other hand, if downstream pressure recovery is sufficient to raise the outlet pressure above the vapor pressure of the liquid, the bubbles will collapse, or implode, producing cavitation. Collapsing of the vapor bubbles releases energy and produces a noise similar to what one would expect if gravel were flowing through the valve. If the bubbles collapse in close proximity to solid surfaces in the valve, the energy released will gradually tear away the material leaving a rough, cinderlike surface as shown in Figure 3-15. Cavitation damage may extend to the adjacent downstream pipeline, if that is where pressure recovery occurs and the bubbles collapse. Obviously, "high recovery" valves tend to be more subject to cavitation, since the downstream pressure is more likely to rise above the liquid's vapor pressure.

Choked Flow

Aside from the possibility of physical equipment damage due to flashing or cavitation, formation of vapor bubbles in the liquid flowstream causes a crowding condition at the vena contracta which tends to limit flow through the valve. So, while the basic liquid sizing equation implies that there is no limit to the amount of flow through a valve as long as the differential pressure across the valve increases, the realities of flashing and cavitation prove otherwise. If valve pressure drop is increased slightly beyond the point where bubbles begin to form, a choked flow condition is reached. With constant upstream pressure, further increases in pressure drop (by reducing downstream pressure) will not produce increased flow through the valve. The limiting pressure differential is designated ΔP_{allow} and the valve recovery coefficient (K_m) is experimentally determined for each valve, in order to relate choked flow for that particular valve to the basic liquid sizing equation. K_m is normally published with other valve capacity coefficients. Figures 3-16 and 3-17 show these flow vs. pressure drop relationships.

Use the following equation to determine the maximum allowable pressure drop that is effective in producing flow. Keep in mind, however, that the limitation on the sizing pressure drop, ΔP_{allow}, does not imply a maximum pressure drop that may be controlled by the valve.

$$\Delta P_{allow} = K_m (P_1 - r_c P_v) \qquad (8)$$

where:

ΔP_{allow} = maximum allowable differential pressure for sizing purposes, psi

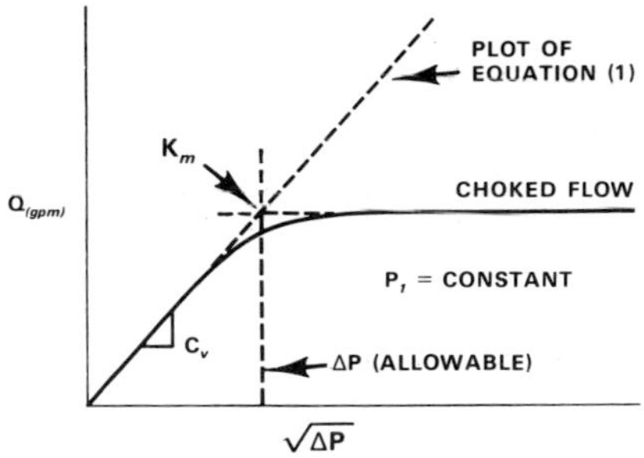

Figure 3-16. Flow Curve Showing C_v and K_m

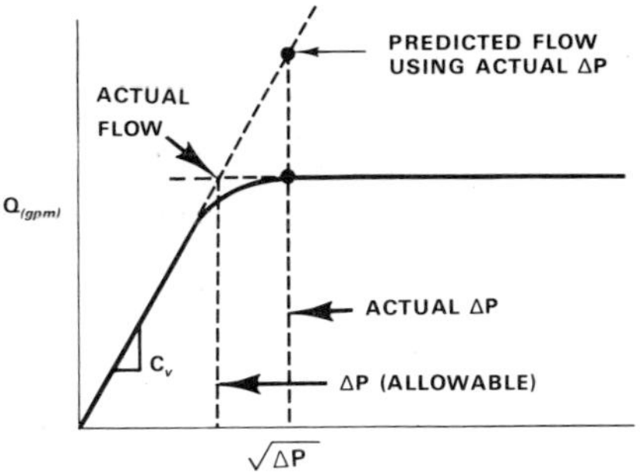

Figure 3-17. Relationship Between Actual ΔP and ΔP Allowable

K_m = valve recovery coefficient from manufacturer's literature

P_1 = body inlet pressure, psia

r_c = critical pressure ratio determined from Figures 3-18 and 3-19

P_v = vapor pressure of the liquid at body inlet temperature, psia (vapor pressures and critical pressures for many common liquids are provided in the tables on pages 130 through 134.)

After calculating ΔP_{allow}, substitute it into the basic liquid sizing equation $Q = C_v\sqrt{\Delta P/G}$ to determine either Q or C_v. If the actual ΔP is less than ΔP_{allow}, then the actual ΔP should be used in the sizing equation.

The equation used to determine ΔP_{allow} should also be used to calculate the valve body differential pressure at which significant cavitation can occur. Minor cavitation will occur at a slightly lower pressure differential than that predicted by the equation, but should produce negligible damage in most globe-style control valves.

Consequently, it can be seen that initial cavitation and choked flow occur nearly simultaneously in globe-style or low-recovery valves.

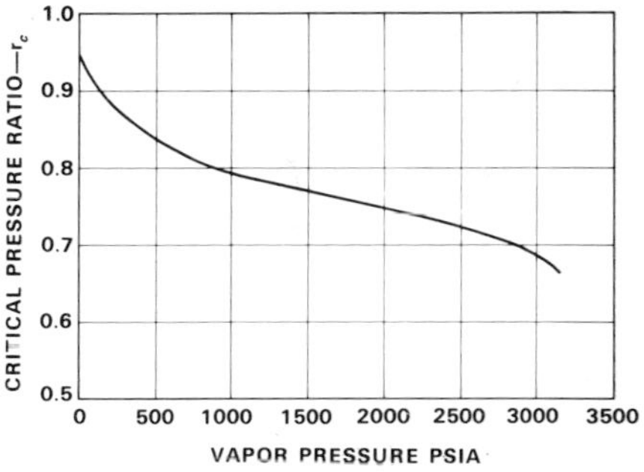

Use this curve for water. Enter on the abscissa at the water vapor pressure at the valve inlet. Proceed vertically to intersect the curve. Move horizontally to the left to read the critical pressure ratio, r_c, on the ordinate.

Figure 3-18. Critical Pressure Ratios for Water

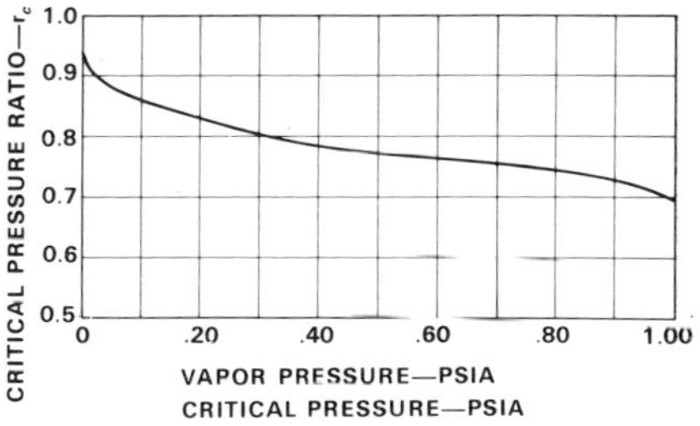

Use this curve for liquids other than water. Determine the vapor pressure/critical pressure ratio by dividing the liquid vapor pressure at the valve inlet by the critical pressure of the liquid. Enter on the abscissa at the ratio just calculated and proceed vertically to intersect the curve. Move horizontally to the left and read the critical pressure ratio, r_c, on the ordinate.

Figure 3-19. Critical Pressure Ratios for Liquids Other than Water

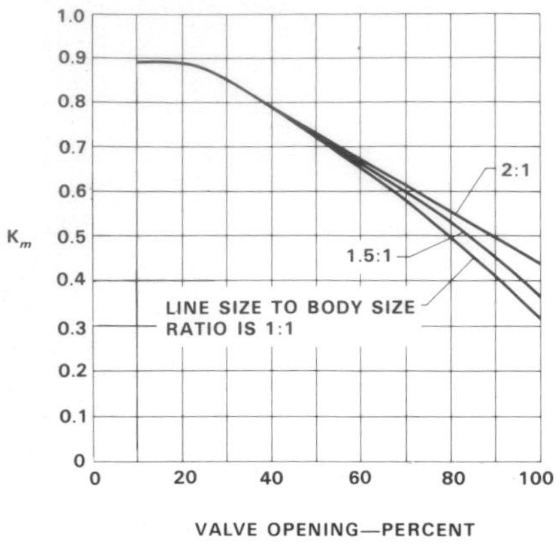

Figure 3-20. K_m Curves for Typical High Recovery Rotary Valves

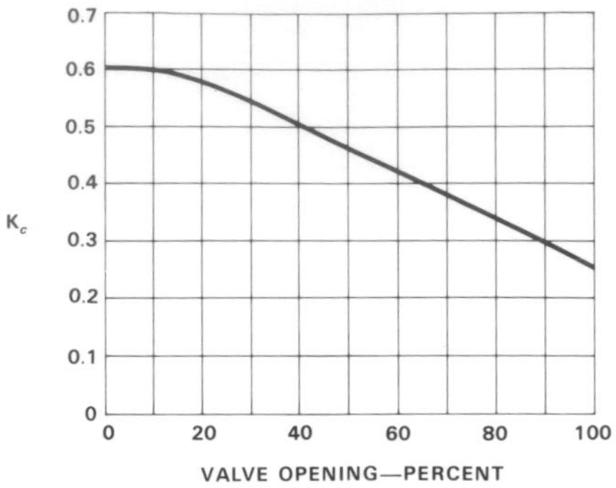

Figure 3-21. K_c Curves for Typical High-Recovery Rotary Valves

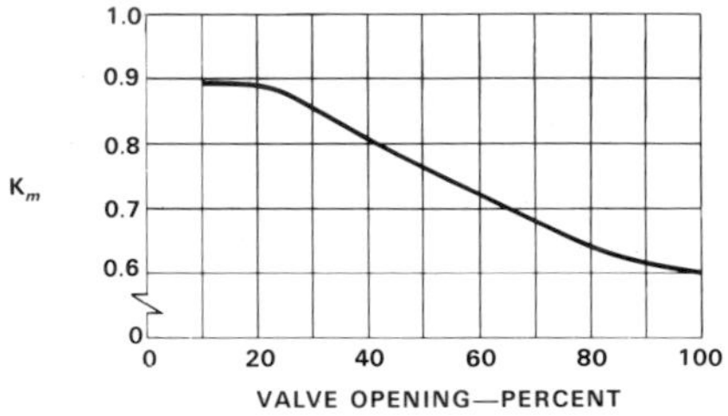

Figure 3-22. K_m Curve for High-Recovery Rotary Valve with Anti-Cavitation Trim

However, in high-recovery valves such as ball or butterfly valves, significant cavitation can occur at pressure drops below that which produces choked flow. So while ΔP_{allow} and K_m are useful in predicting choked flow capacity, a separate cavitation index (K_c) is needed to determine the pressure drop at which cavitation damage will begin (ΔP_c) in high-recovery valves.

The equation can be expressed.

$$\Delta P_c = K_c (P_1 - P_v) \quad (9)$$

This equation can be used anytime outlet pressure is greater than the vapor pressure of the liquid. Figures 3-20 and 3-21 illustrate K_m and K_c curves for typical V-notch ball, high-recovery, rotary valves in liquid service. Note that K_m is considerably higher than K_c throughout the travel range of the valve.

Addition of anti-cavitation trim to the same high-recovery V-notch valve tends to increase the value of K_m in the upper two-thirds of the travel range as shown in Figure 3-22. In other words, choked flow and insipient cavitation will occur at substantially higher pressure drops than was the case without the anti-cavitation accessory.

Liquid Sizing Summary

The most common use of the basic liquid sizing equation is to determine the proper valve size for a given set of service conditions. The first step is to calculate the required C_v by using the sizing equation. The ΔP used in the equation must be the actual valve pressure drop or ΔP_{allow}, whichever is smaller. The second step is to select a valve, from the manufacturer's catalog, with a C_v equal to or greater than the calculated value.

Accurate valve sizing for liquids requires use of the dual coefficients of C_v and K_m. A single coefficient is not sufficient to describe both the capacity and the recovery characteristics of the valve. Also, use of the additional cavitation index factor K_c is appropriate in sizing high recovery valves, which may develop damaging cavitation at pressure drops well below the level of the choked flow.

Summary of Liquid Sizing Nomenclature

C_v = valve sizing coefficient for liquid determined experimentally for each size and style of valve, using water at standard conditions as the test fluid

C_{vc} = calculated C_v coefficient including correction for viscosity

C_{vr} = corrected sizing coefficient required for viscous applications

ΔP = differential pressure, psi

ΔP_{allow} = maximum allowable differential pressure for sizing purposes, psi

ΔP_c = pressure differential at which cavitation damage begins, psi

F_v = viscosity correction factor

G = specific gravity of fluid (water at 60°F = 1.0000)

K_c = dimensionless cavitation index used in determining ΔP_c

K_m = valve recovery coefficient from manufacturer's literature

P_1 = body inlet pressure, psia

P_v = vapor pressure of liquid at body inlet pressure, psia

Q = flow rate capacity, gallons per minute

Q_{max} = designation for maximum flow rate, assuming no viscosity correction required, gallons per minute

Q_{pred} = predicted flow rate after incorporating viscosity correction, gallons per minute

r_c = critical pressure ratio

Summary of Liquid Sizing Equation Applications

(1)—Basic liquid sizing equation. Use to determine proper valve size for a given set of service conditions. (Remember that viscosity effects and valve recovery capabilities are not considered in this basic equation.)

(2)—Use to calculate expected C_v for valve controlling water or other liquids that behave like water.

(3)—Use to find actual required C_v for equation *(2)* after including viscosity correction factor.

(4)—Use to find maximum flow rate assuming no viscosity correction is necessary.

(5)—Use to predict actual flow rate based on equation *(4)* and viscosity factor correction.

(6)—Use to calculate corrected sizing coefficient for use in equation *(7)*.

(7)—Use to predict pressure drop for viscous liquids.

(8)—Use to determine maximum allowable pressure drop that is effective in producing flow.

(9)—Use to predict pressure drop at which cavitation will begin in a valve with high recovery characteristics.

Sizing for Gas or Steam Service

A sizing procedure for gases can be established based on adaptations of the basic liquid sizing equation. By introducing conversion factors to change flow units from gallons-per-minute to cubic-feet-per-hour and to relate specific gravity in meaningful terms of pressure, an equation can be derived for the flow of air at 60°F. Since 60°F corresponds to 520° on the Rankine absolute temperature scale, and since the specific gravity of air at 60°F is 1.0, an additional factor can be included to compare air at 60°F with specific gravity (G) and absolute temperature (T) of any other gas. The resulting equation can be written:

$$Q_{scfh} = 59.64\, C_v P_1 \sqrt{\frac{\Delta P}{P_1}} \sqrt{\frac{520}{GT}} \quad (A)$$

The equation shown above, while valid at very low pressure drop ratios, has been found to be very misleading when the ratio of pressure drop (ΔP) to inlet pressure (P_1) exceeds 0.02. The deviation of actual flow capacity from the calculated flow capacity is indicated in Figure 3-23 and results from compressibility effects and critical flow limitations at increased pressure drops.

Critical flow limitation is the more significant of the two problems mentioned. Critical flow is a choked flow condition caused by increased gas velocity at the vena contracta. When velocity at the vena contracta reaches sonic velocity, additional increases in ΔP by reducing downstream pressure produce no increase in flow. So after critical flow condition is reached (whether at a pressure drop/inlet pressure ratio of about 0.5 for globe valves or at much lower ratios for high recovery valves) the equation above becomes completely useless. If applied, the C_v equation gives a must higher indicated capacity than actually will exist. And in the case of a high recovery valve which reaches critical flow at a low pressure drop ratio (as indicated in Figure 3-24), the critical flow capacity of the valve may be over-estimated by as much as 300 percent.

The problems in predicting critical flow with a C_v-based equation led to establishing a separate gas sizing coefficient based on air flow tests. The coefficient (C_g) was developed experimentally for each type and size of valve to relate critical flow to absolute inlet pressure. By including the correction factor used in the previous equation to compare air at 60°F with other gases at other absolute temperatures, the critical flow equation can be written:

$$Q_{critical} = C_g P_1 \sqrt{520/GT} \quad (B)$$

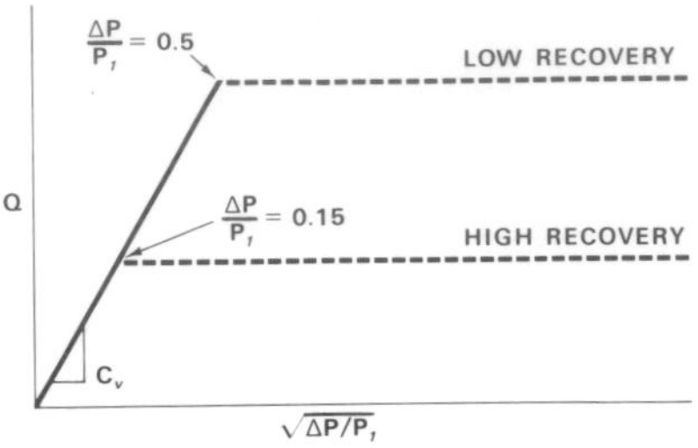

Figure 3-24. Critical Flow for High and Low Recovery Valves with Equal C_v

Universal Gas Sizing Equation

To account for differences in flow geometry among valves, equations *(A)* and *(B)* were consolidated by the introduction of an additional factor (C_1). C_1 is defined as the ratio of the gas sizing coefficient and the liquid sizing coefficient and provides a numerical indicator of the valve's recovery capabilities. In general, C_1 values can range from about 16 to 37, based on the individual valve's recovery characteristics. As shown in the example, two valves with identical flow areas and identical critical flow (C_g) capacities can have widely differing C_1 values dependent on the effect internal flow geometry has on liquid flow capacity through each valve.

Example:

High Recovery Valve

$C_g = 4680$
$C_v = 254$
$C_1 = C_g/C_v = 4680/254 = 18.4$

Low Recovery Valve

$C_g = 4680$
$C_v = 135$
$C_1 = C_g/C_v = 4680/135 = 34.7$

So we see that two sizing coefficients are needed to accurately size valves for gas flow—C_g to predict flow based on physical size or flow area, and C_1 to account for differences in valve recovery characteristics. A blending equation, called the Universal Gas Sizing Equation, combines equations *(A)* and *(B)* by means of a sinusoidal function, and is based on the "perfect gas" laws. It can be expressed in either of the following manners:

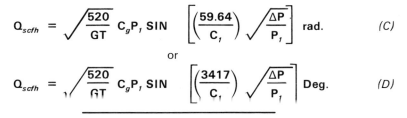

$$Q_{scfh} = \sqrt{\frac{520}{GT}}\, C_g P_1 \,\text{SIN} \left[\left(\frac{59.64}{C_1}\right)\sqrt{\frac{\Delta P}{P_1}}\right] \text{rad.} \qquad (C)$$

or

$$Q_{scfh} = \sqrt{\frac{520}{GT}}\, C_g P_1 \,\text{SIN} \left[\left(\frac{3417}{C_1}\right)\sqrt{\frac{\Delta P}{P_1}}\right] \text{Deg.} \qquad (D)$$

In either form, the equation indicates critical flow when the sine function of the angle designated within the brackets equals unity. The pressure drop ratio at which critical flow occurs is known as the critical pressure drop ratio. It occurs when the sine angle reaches π/2 radians in equation *(C)* or 90 degrees in equation *(D)*. As pressure drop across the valve increases, the sine angle increases from zero up to π/2 radians (90°). If the angle were allowed to increase further, the equations would predict a decrease in flow. Since this is not a realistic situation, the angle must be limited to 90 degrees maximum.

Although "perfect gases," as such, do not exist in nature, there are a great many applications where the Universal Gas Sizing Equation, *(C)* or *(D)*, provides a very useful and usable approximation.

General Adaptation for Steam and Vapors

The density form of the Universal Gas Sizing Equation is the most general form and can be used for both perfect and non-perfect gas applications. Applying the equation requires knowledge of one additional condition not included in previous equations, that being the inlet gas, steam, or vapor density (d_1) in pounds per cubic foot. (Steam density can be determined from tables beginning on page 136 or 148 of this book.)

Then the following adaptation of the Universal Gas Sizing Equation can be applied:

$$Q_{lb/hr} = 1.06\sqrt{d_1 P_1}\, C_g \,\text{SIN} \left(\frac{3417}{C_1}\right)\sqrt{\frac{\Delta P}{P_1}} \text{ Deg.} \qquad (E)$$

Special Equation Form for Steam Below 1000 Psig

If steam applications do not exceed 1000 psig, density changes can be compensated for by using a special adaptation of the Universal Equation. It incorporates a factor for amount of superheat in degrees Fahrenheit (T_{sh}) and also a sizing coefficient (C_s) for steam. Equation *(F)* eliminates the need for finding the density of superheated steam, which was required in Equation *(E)*. At pressures below 1000 psig, a constant relationship exists between the gas sizing coefficient (C_g) and the steam coefficient (C_s). This relationship can be expressed: $C_s = C_g/20$. For higher steam pressure applications, Equation *(E)* must be used.)

$$Q_{lb/hr} = \left[\left(\frac{C_s P_1}{1 + 0.00065 T_{sh}}\right)\right] \text{SIN} \left[\left(\frac{3417}{C_1}\right)\sqrt{\frac{\Delta P}{P_1}}\right] \text{Deg.} \qquad (F)$$

Gas and Steam Sizing Summary
The Universal Gas Sizing Equation can be used to determine the flow of gas through any style of valve. Absolute units of temperature and pressure must be used in the equation. When the critical pressure drop ratio causes the sine angle to be 90 degrees, the equation will predict the value of the critical flow. For service conditions that would result in an angle of greater than 90 degrees, the equation must be limited to 90 degrees in order to accurately determine the critical flow that exists.

Most commonly, the Universal Gas Sizing Equation is used to determine proper valve size for a given set of service conditions. The first step is to calculate the required C_g by using the Universal Gas Sizing Equation. The second step is to select a valve from the manufacturer's catalog. The valve selected should have a C_g which equals or exceeds the calculated value. Be certain that the assumed C_1 value for the C_g calculation matches the C_1 value for the valve selected from the catalog.

It is apparent that accurate valve sizing for gases requires use of the dual coefficients C_g and C_1. A single coefficient is not sufficient to describe both the capacity and the recovery characteristics of the valve.

Proper selection of a control valve for gas service is a highly technical problem with many factors to be considered. Leading valve manufacturers provide technical information, test data, sizing catalogs, nomographs, sizing slide rules, and computer or calculator programs that make valve sizing a simple and accurate procedure.

Summary of Gas and Steam Sizing Nomenclature

$C_1 = C_g/C_v$

C_g = gas sizing coefficient

C_s = steam sizing coefficient

C_v = liquid sizing coefficient

d_1 = density of steam or vapor at inlet, pounds/cu. foot

G = gas specific gravity (air = 1.0)

P_1 = valve inlet pressure, psia

ΔP = pressure drop across valve, psi

$Q_{critical}$ = critical flow rate, scfh

Q_{scfh} = gas flow rate, scfh

$Q_{lb\ hr}$ = steam or vapor flow rate, pounds per hour

T = absolute temperature of gas at inlet, degrees Rankine

T_{sh} = degrees of superheat, °F

Summary of Gas and Steam Sizing Equation Applications

(A)—Use only at very low pressure drop ($\Delta P/P_1$) ratios of 0.02 or less.

(B)—Use only to determine critical flow capacity at a given inlet pressure.

(C) or *(D)*—Universal Gas Sizing Equation. Use to predict flow for either high or low recovery valves, for any gas adhering to the perfect gas laws, and under any service conditions.

(E)—Use to predict flow for perfect or non-perfect gas sizing applications, for any vapor including steam, at any service condition when fluid density is known.

(F)—Use only to determine steam flow when inlet pressure is 1000 psig or less.

Sizing for Liquid-Gas Mixtures

Procedure
Special consideration is required when sizing valves handling mixtures of liquid and gas or liquid and vapor. The equation for required valve C_v for liquid-gas or liquid-vapor mixtures is:

$$C_{vr} = (C_{vl} + C_{vg})\ (1 + F_m) \qquad (I)$$

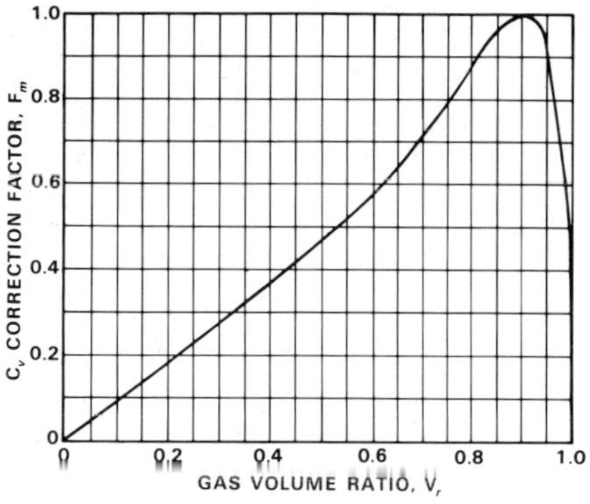

Figure 3-25. C_v Correction Factor, F_m

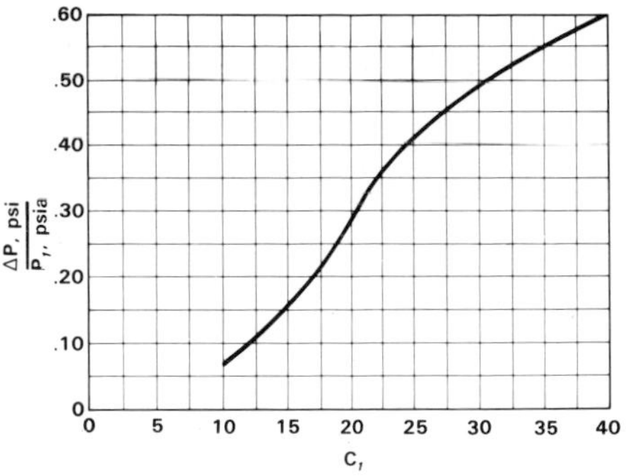

Figure 3-26. Pressure Drop Ratio Resulting in Critical Gas Flow

The value of the correction factor, F_m, is given in Figure 3-25 as a function of the gas volume ratio, V_r. The gas volume ratio for liquid-gas mixtures may be obtained by the equation:

$$V_r = \frac{V_g}{V_l + V_g} = \frac{Q_g}{\dfrac{284\,Q_l P_1}{T_1} + Q_g} \qquad (II)$$

or for liquid-vapor mixtures:

$$V_r = \frac{v_g}{v_g + v_l\left(\dfrac{1 - x}{x}\right)} \qquad (III)$$

If the pressure drop ratio ($\Delta P/P_1$) exceeds the ratio required to give 100% critical gas flow as determined from Figure 3-26, the liquid sizing drop should be limited to the drop required to give 100% critical gas flow.

Because of the possibility of choked flow occurring, the liquid sizing drop may also have to be limited by the equation:

$$\Delta P_{allow} = K_m(P_1 - r_c P_v)^*$$

Summary of Liquid-Gas Mixture Sizing Nomenclature

C_v = Standard liquid sizing coefficient

C_{vr} = C_v required for mixture flow

C_{vl} = C_v for liquid phase

C_g = C_g for gas phase

C_{vg} = C_v required for gas phase = C_g/C_1

C_1 = C_g/C_v ratio for valve

F_m = C_v correction factor

K_m = Valve recovery coefficient

ΔP = Valve pressure drop, psi

P_1 = Valve inlet pressure, psia

P_v = Liquid vapor pressure, psia

Q_g = Gas flow, scfh

Q_l = Liquid flow, gpm

Q_s = Steam or vapor flow, lb/hr

r_c = Critical pressure ratio

T_1 = Inlet temperature, °Rankine (°R = °F + 460°)

V_g = Gas flow, ft³/sec

V_l = Liquid flow, ft³/sec

V_r = Gas volume ratio

v_g = Specific volume of gas phase, ft³/lb

v_l = Specific volume of liquid phase, ft³/lb

x = Quality, lb vapor/lb mixture

*Equation (8) from page 66.

Representative Sizing Coefficients for Single-Ported Globe-Style Valve Bodies

VALVE SIZE (INCHES)	VALVE PLUG STYLE	FLOW CHARACTERISTIC	PORT DIA. (IN.)	RATED TRAVEL (IN.)	SIZING COEFFICIENTS C_v	C_g	C_s	K_m	C_1
1/2	1-Flute **Micro-Flute**™	Equal Percentage	1/4	3/4	0.31	10.0	0.50	.70	32.3
	2-Flute **Micro-Flute**	Equal Percentage	1/4	3/4	0.63	20.0	1.00	.70	31.7
	3-Flute **Micro-Flute**	Equal Percentage	1/4	3/4	0.95	32.0	1.60	.75	33.7
	Micro-Form™	Equal Percentage	1/4	3/4	1.40	48.0	2.40	.75	34.3
	Micro-Form	Equal Percentage	3/8	3/4	2.50	87.0	4.40	.80	34.8
	Micro-Flute	Equal Percentage	1/2	3/4	2.89	99.5	4.98	.89	34.4
	Top-Guided	Equal Percentage	1/2	3/4	4.20	145	7.25	.80	34.5
	Port-Guided	Quick Opening	3/4	7/16	4.06	147	7.35	.85	36.2
	Top-Guided	Quick Opening	3/4	3/4	6.27	227	11.4	.80	36.2
3/4	**Micro-Flute**	Equal Percentage	3/4	3/4	6.26	216	10.8	.87	34.5
	Top-Guided	Equal Percentage	3/4	3/4	8.65	304	15.2	.80	35.1
	Top-Guided	Quick Opening	3/4	3/4	9.08	322	16.1	.80	35.5
1	**Micro-Flute**	Equal Percentage	1	3/4	9.39	355	17.8	.83	37.8
	Micro-Form	Equal Percentage	1	3/4	12.2	467	23.3	.91	38.2
	Cage-Guided	Equal Percentage	1-5/16	3/4	17.4	591	29.6	.90	34.0
		Linear	1-5/16	3/4	20.1	668	33.4	.80	33.2
		Quick Opening	1-5/16	3/4	21.4	690	34.5	.79	32.2
1-1/4	Top-Guided	Equal Percentage	1-1/4	3/4	22.2	785	39.3	.80	35.4
	Top-Guided	Quick Opening	1-1/4	3/4	23.0	805	40.2	.80	35.0
1-1/2	**Micro-Form**	Equal Percentage	1	3/4	17.4	623	31.2	.85	35.8
	Top-Guided	Equal Percentage	1-1/2	3/4	29.1	1000	50.2	.75	34.5
	Top-Guided	Quick Opening	1-1/2	3/4	30.0	1070	53.4	.75	35.6
	Cage-Guided	Equal Percentage	1-7/8	3/4	33.4	1190	59.5	.89	35.6
		Linear	1-7/8	3/4	34.9	1220	61.0	.85	35.0
		Quick Opening	1-7/8	3/4	38.0	1350	67.5	.88	35.6
2	Cage-Guided	Equal Percentage	2-5/16	1-1/8	56.2	2070	104	.85	36.8
		Linear	2-5/16	1-1/8	65.3	2280	114	.83	34.9
		Quick Opening	2-5/16	1-1/8	67.2	2420	121	.86	36.0

2-1/2	Cage-Guided	Equal Percentage	2-7/8	1-1/2	87.2	3100	155	.87	37.4
		Linear	2-7/8	1-1/2	86.5	3220	161	.86	37.2
		Quick Opening	2-7/8	1-1/2	93.1	3470	174	.83	37.2
3	Cage-Guided	Equal Percentage	3-7/16	1-1/2	121	4210	211	.79	34.8
		Linear	3-7/16	1-1/2	135	4680	234	.80	34.7
		Quick Opening	3-7/16	1-1/2	150	5090	255	.76	33.9
4	Cage-Guided	Equal Percentage	4-3/8	2	203	7360	368	.82	36.2
		Linear	4-3/8	2	212	7540	377	.79	35.6
		Quick Opening	4-3/8	2	235	8300	415	.79	35.4
6	Cage-Guided	Equal Percentage	7	2	357	12,900	645	.74	36.1
		Linear	7	2	417	14,400	720	.66	34.5
		Quick Opening	7	2	469	15,700	785	.67	33.5
8	Port-Guided **V-Pup®**	Equal Percentage	8	2	587	20,400	1020	.80	34.8
	Top & Bottom Guided Throttle	Modified Parabolic	8	2	602	20,100	1010	.75	33.4
	Cage-Guided	Equal Percentage	8	2	570	19,000	950	.72	33.3
		Linear	8	2	701	24,400	1220	.70	34.8
		Quick Opening	8	2	787	23,400	1420	.73	36.1
	Cage-Guided	Equal Percentage	8	3	808	23,400	1470	.72	36.4
		Linear	8	3	836	23,900	1500	.72	35.8
		Quick Opening	8	3	875	30,800	1540	.72	35.2
10	Port-Guided V-Port	Modified Parabolic	10	3	987	33,400	1670	.75	33.8
	Port-Guided	Quick Opening	10	3	1280	43,800	2190	.75	34.2
	Top & Bottom-Guided	Quick Opening	10	3	1360	45,500	2330	.75	34.2
12	Port-Guided V-Port	Modified Parabolic	12	3	1180	40,900	2050	.80	34.7
	Top & Bottom-Guided	Quick Opening	12	3	1660	55,300	2770	.75	33.3
	Port-Guided	Quick Opening	12	3	1700	55,600	2830	.75	33.3

Representative Sizing Coefficients for Rotary-Shaft Valve Bodies

VALVE SIZE (INCHES)	VALVE AND TRIM STYLE	DEGREES OF VALVE OPENING	SIZING COEFFICIENTS					
			C_v	C_g	C_s	K_m	C_1	K_c
1	Rotary—V-Notch Ball	90	22.3	684	34.2	.74	30.7	.26
1-1/2	Butterfly—Conventional Disc	60	26.3	662	33.1	.55	25.2	.35
	Butterfly—Conventional Disc	90*	52.0	907	45.3	.30	17.2	.25
	Rotary—V-Notch Ball	90	88.9	2050	103	.55	23.1	.26
2	Rotary—Eccentric Disc	90	75.0	1810	90.6	.48	24.1	.26
	Butterfly—Conventional Disc	60	55.1	1390	69.4	.55	25.2	.35
	Butterfly—Conventional Disc	90*	110	1900	95.0	.30	17.2	.25
	Butterfly—**Fishtail**® Disc	90	91.0	1650	82.3	.43	18.1	.31
	Rotary—V-Notch Ball	90	158	3530	177	.46	22.3	.26
2-1/2	Butterfly—Conventional Disc	60	91.4	2300	115	.55	25.2	.35
	Butterfly—Conventional Disc	90*	182	3150	157	.30	17.2	.25
	Butterfly—**Fishtail** Disc	90	154	2790	139	.43	18.1	.31
3	Rotary—Eccentric Disc	90	193	4310	216	.42	22.3	.26
	Butterfly—Conventional Disc	60	136	3440	172	.55	25.2	.35
	Butterfly—Conventional Disc	90*	273	4710	235	.30	17.2	.25
	Butterfly—**Fishtail** Disc	90	234	4230	211	.43	18.1	.31
	Rotary—V-Notch Ball	90	372	7430	372	.46	20.0	.26
4	Rotary—Eccentric Disc	90	418	8640	432	.36	20.7	.26
	Butterfly—Conventional Disc	60	271	6820	341	.55	25.2	.35
	Butterfly—Conventional Disc	90*	542	9340	467	.30	17.2	.25
	Butterfly—**Fishtail** Disc	90	490	8870	443	.43	18.1	.31
	Rotary—V-Notch Ball	90	575	10,800	540	.37	18.8	.26
6	Rotary—Eccentric Disc	90	900	17,100	855	.33	19.0	.26
	Butterfly—Conventional Disc	60	768	18,800	941	.55	24.5	.35
	Butterfly—Conventional Disc	90*	1750	25,000	1,250	.30	14.3	.25
	Butterfly—**Fishtail** Disc	90	1410	22,500	1120	.43	16.0	.31
	Rotary—V-Notch Ball	90	944	18,100	905	.31	19.2	.26

8	Rotary—Eccentric Disc	90	1920	35,300	1770	.31	18.4	.26
	Butterfly—Conventional Disc	60	1340	32,900	1640	.55	24.5	.35
	Butterfly—Conventional Disc	90*	3050	43,600	2180	.30	14.3	.25
	Butterfly—**Fishtail** Disc	90	2440	39,100	1950	.43	16.0	.31
	Rotary—V-Notch Ball	90	1770	28,900	1450	.28	16.3	.26
10	Rotary—Eccentric Disc	90	3390	60,000	3000	.28	17.7	.26
	Butterfly—Conventional Disc	60	2170	53,100	2650	.55	24.5	.35
	Butterfly—Conventional Disc	90*	4920	70,400	3520	.30	14.3	.25
	Butterfly—**Fishtail** Disc	90	4010	64,200	3210	.43	16.0	.31
	Rotary—V-Notch Ball	90	3160	56,900	2850	.33	18.0	.26
12	Rotary—Eccentric Disc	90	4890	84,100	4200	.27	17.2	.26
	Butterfly—Conventional Disc	60	3180	78,000	3900	.55	24.5	.35
	Butterfly—Conventional Disc	90*	7240	103,000	5180	.30	14.3	.25
	Butterfly—**Fishtail** Disc	90	5990	95,800	4790	.43	16.0	.31
	Rotary—V-Notch Ball	90	4620	83,200	4160	.33	18.0	.26
14	Rotary—Eccentric Disc	90	6800	117,000	5860	.27	17.2	.26
	Butterfly—Conventional Disc	60	3880	95,000	4750	.55	24.5	.35
	Butterfly—Conventional Disc	90*	8810	126,000	6300	.30	14.3	.25
	Butterfly—**Fishtail** Disc	90	7280	116,000	5820	.43	16.0	.31
16	Rotary—Eccentric Disc	90	9470	163,000	8150	.27	17.2	.26
	Butterfly—Conventional Disc	60	5210	127,000	6380	.55	24.5	.35
	Butterfly—Conventional Disc	90*	11,800	169,000	8460	.30	14.3	.25
	Butterfly—**Fishtail** Disc	90	9830	157,000	7860	.43	16.0	.31
	Rotary—V-Notch Ball	90	6760	125,000	6250	.33	18.5	.26
18	Rotary—Eccentric Disc	90	12,000	206,000	10,300	.27	17.2	.26
	Butterfly—Conventional Disc	60	6510	159,000	7980	.55	24.5	.35
	Butterfly—Conventional Disc	90*	14,800	212,000	10,600	.30	14.3	.25
	Butterfly—**Fishtail** Disc	90	12,300	197,000	9850	.43	16.0	.31
20	Rotary—Eccentric Disc	90	14,400	248,000	12,400	.27	17.2	.26
	Butterfly—Conventional Disc	60	8210	201,000	10,000	.55	24.5	.35
	Butterfly—Conventional Disc	90*	18,600	267,000	13,300	.30	14.3	.25
	Butterfly—**Fishtail** Disc	90	15,500	248,000	12,400	.43	16.0	.31

*For on/off service only. For throttling applications, size butterfly valves with conventional discs at 60 degrees open.

- Continued -

Representative Sizing Coefficients for Rotary-Shaft Valve Bodies (Continued)

VALVE SIZE (INCHES)	VALVE AND TRIM STYLE	DEGREES OF VALVE OPENING	SIZING COEFFICIENTS					
			C_v	C_g	C_s	K_m	C_1	K_c
24	Rotary—Eccentric Disc	90	21,600	372,000	18,600	.27	17.2	.26
	Butterfly—Conventional Disc	60	12,200	298,000	14,900	.55	24.5	.35
	Butterfly—Conventional Disc	90*	27,700	396,000	19,800	.30	14.3	.25
	Butterfly—**Fishtail** Disc	90	23,100	370,000	18,500	.43	16.0	.31
	Rotary—V-Notch Ball	90	13,700	248,000	12,400	.33	18.1	.26
30	Butterfly—Conventional Disc	60	19,900	487,000	24,300	.55	24.5	.35
	Butterfly—Conventional Disc	90*	45,200	646,000	32,300	.30	14.3	.25
	Butterfly—**Fishtail** Disc	90	40,300	646,000	32,300	.43	16.0	.31
36	Butterfly—Conventional Disc	60	29,400	721,000	36,100	.55	24.5	.35
	Butterfly—Conventional Disc	90*	66,900	957,000	47,800	.30	14.3	.25
	Butterfly—**Fishtail** Disc	90	61,600	985,000	49,200	.43	16.0	.31
48	Butterfly—Conventional Disc	60	54,200	1,330,000	66,400	.55	24.5	.35
	Butterfly—Conventional Disc	90*	123,000	1,760,000	88,100	.30	14.3	.25
	Butterfly—**Fishtail** Disc	90	116,000	1,850,000	92,400	.43	16.0	.31
60	Butterfly—Conventional Disc	60	85,300	2,090,000	104,000	.55	24.5	.35
	Butterfly—Conventional Disc	90*	194,000	2,770,000	139,000	.30	14.3	.25
	Butterfly—**Fishtail** Disc	90	182,000	2,910,000	145,000	.43	16.0	.31
72	Butterfly—Conventional Disc	60	123,000	3,030,000	151,000	.55	24.5	.35
	Butterfly—Conventional Disc	90*	281,000	4,010,000	201,000	.30	14.3	.25
	Butterfly—**Fishtail** Disc	90	262,000	4,200,000	210,000	.43	16.0	.31

*For on/off service only. For throttling applications, size butterfly valves with conventional discs at 60 degrees open.

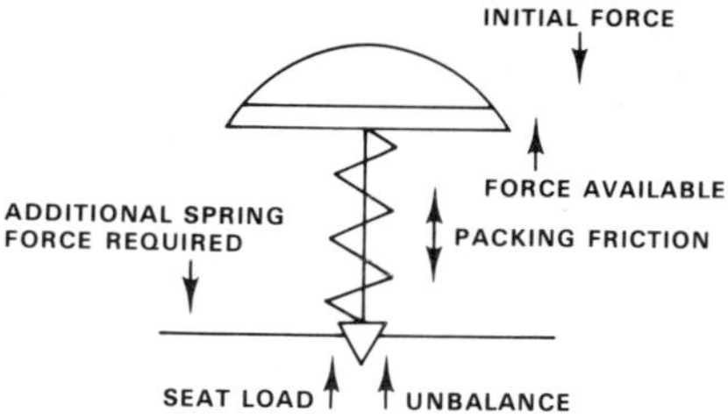

Figure 3-27. Free Body Diagram for Reverse-Acting, Spring-Opposed Diaphragm Actuator on Flow-Tends-To-Open Valve Body

Actuator Sizing

Use of too large an actuator adds unnecessary expense and increased response time to a control valve, while use of an undersized actuator might make it impossible to open the valve or close it completely. However, selection of an optimum-sized actuator for a given control valve application is a subject of greater scope than can be completely detailed here. Consequently, the information furnished is summarized to provide basic knowledge of the factors that must be considered. Complete information and assistance can be provided by representatives of leading valve manufacturers to permit choosing the correct actuator for any specific application.

Actuators for Sliding-Stem Valves

After a valve has been selected to meet given service conditions, the valve must be matched with an appropriate actuator to achieve maximum efficiency. The actuator must provide sufficient force to stroke the valve plug to the fully closed position with sufficient seat loading to meet the required leak class criteria. With spring-return actuators, the spring selected must be sized to properly oppose the force provided by the air supply pressure.

Sizing an actuator involves solving a problem in statics. The forces, and the direction in which each force acts, depend upon actuator design and flow direction through the valve. The free body diagram in Figure 3-27 illustrates the forces involved in achieving static equilibrium. The figure depicts a direct-acting (push-down-to-close) valve body where the flow tends to open the valve plug. The actuator is a reverse-acting spring-and-diaphragm construction that closes the valve in case of supply pressure failure.

To stroke the valve to the fully closed position, the actuator must provde enough force to overcome friction forces and to overcome the unbalance force due to the flow through the valve. The actuator force available is the product of the air supply pressure and the area against which that pressure is applied (i.e., the diaphragm area or piston area). Packing friction varies with stem size, packing material(s), and packing arrangement. Specific friction forces must be obtained from the packing manufacturer or the actuator manufacturer. Other friction forces, such as friction due to metal piston rings, depend on valve design and must be obtained from the valve manufacturer.

The unbalance force is the product of the force of the flowing medium and the area against which that force is applied (either the total port area or, in the case of a "balanced" construction, the specific unbalance area obtained from the valve manufacturer's specifications).

$$\textbf{Unbalance Force} = \Delta P_{shutoff} \textbf{ X Unbalance Area}$$

To meet required leakage criteria, the actuator must provide some seating force beyond that force required to stroke the valve to the fully closed position. The specific force required depends upon valve style and size. Seat load is usually expressed in pounds per lineal inch of port circumference. For a given leak class, valve designs with large ports usually require greater seating load than is required for valves with smaller ports. The seat load is the product of the port circumference and the pounds-per-lineal-inch force recommended by the valve manufacturer.

Seat Load = Port circumference (inches) x Recommended seating force (pounds per lineal inch)

The actuator force available must be greater than the sum of the forces which the actuator force must oppose to achieve static equilibrium. For a spring-opposed diaphragm actuator or a spring-return piston actuator, the spring force (spring rate X travel) must be considered in the equilibrium calculations.

Actuators for Rotary-Shaft Valves

The actuator selected must be capable of providing adequate torque output to overcome the dynamic torque forces on the disc or ball of the valve under flowing conditions. The actuator must also be capable of exceeding the "breakout" torque requirements of the disc or ball at shutoff, in order to initiate rotation of the rotary valve shaft.

Breakout torque requirement determination begins by multiplying the actual pressure drop across the closed valve times a tested breakout torque/pressure drop relationship provided by the valve manufacturer. Another factor is added that includes tested or predicted breakout torque for the body when it is not pressurized. Total calculated valve breakout torque must be less than the maximum allowable breakout torque limit of the actuator size being considered, as published by the actuator manufacturer.

By the same token, total calculated valve dynamic torque must not exceed the maximum allowable actuator dynamic torque limits published by the actuator manufacturer. Dynamic torque requirements are calculated by multiplying the pressure drop that produces critical (gas) or choked (liquid) flow times a pre-calculated effective pressure drop coefficient for the size and style of valve being considered.

Non-Destructive Test Procedures

Successful completion of specific non-destructive examinations is required for valves intended for nuclear service, and may be required by codes or customers in non-nuclear applications, particularly in the Power Industry. Also, successful completion of the examinations may permit uprating of ANSI Standard Class butt-welding end valves to a Special Class rating. The Special Class rating permits use of the butt-welding end valves at higher pressures than allowed for Standard Class valves. Procedures required for uprating to the Special Class are detailed in ANSI Standard B16.34-1977.

While it is certainly not feasible to present complete details of code requirements for non-destructive examinations in this book, we will attempt to summarize the principles and procedures of four major types of non-destructive examinations defined in ANSI, ASME, and ASTM standards.

Magnetic Particle (Surface) Examination

Magnetic particle examination can be used only on materials which can be magnetized. The principle includes application of a direct current across a piece to induce a magnetic field in the piece. Surface or shallow subsurface defects distort the magnetic field to the extent that a secondary magnetic field develops around the defect. If a magnetic powder, either dry or suspended in liquid, is spread over the magnetized piece, areas of distorted magnetic field will be visible, indicating a defect in the piece in the area of distortion. After de-magnetizing the piece by reversing the electric current, it may be possible to weld repair the defect (normal procedure with castings) or it may be necessary to replace the piece (normal procedure with forgings and bar stock parts). After repair or replacement, the magnetic particle examination must be repeated.

Liquid Penetrant (Surface) Examination

This examination method permits detection of surface defects not visible to the naked eye. The surface to be examined is cleaned thoroughly and dried. The liquid penetrant dye, either water or solvent soluble, is applied by dipping, brushing, or spraying, and allowed time to penetrate. Excess penetrant is washed or wiped off (depending on the penetrant used). The surface is again thoroughly dried and a developer (liquid or powder) is applied. Inspection is performed under the applicable light source. (Some developers require use of an ultraviolet or "black" light to expose defective areas.) If defects are discovered and repaired by welding, the piece must be re-examined after repair.

Radiographic (Volumetric) Examination

Radiography of control valve parts works on the principle that X-rays and gamma rays will pass through metal objects which are impervious to light rays and will expose photographic film just as light rays will. The number and intensity of the rays passing through the metal object depend on the density of the object. Subsurface defects represent changes in density of the material and can therefore be photographed radiographically. The piece to be inspected is placed between the X-ray or gamma ray source and the photographic film. Detail and contrast sensitivity are determined by radiographing one or more small flat plates of specified thickness at the same time the test subject is exposed. The small flat plate, called a penetrameter, has serveral holes of specified diameters drilled in it. Its image on the exposed film, along with the valve body or other test subject, makes it possible to determine the detail and contrast sensitivity of the radiograph.

Radiography can detect such casting defects as gas and blowholes, sand spots, internal shrinkage, cracks, hot tears, and internal chills. In castings for nuclear service, some defects such as cracks and hot tears are expressly forbidden and cannot be repaired. The judgement and experience of the radiographer is important, because he must compare the radiograph with the acceptance criteria (American Society for Testing and Materials reference radiographs) to determine the adequacy of the casting. When weld repairs are required, the casting must be radiographed again after the repair.

Ultrasonic (Volumetric) Examination

This method monitors sound wave reflections from the piece being inspected to determine the depth and size of any defects. Ultrasonic examination can detect foreign materials and discontinuities in fine-grained metal and thus lends itself to volumetric examination of structures such as plate, bar, and forgings. The test is normally conducted either with a special oil called a coupler or under water to ensure efficient transmission of sound waves. The sound waves are generated by a crystal probe and are reflected at each interface in the piece being tested, that is, at each outer face of the piece itself and at each face of the damaged or malformed internal portion. These reflections are received by a special microphone and displayed on a cathode ray tube to reveal the location and severity of the defect.

Control Valve Noise

The U.S. Occupational Safety and Health Act of 1970 established maximum permissible noise levels for all industries whose business affects interstate commerce. These maximum sound levels, listed below, have become the accepted noise standard for most regulatory agencies.

Permissible Noise Exposures

Duration Per Day, Hr	Sound Level, dBA
8	90
6	92
4	95
3	97
2	100
1-1/2	102
1	105
1/2	110
1/4 or less	115

The recognition that airborne sound criteria are here to stay has provided the impetus throughout all industry for the acute interest in noise abatement.

Control valves have long been recognized as a major source of excessive noise levels inherent to many fluid process and transmission systems.

Sources of Valve Noise

The major sources of control valve noise are:

1. Mechanical vibration of valve components
2. Hydrodynamic noise
3. Aerodynamic noise

Vibration of valve components is a result of random pressure fluctuations within the valve body and/or fluid impingement upon the movable or flexible parts. The most prevalent source of noise resulting from mechanical vibration is the lateral movement of the valve plug relative to the guide surfaces. Sound produced by this type of vibration will normally have a frequency less than 1500 Hertz and is often described as a metallic rattling. The physical damage incurred by the valve plug and associated guide surfaces is generally of more concern than the noise emitted.

A second source of mechanical vibration noise is a valve component resonating at its natural frequency. Resonant vibration produces a sound that is a single-pitched tone normally having a frequency between 3000 and 7000 Hertz. This type of vibration produces high levels of stress that may ultimately produce fatigue failure of the vibrating part. Valve components susceptible to natural frequency vibration include contoured valve plugs with hollow skirts and flexible members such as the metal seat ring of a ball valve.

Noise that is a by-product of the vibration of valve components is usually of secondary concern and may even be beneficial since it warns that conditions exist which could produce valve failure. Noise resulting from mechanical vibration has for the most part been eliminated by improved valve design and is generally considered a structural problem rather than a noise problem.

The major source of hydrodynamic noise (noise resulting from liquid flow) is cavitation. This noise is caused by the implosion of vapor bubbles that are formed in the cavitation process.

Cavitation occurs in valves controlling liquids when the service conditions are such that the static pressure downstream of the valve is greater than the vapor pressure and at some point within the valve the local static pressure is less than or equal to the liquid vapor pressure. Localized areas of low static pressures within the valve are a result of intense turbulence characterized by high velocity fluctuations or by high main-stream velocity at the vena contracta.

Cavitation may produce severe damage to the solid boundary surfaces that confine the cavitating fluid. Generally speaking, noise produced by cavitation is of secondary concern.

Test results indicate that noise levels from non-cavitating or flashing liquids are quite low and generally would not be considered a noise problem.

The third and major source of control valve noise is due to the Reynolds stresses or shear forces that are a property of turbulent flow. Because of the relative velocities, high intensity levels of noise resulting from turbulent flow are more common to valves handling gas than to those controlling liquids. Noise resulting from turbulent flow of a gas is called aerodynamic noise. Aerodynamic noise can be classified as a non-periodic or random noise with the predominant frequencies occurring between 1000 and 8000 Hertz as shown in Figure 3-28.

Sources of turbulence in gas transmission lines are: obstructions in the flow path, rapid expansion or deceleration of high velocity gas, and directional changes of the fluid stream. Specific areas that are inherently noisy are: headers, pressure regulators, line size expansions, and pipe elbows.

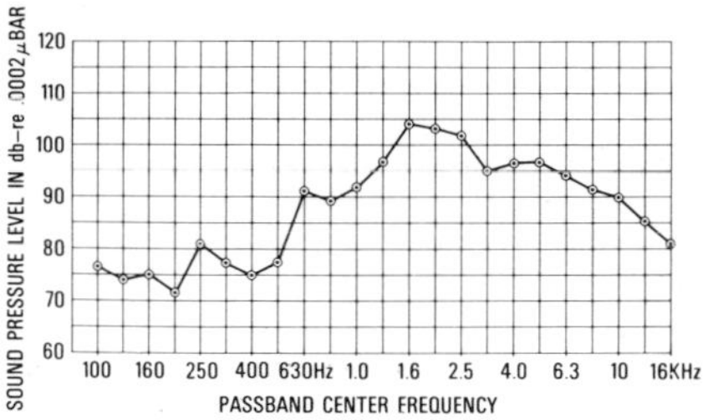

Figure 3-28. Typical Spectrum of Control Valve Noise

Noise Prediction

The establishment of an accurate technique for predicting noise is a prerequisite for good noise abatement programs. Fisher Controls Company has developed a fast and accurate technique for predicting the ambient noise resulting from flow of fluid thru a control valve for any given set of service conditions.

The technique gives consideration to flow parameters relevant to noise generation. These parameters are: pressure differential across the valve, flow coefficient, ratio of pressure differential to inlet pressure, valve geometry, and the size and schedule of adjacent piping. The general technique equation is:

$$SPL = A + B + C + D$$

where:

SPL = overall noise level in decibels (dBA) at a predetermined point in reference to the valve (48″ downstream of the valve outlet and 29″ from the pipe surface)

A = base SPL, in dBA, determined as a function of pressure differential

B = correction in dBA as a function of flow coefficient

C = correction in dBA for valve style and pressure ratio

D = correction in dBA for pipe size and schedule

Noise coefficients used in the equation above are unique values that must be determined by laboratory tests for both compressible and incompressible fluids as a function of valve geometry.

Noise Control

In closed systems (not vented to atmosphere) any noise produced in the process becomes airbone only by transmission through the valves and adjacent piping that contain the flowstream. The sound field in the flowstream forces these solid boundaries to vibrate. The vibrations cause disturbances in the ambient atmosphere that are propagated as sound waves.

Noise control employs either source treatment or path treatment, or both. Source treatment, preventing or attenuating noise at its source, is the most desirable approach, if economically and physically feasible. There are several manners of source treatment available for valves with cage-style trim. Some of them utilize stacked discs creating small, tortuous flow paths or staged pressure drops. These styles are susceptible to plugging as a result of solid particles in the flowstream. Also, multi-staging system pressure drops can result in formation of hydrates in the intermediate stages of pressure reduction and the plugging or blocking of the final stages. This phenomenon is common with hydrocarbons or vapor flow with high moisture content.

The cage-style source treatment approaches recommended by Fisher Controls Company are depicted in Figure 3-29. The upper view shows a cage with many narrow parallel slots designed to minimize turbulence and provide a favorable velocity distribution in the expansion area. This is an economical approach to quiet valve design and can provide 15 to 20 dBA noise reduction with little or no decrease in flow capacity.

The lower view in Figure 3-29 shows a single-stage, cage-style trim designed for optimum noise attenuation where pressure drop ratios ($\Delta P/P_1$) are high.

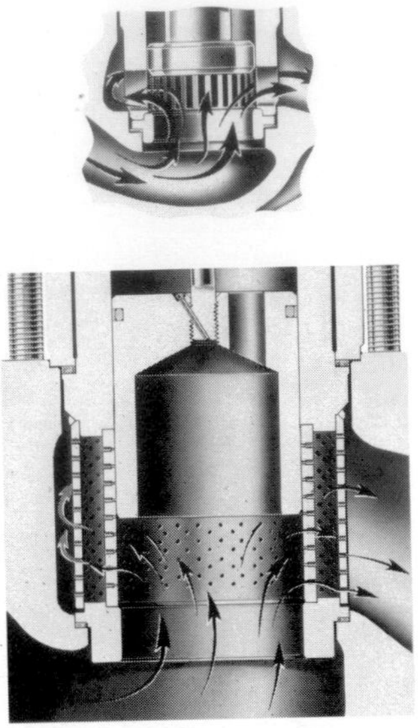

Figure 3-29. Valve Trim Designs for Reducing Aerodynamic Noise

To obtain the desired results, restrictions must be sized and spaced in the primary cage wall so that the noise generated by jet interaction is not greater than the summation of the noise generated by the jets individually.

The construction shown includes a baffle to minimize the noise created by jet interaction at pressure drop ratios of 0.85 or greater. (Baffle flow area is several times greater than the flow area of the primary cage and consequently the baffle creates little or no pressure drop.) For lower $\Delta P/P_1$ ratios (less than 0.85) the baffle is not required and the degree of noise attenuation provided depends on the size and spacing of the restrictions in the primary cage wall. Proper sizing and spacing of the restrictions provides equivalent or better noise attenuation results than the other methods discussed. Besides reducing valve noise by as much as 30 dBA, this design is less subject to plugging than some of the others mentioned.

For control valve applications operating at high pressure ratios ($\Delta P/P_1 > 0.8$) the series restriction approach, splitting the total pressure drop between the control valve and a fixed restriction (diffuser) downstream of the valve can be very effective in minimizing the noise. In order to optimize the effectiveness of a diffuser, it must be designed (special shape and sizing) for each given installation so that the noise levels generated by the valve and diffuser are equal. Figure 3-30 shows a typical installation.

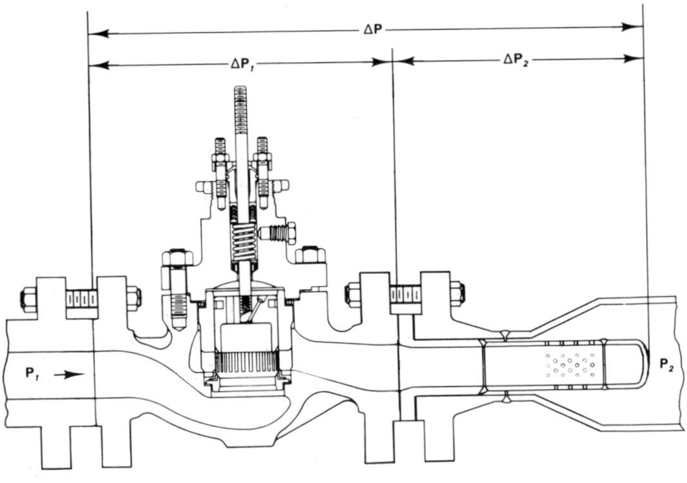

Figure 3-30. Valve and Inline Diffuser Combination

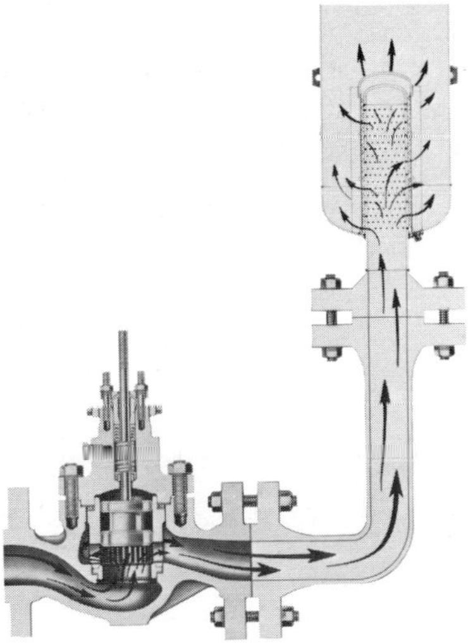

Figure 3-31. Valve and Vent Diffuser Combination

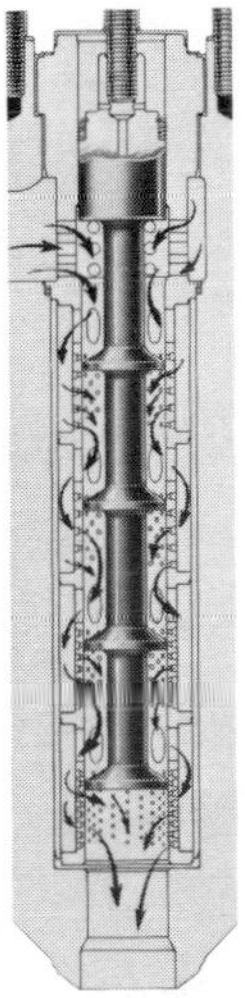

Figure 3-32. Special Valve Design to Eliminate Cavitation

Control systems venting to atmosphere are generally very noisy because of the high pressure ratios and high exit velocities involved. Dividing the total pressure drop between the actual vent and an upstream control valve, by means of a vent diffuser, quiets both the valve and the vent. A properly sized vent diffuser and valve combination, such as that shown in Figure 3-31, can reduce the overall system noise level as much as 40 dBA.

Source treatment for noise problems associated with control valves handling liquid is directed primarily at eliminating or minimizing cavitation. Because flow conditions that will produce cavitation can be accurately predicted, valve noise resulting from cavitation can be eliminated by application of appropriate limits to the service conditions at the valve by use of break-down orifices, valves in series, etc. Another approach to source treatment is use of special valve trim that utilizes the series restriction concept to eliminate cavitation as shown in Figure 3-32.

A second approach to noise control is that of path treatment. The fluid stream is an excellent noise transmission path. When critical flow exists (fluid velocity at the vena contracta is at least at the sonic level), the vena contracta acts as a barrier to the propagation of sound upstream via the fluid. At sub-critical flow, however, valve noise can be propagated in the upstream direction almost as efficiently as it is downstream. The impedance to the transmission of noise upstream at sub-critical flow is primarily a function of valve geometry. The valve geometry that provides a direct line of sight through the valve (i.e., ball valves and butterfly valves), offers little resistance to noise propagation. Glove style valves provide approximately 10 dB attenuation. In any path treatment approach to control valve noise abatement, consideration must be given to the amplitude of noise radiated by both the upstream and downstream piping. Path treatment consists of increasing the impedance of the transmission path to reduce the acoustic energy that is communicated to the receiver.

Dissipation of acoustic energy by use of acoustical absorbent materials is one of the most effective methods of

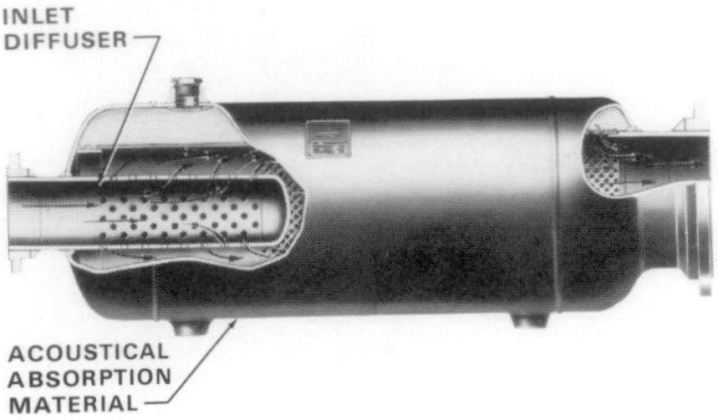

Figure 3-33. Typical In-line Silencer

path treatment. Whenever possible the acoustical material should be located in the flow stream either at or immediately downstream of the noise source. In gas transmission systems, inline silencers effectively dissipate the noise within the fluid stream and attenuate the noise level transmitted to the solid boundaries. Where high mass flow rates and/or high pressure ratios across the valve exist, inline silencers, such as that shown in Figure 3-33, are often the most realistic and economical approach to noise control. Use of absorption-type inline silencers can provide almost any degree of attenuation desired. However, economic considerations generally limit the insertion loss to approximately 25 dBA.

Noise that cannot be eliminated within the boundaries of the flow stream must be eliminated by external treatment. This approach to the abatement of control valve noise suggests the use of heavy walled piping, acoustical insulation of the exposed solid boundaries of the fluid stream, use of insulated boxes, buildings, etc. to isolate the noise source.

Path treatment such as heavy wall pipe or external acoustical insulation can be a very economical and effective technique for localized noise abatement. However, noise is propagated for long distances via the fluid stream and the effectiveness of the heavy wall pipe or external insulation ends where the treatment ends.

Noise Summary

The amount of noise that will be generated by a proposed control valve installation can be quickly and accurately predicted by use of documented procedures available from many valve manufacturers. Leading manufacturers can also provide computer programs for large or intermediate computers and pre-programmed tapes for hand-held programmable calculators to facilitate valve selection based on noise requirements. These aids permit proper selection of equipment (such as that shown in Figures 3-34 and 3-35) to provide solutions for most control valve noise problems.

Figure 3-34. Noise Abatement Cages for Globe-style Valve Bodies

Figure 3-35. Cage and Tube Bundle to Reduce Hydrodynamic Cavitation Noise

With increasing interest on the environmental impact of all aspects of industry, there will be increasing demands for noise abatement procedures and equipment. The technology and hardware associated with noise abatement are continually being refined. Contacting a representative of one of the leading valve manufacturers is the best way to be assured of the latest noise abatement sizing and selection techniques.

Section 4

Special Control Valves

Valves for Special Applications

As discussed previously, "standard" control valves can be used to handle a very wide range of control applications. The range of "standard" applications can be defined as being encompassed by: atmospheric pressure and 6000 psig (414 bar), minus 150°F (−101°C) and 450°F (232°C), flow coefficient C_v values of 1.0 and 25,000, and the limits imposed by common industrial standards. Certainly corrosiveness and viscosity of the fluid, leakage rates, and the many other factors mentioned at the beginning of Part III of this book demand consideration even for "standard" applications. But perhaps the need for careful consideration of valve selection is even more critical for applications outside the "standard" limits mentioned above. This chapter discusses some of the "special" applications and control valve modifications useful in controlling them, designs and materials for severe service, and test requirements for control valves used in nuclear power plant service.

High Pressure Control Valves

Modern industrial processes frequently utilize working pressures above 6000 psig (414 bar). Widespread usage of plastic products has created an expanding market for high pressure valves used in production of polyethylene. Pressures up to 50,000 psig (3450 bar) are not unusual. At such high pressures, the techniques and methods used to seal valve bodies are very important. Usually the valve body is of two-piece angle design with the seat ring clamped between the two body halves. The seat ring-to-body seal is made with a retained, metallic, hollow O-ring. The inside diameter of the O-ring is perforated to allow line pressure to enter the hollow cross-section of the O-ring. As pressure builds up, the O-ring tends to "inflate", creating a tight seal between the body and seat ring. The exterior surface of the O-ring is usually plated with soft silver to assist in forming the seal.

Line connections for high pressure service also are normally "self-energizing" or pressure-assisted. They usually rely on the deformation of a ring at the gasket face to provide a tight seal. Three of the more common line connection seals are shown in Figure 4-1. The line connection used is at the buyer's option and is not furnished with the control valve. However, the intended connection style must be specified to the valve manufacturer so that the body ends can be properly machined and threaded. [For ratings up to 10,000 psig (690 bar), flanged end connections are available.]

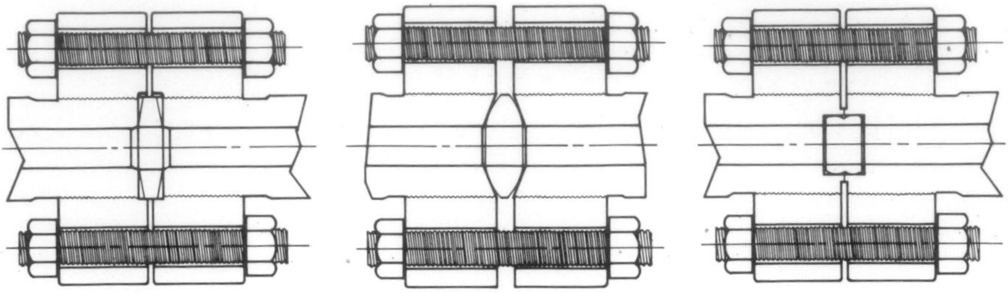

Figure 4-1. Typical Line Connections for High Pressure Valve Bodies

Valve stem packing tolerances become more critical for high-pressure units. At high pressures, elastomer packing can be extruded through very small clearances. Packing material is generally a TFE compound impregnated with glass to make it more resistant to extrusion. Valve stems are subject to much higher stresses than in standard control valve service, so they are made of higher strength material, such as hardened Type 4140 steel. The stem must be short and well guided to prevent column action and should be hard chrome plated to prevent galling caused by the high unit pressure contact with the packing.

Closed-die forgings are used for high pressure valve bodies. The material is usually heat-treated Type 4340 steel if the intended pressure rating is 50,000 psig (3450 bar). For ratings to 10,000 psig (690 bar), annealed Type 316 stainless steel can be used. The forging process provides bodies that are free of voids and that can be heat treated to high strength levels without losing ductility. Figure 4-2 shows an internal view of the components used in a high pressure valve body. Note that optional steam tracing lines are shown which permit raising the temperature of the body before admitting high pressure fluid. Steam tracing can increase the ductility and impact strength of the material.

Various trim materials are used in high pressure control valves. When pressure drops are low, hardened stainless steel or cobalt-chromium alloys are adequate. For higher pressure drops, the valve plug tip may be furnished in tungsten carbide for excellent resistance to abrasion and erosion.

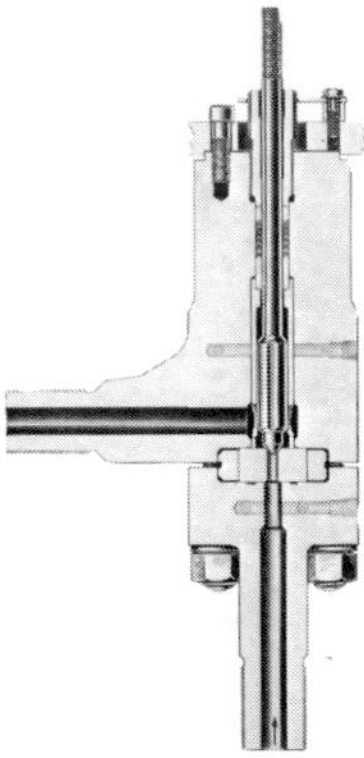

Figure 4-2. Forged Valve Body Assembly for Service to 50,000 PSIG (3450 Bar)

High pressure valves can be actuated by a variety of actuators ranging from standard piston or diaphragm models (Figure 4-3) to the more sophisticated pneumatic and electro-hydraulic actuators shown in Figure 4-4 and 4-5. The dual-piston pneumatic model (Figure 4-4) was specifically designed for polyethylene let-down service where very short overall valve plug travel was required. The actuator shown (Figure 4-4) provides precise control of valve stem movement through a crank and screw assembly. Each of the actuator cylinders includes its own positioner, making it easy to

Figure 4-3. High Pressure Control Valve with Flanged End Connections and Diaphragm Actuator

split controller output so that one cylinder operates on the 3 to 9 psig (0.2 to 0.6 bar) portion and the other on the 9 to 15 psig (0.6 to 1.0 bar) portion.

High Temperature Control Valves

Control valves for service at temperatures above 450°F (232°C) must be designed and specified with the temperature conditions in mind. At elevated temperatures, such as may be encountered in boiler feedwater systems and superheater bypass systems, the standard materials of control valve construction may be inadequate. For instance, plastics, elastomers, and standard gaskets are generally unsuitable and must be replaced by more durable materials. Metal-to-metal seating materials are always used. Semi-metallic or laminated graphite packing materials are commonly used, and spiral-wound stainless steel and asbestos gaskets are necessary.

Chrome-moly steels are often used for the valve body castings for temperatures above 1000°F (538°C), but above 1050°F (566°C) ASTM A217

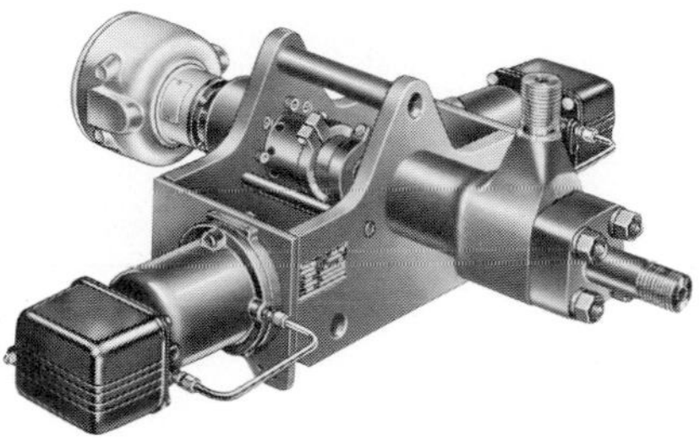

Figure 4-4. Control Valve Assembly Designed for Polyethylene Production

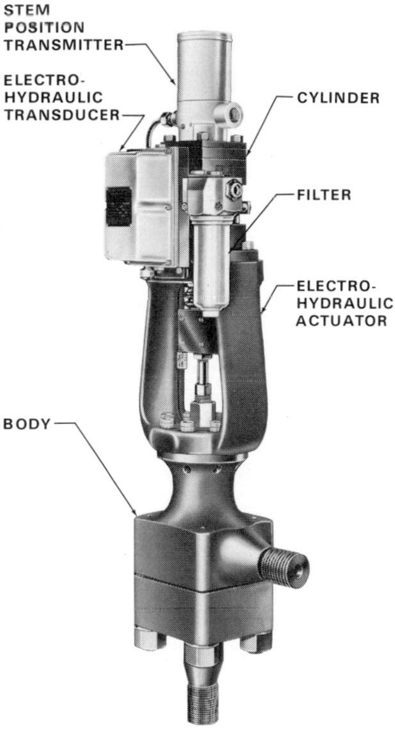

Figure 4-5. High Pressure Control Valve with Electro-Hydraulic Actuator

Grade WC9 is subject to oxidation and scaling. ASTM A217 Grade C5 has the same shortcoming above 1100°F (593°C). So for temperatures on up to 1500°F (816°C) the material usually selected is ASTM A351 Grade CF-8M, Type 316 stainless steel.

Extension bonnets are used to help protect packing box parts from

Figure 4-6. Control Valve for Service to 1500°F (816°C)

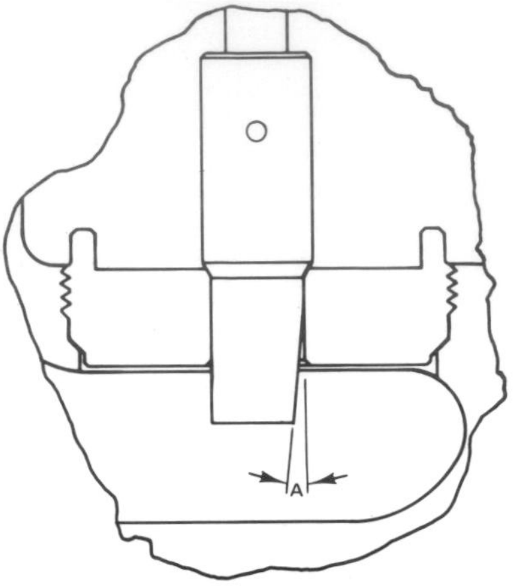

Figure 4-7. Angle of Flat "A" Determines Control of Small Flow Rates

extremely high temperatures. Some rotary-shaft control valves have optional refractory liners for additional heat resistance. A valve such as that shown in Figure 4-6 is suitable for high temperature service as well as for pressures above the limits of ANSI Class 2500 ratings. It incorporates the qualities mentioned above and also includes trim materials such as chrome-plated Type 316 stainless steel, cobalt-based Alloy 6, and high-vanadium, high-chromium steels for additional resistance to high working temperatures.

Small-Flow Control Valves

Many applications exist in laboratories, pilot plants, and the commerical process industries where control of extremely small flow rates is necessary. Using special trim in a standard control valve body is a common way of handling these situations, and provides economy in reducing need for spare parts inventory for special valves and actuators. By utilizing standard control valve travel ranges and accessories, accurate flow control can be maintained at very low rates. The special trim parts used are normally only two—a reduced-port seat ring and a valve plug with a tapered flat milled on one side-as shown in Figure 4-7. These parts are machined to very close tolerances and are usually made of a hardened stainless steel or hard faced with Alloy 6 to minimize erosion. Using a 3/16-inch diameter port, the construction shown can be provided with a C_v flow coefficient of only 0.075 at fully open 3/4-inch travel.

Large-Flow Control Valves

Generally speaking, globe-style valves larger than 12-inch, ball or eccentric disc valves larger than 24-inch, and butterfly valves larger than 72-inch fall in the "special valve" category. As valve sizes increase arithmetically, static pressure loads at shutoff increase geometrically. Consequently then, shaft strength, bearing loads, unbalance forces, and available actuator thrust all become of greater significance with increasing valve size. Normally maximum allowable pressure drop is reduced on large valves to keep design and actuator requirements within reasonable limits. Even with lowered working pressure ratings, the flow capacity of some of the large-flow valves is awesome. For instance, the 72-inch butterfly valve would deliver up to 281,000 gallons of water per minute per psi of differential pressure. Capacity of this magnitude could be applied in the circulating water systems of Power Industry installations.

Naturally, actuator requirements are severe, and long-stroke, double-acting pneumatic piston or electric actuators are usually specified for large-flow applications. Installation and maintenance procedures are complicated by the physical size and weight of the valve and actuator components. Heavy-duty hoists are required for installation of the valve body assembly into the pipeline and also for removal or replacement of major trim parts. Maintenance personnel must follow the manufacturers' instruction manuals closely to minimize risk of injury. Extra caution is required in adjustment of large butterfly valve seals for tight shutoff when those adjustments must be made from inside the pipeline downstream of the valve. Any such maintenance requires that the actuator linkage be positively blocked so that the valve remains closed.

Noise levels must be carefully considered in all large-flow installations since sound pressure levels increase in direct proportion to flow magnitude. To keep valve-originated noise within tolerable limits, large fabricated valve body designs, such as that shown in Figure 4-8, have been developed. These bodies are normally of cage-style construction, using unusually long valve plug travel, a great number of small flow openings through the wall of the cage, and an expanded outlet line connection to minimize noise output and reduce fluid velocity. Often the inlet connection and inlet portion of the fabricated valve body are designed for higher pressure than are the remainder of the body shell and the expanded outlet connection. When such a construction is used, the body is rated according to the maximum allowable working pressure of the outlet portion. Overpressure protection equipment must be included in the downstream system to ensure that the body shell and outlet connection are not subjected to pressure in excess of the rated capability.

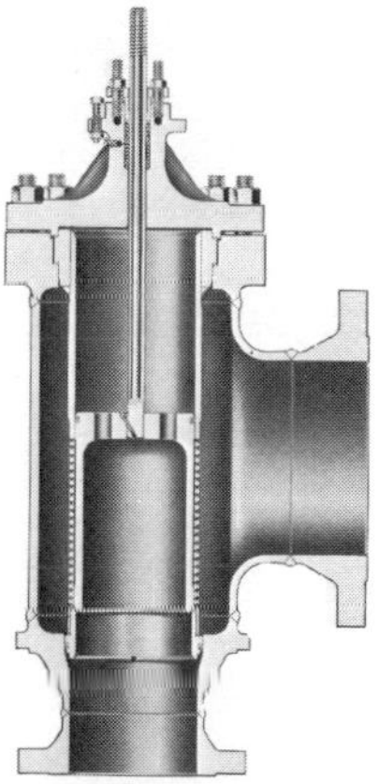

Figure 4-8. Large Flow Valve Body for Noise Attenuation Service

Cryogenic Service Valves

Cryogenics is the science dealing with materials and processes at temperatures below minus 150°F (−101°C). With increasing production and use of fluids such as liquefied hydrogen, oxygen, fluorine, nitrogen, and methane, the need for low-temperature fluid control has become commonplace. But standard control valves often cannot handle cryogenic applications satisfactorily.

To maintain cryogenic process efficiency, heat influx into the system must be kept at a minimum. Consequently, pipelines are usually heavily insulated and control valves are often placed inside insulated cold-boxes. A large portion of the heat influx that occurs is caused by conduction through control valve parts that extend beyond the insulated area. To minimize that heat influx, thin-walled bonnet extensions and small-diameter valve stems are used. Austenitic (300 Series) stainless steels are used for these parts to take advantage of the low conductivity of the material. Also, the extension bonnet is sometimes fabricated to keep wall section thickness to a minimum and the valve body itself is often of the weld-end variety to eliminate unnecessary weight common to flanged constructions. Keeping valve assembly weight to a minimum is advantageous in that the mass which must be cooled from ambient temperature to cryogenic

Figure 4-9. Control Valve for Cryogenic Service

operating temperature at start-up is lessened. Valve body walls are carefully contoured for the same purpose.

Gasketed joints are avoided whenever possible to avoid the possibility of leakage which would damage the insulation of the cold box and necessitate costly maintenance and downtime. A leak-tight stem seal is also important, but is often difficult to maintain since most elastomer and plastic materials become hard and brittle at temperatures below −50°F (−46°C). Use of a valve with a long extension bonnet, such as that shown in Figure 4-9, provides the solution. The extension bonnet, which should extend four to six inches beyond the cold-box as shown in figure 4-10, provides space for a slight boil-off of the cold liquid. When installed so that the extension bonnet slants at least 20 degrees above horizontal, the vapor pocket resulting from liquid boil-off prevents the cold liquid from contacting the stem seal packing area.

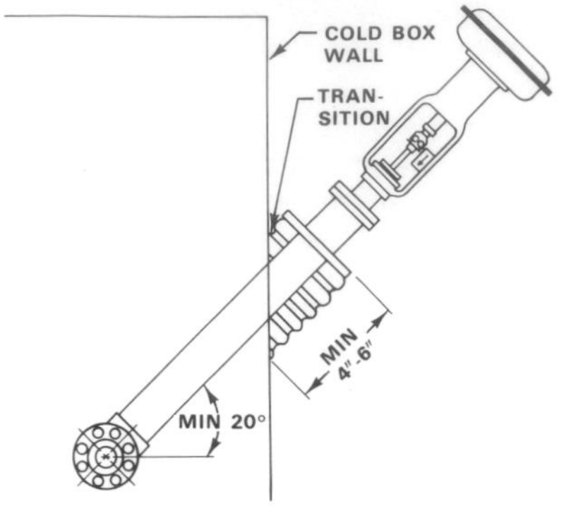

Figure 4-10. Cold Box Installation

Most valve manufacturers can provide valves, similar to that shown in Figure 4-9, designed specifically for cryogenic service. These valves are usually limited to 4-inch size due to high heat influx given by large warming extensions. For applications requiring larger valve sizes, ball and butterfly valves can be modified by the addition of fabricated extension bonnets. Both types are relatively economical and are suited to cryogenic service due to their low cool-down weights. To minimize gasketing problems, the gasket surfaces of the valve and pipeline must be provided with a better finish than on standard service valves. This helps to compensate for loss of gasket resilience at cryogenic temperatures.

Standard throttling globe-style control valves are also frequently used in cryogenic service. Normally they are used in insulated pipelines and include fabricated extension bonnets so that the actuator and packing box are outside the insulated area. Valve body material is most often ASTM A351 Grade CF8M Type 316 stainless steel. Internal parts must be made of materials compatible with the fluid controlled, and must also have rates of thermal contraction comparable to the body material to avoid internal leakage during cycling temperature conditions. A liquid seal may be used around the stem at the bottom of the bonnet extension to help maintain a pocket of insulating vapor within the bonnet extension and keep the cryogenic liquid away from the packing area. Standard ANSI-class valves may have to be derated for cryogenic service due to reduced bonnet bolting strength at very low temperatures.

Control Valves for Nuclear Service

Since 1970 U.S. manufacturers and suppliers of components for nuclear power plants have been subject to the requirements of Appendix B, Title 10, Part 50 of the Code of Federal Regulations entitled "Quality Assurance Criteria for Nuclear Power Plants and Fuel Reprocessing Plants." The enforcement agency for this regulation is the U.S. Nuclear Regulatory Commission. Ultimate responsibility of proof of compliance to Appendix B rests with the owner of the plant, but he must in turn rely on the manufacturers of the various plant components to provide documented evidence that the components were manufactured, inspected, and tested by proven techniques performed by qualified personnel according to documented procedures.

In keeping with the requirements of the Code of Federal Regulations, most nuclear power plant components are specified in accordance with Section III of the ASME Boiler and Pressure Vessel Code entitled "Nuclear Power Plant Components." All aspects of the manufacturing process must be documented in a quality control manual and audited and certified by ASME prior to actual manufacture of the components. All subsequent manufacturing materials and operations are to be checked by an authorized inspector. All valves manufactured in accordance with Section III requirements receive an ASME code nameplate and an "N" stamp symbolizing acceptability for service in nuclear power plant applications. The Code requirements ensure strength and pressure integrity of the pressure-retaining parts. Section III defines pressure-retaining parts as the body, bonnet, disc or valve plug, and bolting.

Section III does not apply to parts not associated with the pressure retaining function, to actuators and accessories unless they are pressure retaining parts, to deterioration of valve components due to radiation, corrosion, erosion, seismic or environmental qualifications, or to cleaning, painting, or packaging requirements. (However, customer specifications normally cover these areas.) Section III *does* apply to materials used for pressure retaining parts, to design criteria, to fabrication procedures, to non-destructive test procedures for pressure retaining parts, to hydrostatic testing, and to marking and stamping procedures. ASME Section III is revised by means of semi-annual addenda which may be used after date of issue, and which become mandatory six months after date of issue.

Valves Subject to Sulfide Stress Cracking

The National Association of Corrosion Engineers, recognizing the problems of sulfide stress cracking (SSC) and hydrogen embrittlement in gas and oil industry valves, have prepared NACE Standard MR-01-75 setting material guidelines for selection of valves to be used in "sour gas" service. The following statements, while based on the standard mentioned, cannot be presented in the detail furnished in the standard itself and do not guarantee suitability for any given material in hydrogen sulfide-containing sour environments. The reader is urged to refer to the complete standard prior to selecting control valves for "sour gas" service. Additionally, the reader should be aware that portions of this standard have been mandated by statute in many states of the U.S.A.

- Most ferrous metals can become susceptible to SSC due to hardening by heat treatment and/or cold work. Conversely, many ferrous metals can be heat treated to improve resistance to SSC.

- Carbon and low-alloy steels should be heat treated to a maximum hardness of HRC 22 (Rockwell "C" Hardness Scale) to improve resistance to SSC.

- Cast iron is not permitted for use as a pressure-containing member in equipment covered by some American Petroleum Institute standards and should not be used in non-pressure containing internal valve parts without the approval of the purchaser.

• Austenitic stainless steels are most resistant to SSC in the annealed condition; some other stainless steels are acceptable up to HRC 35.

• Copper-base alloys are generally not to be used in critical parts of a valve without the approval of the purchaser.

• Some high-strength alloys are acceptable under specified conditions.

• Chrome, nickel, and cadmium plating offer no protection from SSC.

• Most weld repairs or fabrication welds require post-weld heat treatment to assure a maximum hardness of HRC 22.

• Conventional identification stamping is permissible in low stress areas, such as on the outside diameter of line flanges.

• The standard precludes using ASTM A193 Grade B7 bolting for some applications. Therefore, it may be necessary to derate valves originally designed to use this bolting.

Section 5

Installation and Maintenance

Control Valve Installation

Correct sizing and selection procedures, proper installation techniques, and periodic preventive maintenance are all factors that can lengthen control valve service life. Most valve manufacturers furnish detailed installation and operation instructions with each valve. These instruction sheets normally outline specific installation and maintenance procedures which apply to the particular valve described. Naturally, the specific instructions should be read by the purchaser prior to valve installation and closely followed during installation and operation. The suggestions furnished below are general in nature and should not take precedence over the valve manufacturer's detailed instructions for a particular valve.

Use a Recommended Piping Arrangement

The Instrument Society of America has published a Recommended Practice, ISA RP-4.2, on Standard Control Valve Manifold Designs to promote uniform control valve installations. Following one of the recommended practices, such as those described in Figures 5-1 and 5-2, will be of benefit in the event that piping components have to be replaced due to changing service requirements. The dimensions shown are for carbon steel valves and fittings, but the general arrangement of parts can be applied to installations with cast iron valves and fittings.

Be Sure the Pipeline is Clean

Foreign material in the pipeline could damage the seating surface of the valve, or even obstruct the movement of the valve plug or disc so that the valve could not shut off properly. To help reduce the possibility of a dangerous situation occurring, all pipelines should be blown out with air prior to valve installation. Make sure pipe scale, metal chips, welding slag, and other foreign materials are removed. Also, if the valve has screwed end connections, a good grade of pipe sealant compound should be applied to the male pipeline threads only. Do not use sealant on the female threads in the valve body because excess compound on the female threads would be forced into the valve body. This could cause sticking of the valve plug or accumulation of dirt which would prevent good valve shutoff.

Inspect the Control Valve Before Installation

While valve manufacturers take steps to prevent shipment damage, such damage is possible and should be discovered and reported before the valve is installed.

Type I Control Valve Manifold

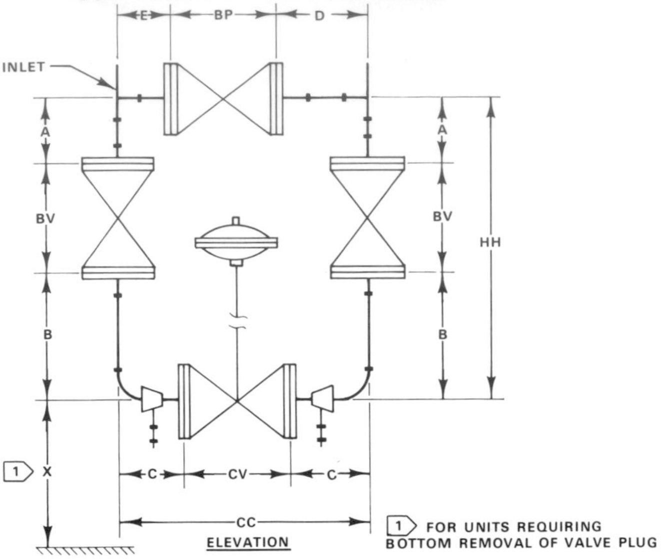

Figure 5-1. Control Valve Installation for Low Pressure Drop Applications

Table of Dimensions
(All Dimensions Given in Inches)

Manifold Rating	Manifold Size	Control Valve Size	CV*	BV	BP	CC	HH	A	B	C	D	E	X
With ANSI Class 300 Flanges	2	1-1/2	9.25	8.50	10.50	26.75	39.00	8.75	21.62	8.69	10.88	5.25	22.62
	3	2	10.50	11.12	12.50	29.12	41.50	9.50	20.75	9.25	10.00	6.50	26.62
	3	1-1/2	9.25	11.12	12.50	29.12	41.50	9.50	20.75	9.88	10.00	6.50	26.62
	4	3	12.50	12.00	14.00	34.88	42.12	10.88	19.12	11.12	13.25	7.50	29.50
	4	2	10.50	12.00	14.00	34.88	42.12	10.88	19.12	12.12	13.25	7.50	29.50
	6	4	14.50	15.88	15.88	44.38	53.50	17.12	20.38	14.88	18.88	9.50	39.00
	6	3	12.50	15.88	15.88	44.38	53.50	17.12	20.38	15.88	18.88	9.50	39.00
	8	6	18.62	16.50	16.50	54.50	56.62	22.00	18.00	17.88	26.50	11.38	45.50
	8	4	14.50	16.50	16.50	54.50	56.62	22.00	18.00	19.94	26.50	11.38	45.50
With ANSI Class 150 Flanges	2	1-1/2	9.25	7.00	8.00	26.75	39.00	10.25	21.62	8.69	13.62	5.00	22.62
	3	2	10.50	8.00	9.50	29.12	41.50	12.62	20.75	9.25	13.38	6.12	26.62
	3	1-1/2	9.25	8.00	9.50	29.12	41.50	12.62	20.75	9.88	13.38	6.12	26.62
	4	3	12.50	9.00	11.50	34.88	42.12	13.88	19.12	11.12	16.12	7.12	29.50
	4	2	10.50	9.00	11.50	34.88	42.12	13.88	19.12	12.12	16.12	7.12	29.50
	6	4	14.50	10.50	10.50	44.38	53.50	22.50	20.38	14.88	24.62	9.12	39.00
	6	3	12.50	10.50	10.50	44.38	53.50	22.50	20.38	15.88	24.62	9.12	39.00
	8	6	18.62	11.50	11.50	54.50	56.62	27.00	18.00	17.88	31.88	11.00	45.50
	8	4	14.50	11.50	11.50	54.50	56.62	27.00	18.00	19.94	31.88	11.00	45.50

*Control valve dimensions in accordance with ISA S4.01.1-1977. All control valve dimensions are ANSI Class 300 flanged.

Type VI Control Valve Manifold

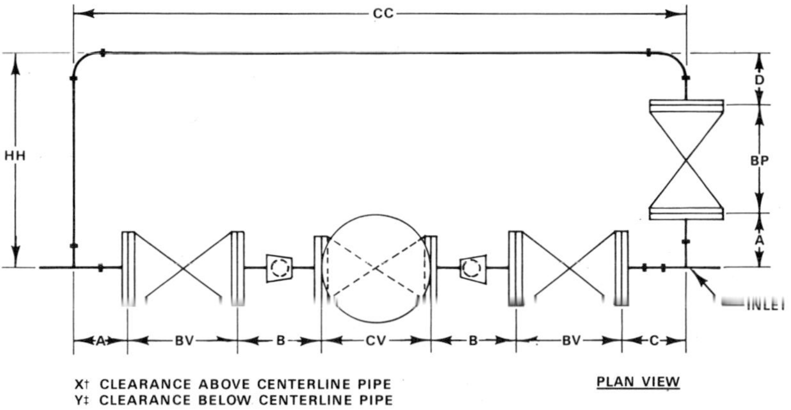

Figure 5-2. Control Valve Installation for High Pressure Drop Applications

Table of Dimensions

(All Dimensions Given in Inches)

Manifold Rating	Manifold Size	Control Valve Size	CV*	BV	BP	CC	HH	A	B	C	D	X†	Y‡
With ANSI Class 300 Flanges	2	1-1/2	9.25	8.50	10.50	57.50	20.62	5.25	8.44	8.75	4.75	22.62	36.62
	3	2	10.50	11.12	12.50	66.50	25.25	6.50	8.69	9.50	6.12	26.62	38.50
	3	1-1/2	9.25	11.12	12.50	66.50	25.25	6.50	9.31	9.50	6.12	26.62	38.50
	4	3	12.50	12.00	14.00	73.50	29.00	7.50	9.12	10.88	7.38	29.50	39.12
	4	2	10.50	12.00	14.00	73.50	29.00	7.50	10.12	10.88	7.38	29.50	39.12
	6	4	14.50	15.88	15.88	96.25	35.38	9.50	11.50	17.12	9.88	39.00	50.00
	6	3	12.50	15.88	15.88	96.25	35.38	9.50	12.50	17.12	9.88	39.00	50.00
	8	6	18.62	16.50	16.50	108.75	40.38	11.38	11.69	22.00	12.38	45.50	51.75
	8	4	14.50	16.50	16.50	108.75	40.38	11.38	13.75	22.00	12.38	45.50	51.75
With ANSI Class 150 Flanges	2	1-1/2	9.25	7.00	8.00	55.25	17.62	5.00	8.19	10.25	4.50	22.62	36.62
	3	2	10.50	8.00	9.50	62.25	21.50	6.12	8.31	12.62	5.75	26.62	38.50
	3	1-1/2	9.25	8.00	9.50	62.25	21.50	6.12	8.94	12.62	5.75	26.62	38.50
	4	3	12.50	9.00	11.50	69.38	25.75	7.12	8.75	13.88	7.00	29.50	39.12
	4	2	10.50	9.00	11.50	69.38	25.75	7.12	9.75	13.88	7.00	29.50	39.12
	6	4	14.50	10.50	10.50	89.75	29.25	9.12	11.12	22.50	9.50	39.00	50.00
	6	3	12.50	10.50	10.50	89.75	29.25	9.12	12.12	22.50	9.50	39.00	50.00
	8	6	18.62	11.50	11.50	102.62	34.62	11.00	11.31	27.00	12.00	45.50	51.75
	8	4	14.50	11.50	11.50	102.62	34.62	11.00	13.38	27.00	12.00	45.50	51.75

*Control valve dimensions in accordance with ISA S4.01.1-1977. All control valve dimensions are ANSI Class 300 flanged.

†Clearance above centerline of pipe for units requiring top removal of valve plug.

‡Clearance below centerline of pipe for units requiring bottom removal of valve plug.

DO NOT INSTALL A CONTROL VALVE KNOWN TO HAVE BEEN DAMAGED IN SHIPMENT. Before installation check for and remove all shipping stops and protective plastic plugs or gasket surface covers. Check inside the valve body to make sure no foreign objects are present.

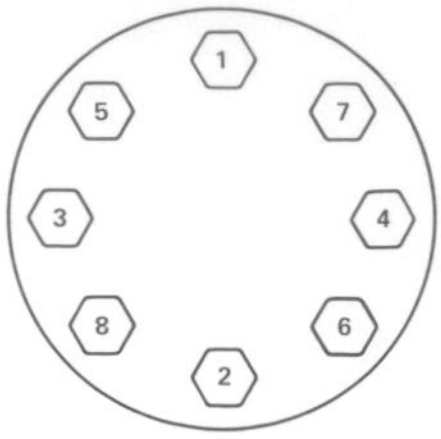

Figure 5-3. Recommended Bolt Tightening Sequence for Uniform Gasket Loading

Use Good Piping Practice

Most control valves can be installed in any position. However, the most common method is with the actuator vertical and above the valve body. If horizontal actuator mounting is necessary, consider the possibility of providing additional vertical support for the actuator. Be sure the body is installed so that fluid flow will be in the direction indicated by the flow arrow on the body.

Be sure ample room is allowed above and/or below the valve installation to permit easy removal of the actuator or valve plug for inspection and maintenance procedures. Clearance distances are normally available from the valve manufacturer in the form of certified dimension drawings. For flanged valve bodies, be sure the flanges are properly aligned to provide uniform contact on the gasket surfaces. Snug up the bolts gently in establishing proper flange alignment and then finish tightening them in a criss-cross pattern as depicted in Figure 5-3. This will avoid uneven gasket loading and will help in preventing leaks, as well as avoiding the possibility of damaging, or even breaking, the flange itself. This precaution is particularly important when connecting flanges of different materials, such as would be the case when a cast iron body is bolted between steel pipeline flanges.

Pressure taps installed upstream and downstream of the control valve are useful for checking flow capacity or pressure drop. Such taps should be located in straight runs of pipe, away from elbows, reducers, or expanders, to minimize inaccuracies resulting from fluid turbulence.

Use 1/4-inch or 3/8-inch tubing or pipe from the pressure connection on the actuator to the controller. Try to keep this distance relatively short and try to minimize the number of fittings and elbows in order to reduce system time lag. If long distances are involved, a valve positioner or a booster should be used on the control valve.

Control Valve Maintenance

In order to perform even routine maintenance procedures on a control valve, it is important that the maintenance man have a thorough understanding of the fundamental construction and operation of the valve. Without this knowledge, the equipment could be damaged inadvertently, or could cause injury to the maintenance man and others in the area. Most valve manufacturers provide suggested safety measures in their detailed instruction and operation manuals. Usually, a sectional drawing of the equipment is also furnished to help in understanding the operation of the equipment as well as to provide identification of component parts..

In all major types of control valves, the actuator provides force to position a movable valve plug, disc, or ball in relation to a stationary seat ring or sealing surface. The moveable member should respond freely to changes in actuator loading pressure. If proper operation is not being received, service is indicated. Before any maintenance procedures are started, be sure that all line pressure is shut off and released from the valve body and also that all pressure to the actuator is shut off and captive pressure gradually relieved. Failure to take adequate precautions could create a situation that would damage the equipment or injure personnel.

Often corporate maintenance policy or existing codes require preventive maintenance on a regular schedule. Usually such programs include inspection for damage of all major valve components and replacement of all gaskets, O-ring seals, diaphragms, and other elastomer parts. Following is a series of commonly performed maintenance procedures and some general instructions for performing each procedure. The reader is reminded that specific, detailed maintenance procedure instructions are normally furnished with control valve equipment and should be carefully followed.

Replacing Actuator Diaphragm

After isolating the valve from all pressure, relieve all spring compression in the main spring, if possible. (On some spring and diaphragm actuators for use on rotary-shaft valve bodies, spring compression is not externally adjustable. Initial spring compression is set at the factory and does not need to be released in order to change the diaphragm.) Remove the upper diaphragm case. On direct-acting actuators, the diaphragm can be lifted out and replaced with a new one. On reverse-acting actuators, the diaphragm head assembly must be dismantled to change the diaphragm.

Most pneumatic spring-and-diaphragm actuators utilize a molded diaphragm for control valve service. The molded diaphragm facilitates installation, provides a relatively uniform effective area throughout the valve's travel range, and permits greater travel than could be possible if a flat-sheet diaphragm were used. If a flat-sheet diaphragm is used in an emergency repair situation, it should be replaced with a molded diaphragm as soon as possible.

When re-assembling the diaphragm case, tighten the cap screws around the perimeter of the case firmly and evenly to prevent leakage.

Replacing Stem Packing

Bonnet packing, which provides the pressure seal around the stem of a globe-style or angle-style valve body, may need to be replaced if leakage develops around the stem, or if the valve is completely disassembled for other maintenance or inspection. Before starting to remove packing nuts, make sure there is no pressure in the valve body.

If the packing is of the split ring variety, it can be removed (with considerable difficulty) without removing the actuator by digging it out of the packing box with a narrow, sharp tool. This is not recommended, because the wall of the packing box or the stem could easily be scratched, thereby causing leakage when the new packing was installed.

Don't try to blow out the old packing rings by applying pressure to the lubricator hole in the bonnet. This can be dangerous and frequently doesn't work very well anyway. (Many packing arrangements have about half of the rings below the lubricator opening.)

The approved method is to:

1. Separate the valve stem and actuator stem connection.

2. Remove the actuator from the valve body.

3. Remove the bonnet and pull out the valve plug and stem.

4. Insert a rod (preferably slightly larger than the stem) through the bottom of the packing box and push or drive the old packing out the top of the bonnet. (Don't use the valve plug stem because the threads could be damaged in the process.)

5. Clean the packing box. Inspect the stem for scratches or imperfections that could damage new packing.

6. Check the valve plug, seat ring, and trim parts as appropriate.

7. Re-assemble the valve body and put the bonnet in position.

8. Tighten body/bonnet bolting in sequence similar to that described for flanges on page 100.

9. Slide new packing parts over the stem in proper sequence, being careful that the stem threads do not damage the packing rings.

10. Install the packing follower, flange, and packing nuts.

11. For spring-loaded TFE V-ring packing, tighten the packing nuts as far as they will go. For other varieties, tighten in service only enough to prevent leakage.

12. Replace and tighten the actuator onto the body. Position and tighten the stem connector to provide desired valve plug travel.

Replacing Threaded Seat Rings

Many conventional sliding-stem control valves use threaded-in seat rings. Severe service conditions can cause damage to the seating surface of the seat ring(s) so that the valve does not shut off satisfactorily. In that event, replacement of the seat ring(s) will be necessary.

Before trying to remove the seat ring(s), check to see if the ring has been tack-welded to the valve body. If so, cut away the weld and apply penetrating oil to the seat ring threads before trying to remove the ring. The following procedure for seat ring removal assumes that a seat ring puller, such as that shown in Figure 5-4, is being used. If a puller is not available, a lathe or boring mill may be used to remove the ring(s).

1. Place the proper size seat lug bar across the seat ring so that the bar contacts the seat lugs as shown.

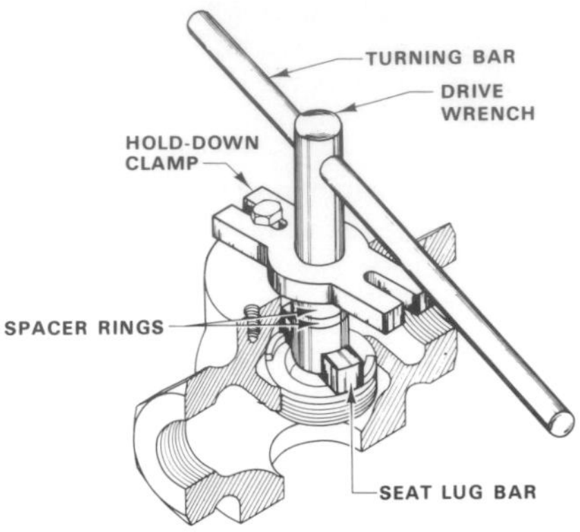

Figure 5-4. Seat Ring Puller

2. Insert drive wrench and place enough spacer rings over the wrench so that the hold-down clamp will rest about 1/4-inch above the body flange.

Slip hold-down clamp onto drive wrench and secure the clamp to the body with two cap screws (or hex nuts for steel bodies) from the bonnet. Do not tighten cap screws or nuts.

3. Use turning bar to unscrew the seat ring. Stuck seat rings may require additional force on the turning bar. Slip a 3- to 5-foot length of pipe over one end of the turning bar, and while applying a steady force, hit the other end of the bar with a heavy hammer to break the ring loose. In addition, a large pipe wrench can be used on the drive wrench near the hold-down clamp.

4. After the seat ring is loose, alternately unscrew the flange bolts (or nuts) on the hold-down clamp and continue to unscrew seat ring.

5. Before installing new ring(s), thoroughly clean threads in the body port(s). Apply pipe compound to the threads of the new seat ring(s).

Note

On double-port bodies, one of the seat rings is smaller than the other. On direct-acting valves (push-down-to-close action), install the smaller ring in the body port farther from the bonnet before installing the larger ring. On reverse-acting valves (push-down-to-open action), install the smaller ring in the body port closer to the bonnet before installing the larger ring.

Screw the ring(s) into the body. Use the seat ring puller, lathe, or boring mill to tighten seat rings in the body. Remove all excess pipe compound after tightening. The seat ring can be spot welded in place to ensure that it does not loosen.

6. Reassemble the valve.

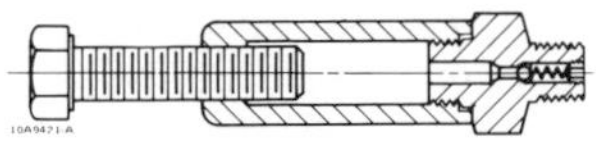

LUBRICATOR

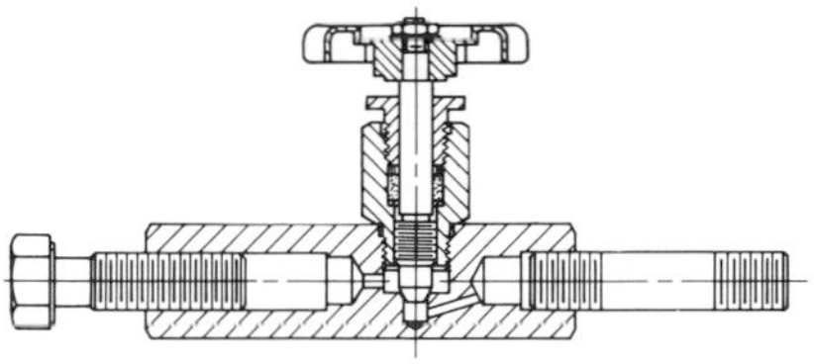

LUBRICATOR/ISOLATING VALVE

Figure 5-5. Lubricator and Lubricator/ Isolating Valve

Grinding Metal Seats

A certain amount of leakage should be expected with metal-to-metal seating in any globe-style valve body. If the leakage becomes excessive, however, the condition of the seating surfaces of the valve plug and seat ring can be improved by grinding. Large nicks should be machined out rather than ground out. Many grinding compounds are available commercially. Use one of good quality or make your own with a mixture of 600-grit silicon carbide compound and solidified vegetable oil. White lead should be applied to the seat to prevent excessive cutting or tearing during grinding. In cage-style constructions the bonnet or bottom flange must be bolted to the body with the gaskets in place during the grinding procedure to position the cage and seat ring properly and to help align the valve plug with the seat ring. A simple grinding tool can be made from a piece of strap iron locked to the valve plug stem with nuts.

On double-port bodies, the top ring normally grinds faster than the bottom ring. Under these conditions, continue to use grinding compound and white lead on the bottom ring, but use only a polishing compound (rottenstone and oil) on the top ring. If either of the ports continues to leak, use more grinding compound on the seat ring that is not leaking and polishing compound on the other ring. This procedure grinds down the seat ring that is not leaking until both seats touch at the same time. Never leave one seat ring dry while grinding the other.

After grinding, remove bonnet or bottom flange, clean seating surfaces, and test for shutoff. Repeat grinding procedure if leakage is still excessive.

Lubricating Control Valve Packing

A lubricator or lubricator/isolating valve (as shown in Figure 5-5) is required for semi-metallic packing and is recommended for graphited asbestos and TFE-impregnated asbestos packing. The lubricator or lubricator/ isolating valve combination should be installed on the side of the valve bonnet, replacing the pipe plug used with packing types not requiring lubrication. Use Dow Corning X-2 lubricant or equivalent for standard service up to 450°F (232°C) and Hooker Chemical Corporation Fluorolube lubricant or equivalent for chemical service up to 300°F (149°C). With lubricator, isolating valve, and pipe nipple (if used) completely filled with lubricant and installed on bonnet, open isolating valve (if used) and rotate lubricator bolt a full turn clockwise to force lubricant into the packing box. Close the isolating valve after each lubrication.

Adjusting Travel and Connecting Stem

Sliding-Stem Control Valves

Part names used throughout the following section are shown in Figure 5-6. The procedure is appropriate for sliding-stem valves with either spring-and-diaphragm or piston actuators. When performing the travel adjustment procedure, be careful to avoid damaging the valve plug stem. Scratches on the stem can lead to packing leakage. If the unit includes a bellows seal bonnet, the stem must not be rotated or the bellows will be damaged. On all other units, the stem may be rotated for minor travel adjustment, but the valve plug should not be in contact with the seat ring during rotation of the stem.

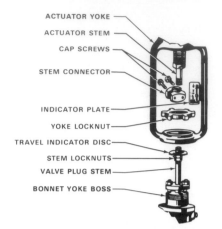

Figure 5-6. Exploded View of Stem Connection Components

1. Assemble the body and mount the actuator. Screw the stem locknuts onto the valve plug stem and set the travel indicator disc on the locknuts with the "cupped" portion downward. Leave enough threads exposed above the disc for the stem connector.

2. Be sure the actuator stem is in the position that equates with the "closed" valve plug position—fully "down" for push-down-to-close valve styles; fully "up" for push-down-to-open valve styles. To achieve this condition, it will often be necessary to pressure load the actuator to properly position the stem.

3. Move the valve plug to the "closed" position, contacting the seat ring.

4. Change actuator loading pressure in order to move the actuator stem 1/8-inch. Install the stem connector, clamping the actuator stem to the valve plug stem.

5. Cycle the actuator to check availablity of desired total travel and that the valve plug seats before the actuator contacts the upper travel stop. Minor adjustments in total travel can be made, if necessary, by loosening the stem connector **slightly,** tightening the locknuts together, and screwing the stem either into or out of the stem connector by means of a wrench on the locknuts. If overall travel increase is desired, the increase must be less than the 1/8-inch the actuator rod was moved in step 4 above, or the valve will not shut off.

6. If the total travel is adequate, tighten the stem connector securely, lock the travel indicator disc against the connector with the locknuts, and adjust the indicator plate on the yoke to show valve plug position.

7. Provide a gauge to measure the pressure to the actuator. Make a final adjustment on the actuator or its positioner to set the starting point of valve travel and to obtain full travel for the desired instrument range.

Rotary-Shaft Control Valves

As shown in Figures 5-7 and 5-8, there are a variety of actuator mounting styles and positions possible with rotary-shaft control valve bodies. Specific adjustment procedures vary depending on whether desired valve action is push-down-to-close or push-down-to-open. The connecting linkage between the actuator and the valve body normally includes a lever which is attached to the valve shaft by means of a key and keyway slot or by mating multiple cut splines on the lever and shaft. A rod end bearing and turnbuckle usually connect the lever to the

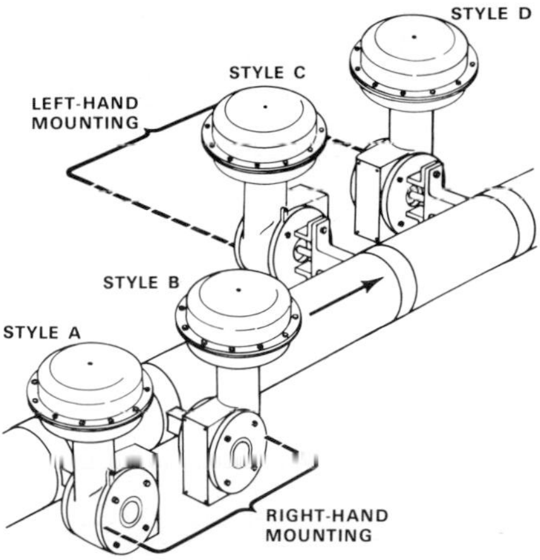

Figure 5-7. Mounting Styles for Actuators on Rotary-Shaft Control Valve Bodies

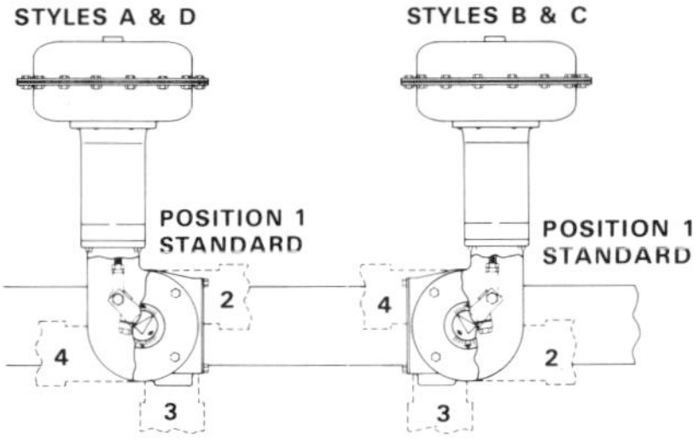

Figure 5-8. Mounting Positions for Actuators on Rotary-Shaft Control Valve Bodies

actuator stem. The valve shaft and disc or V-notched ball are stamped with indicating marks to show proper

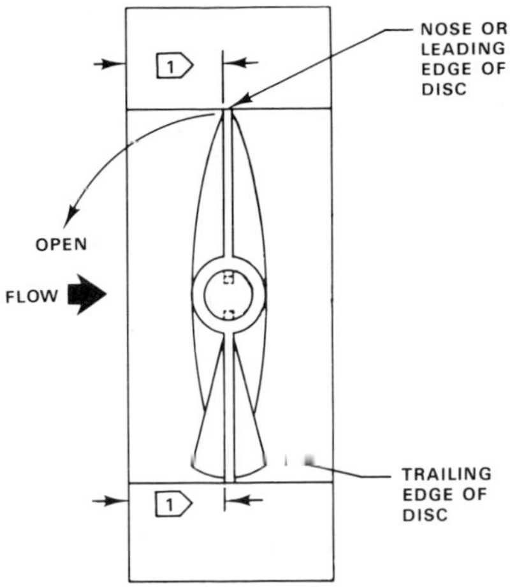

1 EQUAL MEASUREMENTS BETWEEN VALVE FACE AND DISC EDGE AT TOP AND BOTTOM ENSURE FULLY CLOSED DISC.

Figure 5-9. Check for Proper Disc Closure

orientation for mating splines. Similar indicating marks are used to show shaft and lever orientation. Fine adjustment is accomplished by lengthening or shortening the turnbuckle to achieve full disc or V-notch ball closure at 0° indicated rotation.

For disc-style rotary valves, fine travel adjustment should be performed with the valve body out of the pipeline so that measurements can be made as suggested in Figure 5-9. Refer to the manufacturer's instruction manuals for specific adjustment details for the body and actuator being used.

Section 6

Conversions and Equivalents

Length Equivalents

Multiply Number of ↘ by ↘ To Obtain	Meters	Inches	Feet	Millimeters	Miles	Kilometers
Meters	1	39.37	3.2808	1000	0.0006214	0.001
Inches	0.0254	1	0.0833	25.4	0.00001578	0.0000254
Feet	0.3048	12	1	304.8	0.0001894	0.0003048
Millimeters	0.001	0.03937	0.0032808	1	0.0000006214	0.000001
Miles	1609.35	63,360	5,280	1,609,350	1	1.60935
Kilometers	1,000	39,370	3280.83	1,000,000	0.62137	1

1 meter = 100 centimeters = 1000 millimeters = 0.001 kilometers = 1,000,000 micrometers
To convert metric units, merely adjust the decimal point.
1 millimeter = 1000 microns = 0.03937 inches = 39.37 mils.

Whole Inch-Millimeter Equivalents

In.	0	1	2	3	4	5	6	7	8	9
	mm									
0	0.0	25.4	50.8	76.2	101.6	127.0	152.4	177.8	203.2	228.6
10	254.0	279.4	304.8	330.2	355.6	381.0	406.4	431.8	457.2	482.6
20	508.0	533.4	558.8	584.2	609.6	635.0	660.4	685.8	711.2	736.6
30	762.0	787.4	812.8	838.2	863.6	889.0	914.4	939.8	965.2	990.6
40	1016.0	1041.4	1066.8	1092.2	1117.6	1143.0	1168.4	1193.8	1219.2	1244.6
50	1270.0	1295.4	1320.8	1346.2	1371.6	1397.0	1422.4	1447.8	1473.2	1498.6
60	1524.0	1549.4	1574.8	1600.2	1625.6	1651.0	1676.4	1701.8	1727.2	1752.6
70	1778.0	1803.4	1828.8	1854.2	1879.6	1905.0	1930.4	1955.8	1981.2	2006.6
80	2032.0	2057.4	2082.8	2108.2	2133.6	2159.0	2184.4	2209.8	2235.2	2260.6
90	2286.0	2311.4	2336.8	2362.2	2387.6	2413.0	2438.4	2463.8	2489.2	2514.6
100	2540.0	2565.4	2590.8	2616.2	2641.6	2667.0	2692.4	2717.8	2743.2	2768.6

Note: All values in this table are exact, based on the relation 1 in = 25.4 mm. By manipulation of the decimal point any decimal value or multiple of an inch may be converted to its exact equivalent in millimeters.

Fractional Inches To Millimeters

(1 Inch = 25.4 Millimeters)

In.	0	1/16	1/8	3/16	1/4	5/16	3/8	7/16	1/2	9/16	5/8	11/16	3/4	13/16	7/8	15/16
	mm															
0	0.0	1.6	3.2	4.8	6.4	7.9	9.5	11.1	12.7	14.3	15.9	17.5	19.1	20.6	22.2	23.8
1	25.4	27.0	28.6	30.2	31.8	33.3	34.9	36.5	38.1	39.7	41.3	42.9	44.5	46.0	47.6	49.2
2	50.8	52.4	54.0	55.6	57.2	58.7	60.3	61.9	63.5	65.1	66.7	68.3	69.9	71.4	73.0	74.6
3	76.2	77.8	79.4	81.0	82.6	84.1	85.7	87.3	88.9	90.5	92.1	93.7	95.3	96.8	98.4	100.0
4	101.6	103.2	104.8	106.4	108.0	109.5	111.1	112.7	114.3	115.9	117.5	119.1	120.7	122.2	123.8	125.4
5	127.0	128.6	130.2	131.8	133.4	134.9	136.5	138.1	139.7	141.3	142.9	144.5	146.1	147.6	149.2	150.8
6	152.4	154.0	155.6	157.2	158.8	160.3	161.9	163.5	165.1	166.7	168.3	169.9	171.5	173.0	174.6	176.2
7	177.8	179.4	181.0	182.6	184.2	185.7	187.3	188.9	190.5	192.1	193.7	195.3	196.9	198.4	200.0	201.6
8	203.2	204.8	206.4	208.0	209.6	211.1	212.7	214.3	215.9	217.5	219.1	220.7	222.3	223.8	225.4	227.0
9	228.6	230.2	231.8	233.4	235.0	236.5	238.1	239.7	241.3	242.9	244.5	246.1	247.7	249.2	250.8	252.4
10	254.0	255.6	257.2	258.8	260.4	261.9	263.5	265.1	266.7	268.3	269.9	271.5	273.1	274.6	276.2	277.8

Additional Fractional/Decimal Inch—Millimeter Equivalents

INCHES		MILLI-METERS	INCHES		MILLI-METERS	INCHES		MILLI-METERS
Frac-tions	Decimals		Frac-tions	Decimals		Frac-tions	Decimals	
	.00394	.1		.2	5.08		.44	11.176
	.00787	.2	13/64	.203125	5.1594		.45	11.430
	.01	.254		.21	5.334	29/64	.453125	11.5094
	.01181	.3	7/32	.21875	5.5562		.46	11.684
1/64	.015625	.3969		.22	5.588	15/32	.46875	11.9062
	.01575	.4		.23	5.842		.47	11.938
	.01969	.5	15/64	.234375	5.9531		.47244	12.0
	.02	.508		.23622	6.0		.48	12.192
	.02362	.6		.24	6.096	31/64	.484375	12.3031
	.02756	.7	1/4	.25	6.35		.49	12.446
	.03	.762		.26	6.604	1/2	.50	12.7
1/32	.03125	.7938	17/64	.265625	6.7469		.51	12.954
	.0315	.8		.27	6.858		.51181	13.0
	.03543	.9		.27559	7.0	33/64	.515625	13.0969
	.03937	1.0		.28	7.112		.52	13.208
	.04	1.016	9/32	.28125	7.1438		.53	13.462
3/64	.046875	1.1906		.29	7.366	17/32	.53125	13.4938
	.05	1.27	19/64	.296875	7.5406		.54	13.716
	.06	1.524		.30	7.62	35/64	.546875	13.8906
1/16	.0625	1.5875		.31	7.874		.55	13.970
	.07	1.778	5/16	.3125	7.9375		.55118	14.0
5/64	.078125	1.9844		.31496	8.0		.56	14.224
	.07874	2.0		.32	8.128	9/16	.5625	14.2875
	.08	2.032	21/64	.328125	8.3344		.57	14.478
	.09	2.286		.33	8.382	37/64	.578125	14.6844
3/32	.09375	2.3812		.34	8.636		.58	14.732
	.1	2.54	11/32	.34375	8.7312		.59	14.986
7/64	.109375	2.7781		.35	8.89		.59055	15.0
	.11	2.794		.35433	9.0	19/32	.59375	15.0812
	.11811	3.0	23/64	.359375	9.1281		.60	15.24
	.12	3.048		.36	9.144	39/64	.609375	15.4781
1/8	.125	3.175		.37	9.398		.61	15.494
	.13	3.302	3/8	.375	9.525		.62	15.748
	.14	3.556		.38	9.652	5/8	.625	15.875
9/64	.140625	3.5719		.39	9.906		.62992	16.0
	.15	3.810	25/64	.390625	9.9219		.63	16.002
5/32	.15625	3.9688		.39370	10.0		.64	16.256
	.15748	4.0		.40	10.16	41/64	.640625	16.2719
	.16	4.064	13/32	.40625	10.3188		.65	16.510
	.17	4.318		.41	10.414	21/32	.65625	16.6688
11/64	.171875	4.3656		.42	10.668		.66	16.764
	.18	4.572	27/64	.421875	10.7156		.66929	17.0
3/16	.1875	4.7625		.43	10.922		.67	17.018
	.19	4.826		.43307	11.0	43/64	.671875	17.0656
	.19685	5.0	7/16	.4375	11.1125		.68	17.272

- Continued -

Additional Fractional/Decimal Inch—Millimeter Equivalents (Continued)

INCHES		MILLI-METERS	INCHES		MILLI-METERS	INCHES		MILLI-METERS
Fractions	Decimals		Fractions	Decimals		Fractions	Decimals	
11/16	.6875	17.4625	51/64	.796875	20.2406		.90551	23.0
	.69	17.526		.80	20.320	29/32	.90625	23.0188
	.70	17.78		.81	20.574		.91	23.114
45/64	.703125	17.8594	13/16	.8125	20.6375		.92	23.368
	.70866	18.0		.82	20.828	59/64	.921875	23.4156
	.71	18.034		.82677	21.0		.93	23.622
23/32	.71875	18.2562	53/64	.828125	21.0344	15/16	.9375	23.8125
	.72	18.288		.83	21.082		.94	23.876
	.73	18.542		.84	21.336		.94488	24.0
47/64	.734375	18.6531	27/32	.84375	21.4312		.95	24.130
	74	18.796		.85	21.590	61/64	.953125	24.2094
	.74803	19.0	55/64	.859375	21.8281		.96	24.384
3/4	.75	19.050		.86	21.844	31/32	.96875	24.6062
	.76	19.304		.86614	22.0		.97	24.638
49/64	.765625	19.4469		.87	22.098		.98	24.892
	.77	19.558	7/8	.875	22.225		.98425	25.0
	.78	19.812		.88	22.352	63/64	.984375	25.0031
25/32	.78125	19.8438		.89	22.606		.99	25.146
	.78740	20.0	57/64	.890625	22.6219	1	1.00000	25.4000
	.79	20.066		.90	22.860			

Note: Round off decimal points to provide no more than the desired degree of accuracy.

Area Equivalents

Multiply Number of by → To Obtain	Square Meters	Square Inches	Square Feet	Square Miles	Square Kilometers
Square Meters	1	1549.99	10.7639	3.861×10^{-7}	1×10^{-6}
Square Inches	0.0006452	1	6.944×10^{-3}	2.491×10^{-10}	6.452×10^{-10}
Square Feet	0.0929	144	1	3.587×10^{-8}	9.29×10^{-8}
Square Miles	2,589,999	. . .	27,878,400	1	2.59
Square Kilometers	1,000,000	. . .	10,763,867	0.3861	1

1 square meter = 10,000 square centimeters.
1 square millimeter = 0.01 square centimeter = 0.00155 square inches.

Volume Equivalents

To Obtain → by Multiply Number of	Cubic Decimeters (Liters)	Cubic Inches	Cubic Feet	U.S. Quart	U.S. Gallon	Imperial Gallon	U.S. Barrel (Petroleum)
Cubic Decimeters (Liters)	1	61.0234	0.03531	1.05668	0.264178	0.220083	0.00629
Cubic Inches	0.01639	1	5.787×10^{-4}	0.01732	0.004329	0.003606	0.000103
Cubic Feet	28.317	1728	1	29.9221	7.48055	6.22888	0.1781
U.S. Quart	0.94636	57.75	0.03342	1	0.25	0.2082	0.00595
U.S. Gallon	3.78543	231	0.13368	4	1	0.833	0.02381
Imperial Gallon	4.54374	277.274	0.16054	4.80128	1.20032	1	0.02877
U.S. Barrel (Petroleum)	158.98	9702	5.6146	168	42	34.973	1

1 cubic meter = 1,000,000 cubic centimeters.
1 liter = 1000 milliliters = 1000 cubic centimeters.

Volume Rate Equivalents

To Obtain → by Multiply Number of	Liters Per Minute	Cubic Meters Per Hour	Cubic Feet Per Hour	Liters Per Hour	U.S. Gallon Per Minute	U.S. Barrel Per Day
Liters Minute	1	0.06	2.1189	60	0.264178	9.057
Cubic Meters Per Hour	16.667	1	35.314	1000	4.403	151
Cubic Feet Per Hour	0.4719	0.028317	1	28.317	0.1247	4.2746
Liters Per Hour	0.016667	0.001	0.035314	1	0.004403	0.151
U.S. Gallon Per Minute	3.785	0.2273	8.0208	227.3	1	34.28
U.S. Barrel Per Day	0.1104	0.006624	0.23394	6.624	0.02917	1

Pressure Equivalents

Multiply Number of / by / To Obtain →	Kg. Per Sq. Cm.	Lb. Per Sq. In.	Atm.	Bar	In. of Hg.	Kilopascals	In. of Water	Ft. of Water
Kg. Per Sq. Cm.	1	14.22	0.9678	0.98067	28.96	98.067	394.05	32.84
Lb. Per Sq. In.	0.07031	1	0.06804	0.06895	2.036	6.895	27.7	2.309
Atm.	1.0332	14.696	1	1.01325	29.92	101.325	407.14	33.93
Bar	1.01972	14.5038	0.98692	1	29.53	100	402.156	33.513
In. of Hg.	0.03453	0.4912	0.03342	0.033864	1	3.3864	13.61	1.134
Kilopascals	0.0101972	0.145038	0.0098696	0.01	0.2953	1	4.02156	0.33513
In. of Water	0.002538	0.0361	0.002456	0.00249	0.07349	0.249	1	0.0833
Ft. of Water	0.03045	0.4332	0.02947	0.029839	0.8819	2.9839	12	1

1 ounce/sq. inch = 0.0625 lbs./sq. inch.

Mass Conversion—Pounds to Kilograms

(1 pound = 0.4536 kilogram)

Pounds	0	1	2	3	4	5	6	7	8	9
	Kilograms									
0	0.00	0.45	0.91	1.36	1.81	2.27	2.72	3.18	3.63	4.08
10	4.54	4.99	5.44	5.90	6.35	6.80	7.26	7.71	8.16	8.62
20	9.07	9.53	9.98	10.43	10.89	11.34	11.79	12.25	12.70	13.15
30	13.61	14.06	14.52	14.97	15.42	15.88	16.33	16.78	17.24	17.69
40	18.14	18.60	19.05	19.50	19.96	20.41	20.87	21.32	21.77	22.23
50	22.68	23.13	23.59	24:04	24.49	24.95	25.40	25.86	26.31	26.76
60	27.22	27.67	28.12	28.58	29.03	29.48	29.94	30.39	30.84	31.30
70	31.75	32.21	32.66	33.11	33.57	34.02	34.47	34.93	35.38	35.83
80	36.29	36.74	37.20	37.65	38.10	38.56	39.01	39.46	39.92	40.37
90	40.82	41.28	41.73	42.18	42.64	43.09	43.55	44.00	44.45	44.91

Pressure Conversion—Pounds per Square Inch to Bar*

Pounds Per Square Inch	0	1	2	3	4	5	6	7	8	9
	Bar									
0	0.000000	0.068948	0.137895	0.206843	0.275790	0.344738	0.413685	0.482633	0.551581	0.620528
10	0.689476	0.758423	0.827371	0.896318	0.965266	1.034214	1.103161	1.172109	1.241056	1.310004
20	1.378951	1.447899	1.516847	1.585794	1.654742	1.723689	1.792637	1.861584	1.930532	1.999480
30	2.068427	2.137375	2.206322	2.275270	2.344217	2.413165	2.482113	2.551060	2.620008	2.688955
40	2.757903	2.826850	2.895798	2.964746	3.033693	3.102641	3.171588	3.240536	3.309484	3.378431
50	3.447379	3.516326	3.585274	3.654221	3.723169	3.792117	3.861064	3.930012	3.998959	4.067907
60	4.136854	4.205802	4.274750	4.343697	4.412645	4.481592	4.550540	4.619487	4.688435	4.757383
70	4.826330	4.895278	4.964225	5.033173	5.102120	5.171068	5.240016	5.308963	5.377911	5.446858
80	5.515806	5.584753	5.653701	5.722649	5.791596	5.860544	5.929491	5.998439	6.067386	6.136334
90	6.205282	6.274229	6.343177	6.412124	6.481072	6.550019	6.618967	6.687915	6.756862	6.825810
100	6.894757	6.963705	7.032652	7.101600	7.170548	7.239495	7.308443	7.377390	7.446338	7.515285

*To convert to kilopascals, move decimal point two positions to right; to convert to Megapascals, move decimal point one position to left. For example, 30 psi = 2.068427 bar = 206.8427 kPa = 0.2068427 MPa.

Note: Round off decimal points to provide no more than the desired degree of accuracy.

Temperature Conversion Tables

Temperature Conversion Formulas

To Convert From	To	Substitute in Formula
Degrees Celsius	Degrees Fahrenheit	(°C x 9/5) + 32
Degrees Celsius	Kelvin	(°C + 273.16)
Degrees Fahrenheit	Degrees Celsius	(°F −32) x 5/9
Degrees Fahrenheit	Degrees Rankin	(°F + 459.69)

Temperature Conversions

°C	Temp. in °C or °F to be Converted	°F	°C	Temp. in °C or °F to be Converted	°F	°C	Temp. in °C or °F to be Converted	°F
−273.16	−459.69		−90.00	−130	−202.0	−17.8	0	32.0
−267.78	−450		−84.44	−120	−184.0	−16.7	2	35.6
−262.22	−440		−78.89	−110	−166.0	−15.6	4	39.2
−256.67	−430		−73.33	−100	−148.0	−14.4	6	42.8
−251.11	−420		−70.56	−95	−139.0	−13.3	8	46.4
−245.56	−410		−67.78	−90	−130.0	−12.2	10	50.0
−240.00	−400		−65.00	−85	−121.0	−11.1	12	53.6
−234.44	−390		−62.22	−80	−112.0	−10.0	14	57.2
−228.89	−380		−59.45	−75	−103.0	−8.89	16	60.8
−223.33	−370		−56.67	−70	−94.0	−7.78	18	64.4
−217.78	−360		−53.89	−65	−85.0	−6.67	20	68.0
−212.22	−350		−51.11	−60	−76.0	−5.56	22	71.6
−206.67	−340		−48.34	−55	−67.0	−4.44	24	75.2
−201.11	−330		−45.56	−50	−58.0	−3.33	26	78.8
−195.56	−320		−42.78	−45	−49.0	−2.22	28	82.4
−190.00	−310		−40.00	−40	−40.0	−1.11	30	86.0
−184.44	−300		−38.89	−38	−36.4	0	32	89.6
−178.89	−290		−37.78	−36	−32.8	1.11	34	93.2
−173.33	−280		−36.67	−34	−29.2	2.22	36	96.8
−169.53	−273.16	−459.69	−35.56	−32	−25.6	3.33	38	100.4
−168.89	−272	−457.6	−34.44	−30	−22.0	4.44	40	104.0
−167.78	−270	−454.0	−33.33	−28	−18.4	5.56	42	107.6
−162.22	−260	−436.0	−32.22	−26	−14.8	6.67	44	111.2
−156.67	−250	−418.0	−31.11	−24	−11.2	7.78	46	114.8
−151.11	−240	−400.0	−30.00	−22	−7.6	8.89	48	118.4
−145.56	−230	−382.0	−28.89	−20	−4.0	10.0	50	122.0
−140.00	−220	−364.0	−27.78	−18	−0.4	11.1	52	125.6
−134.44	−210	−346.0	−26.67	−16	3.2	12.2	54	129.2
−128.89	−200	−328.0	−25.56	−14	6.8	13.3	56	132.8
−123.33	−190	−310.0	−24.44	−12	10.4	14.4	58	136.4
−117.78	−180	−292.0	−23.33	−10	14.0	15.6	60	140.0
−112.22	−170	−274.0	−22.22	−8	17.6	16.7	62	143.6
−106.67	−160	−256.0	−21.11	−6	21.2	17.8	64	147.2
−101.11	−150	−238.0	−20.00	−4	24.8	18.9	66	150.8
−95.56	−140	−220.0	−18.89	−2	28.4	20.0	68	154.4

- Continued -

Temperature Conversions (Continued)

°C	Temp. in °C or °F to be Converted	°F	°C	Temp. in °C or °F to be Converted	°F	°C	Temp. in °C or °F to be Converted	°F
21.1	70	158.0	204.4	400	752.0	454.4	850	1562.0
22.2	72	161.6	210.0	410	770.0	460.0	860	1580.0
23.3	74	165.2	215.6	420	788.0	465.6	870	1598.0
24.4	76	168.8	221.1	430	806.0	471.1	880	1616.0
25.6	78	172.4	226.7	440	824.0	476.7	890	1634.0
26.7	80	176.0	232.2	450	842.0	482.2	900	1652.0
27.8	82	179.6	237.8	460	860.0	487.8	910	1670.0
28.9	84	183.2	243.3	470	878.0	493.3	920	1688.0
30.0	86	186.8	248.9	480	896.0	498.9	930	1706.0
31.1	88	190.4	254.4	490	914.0	504.4	940	1724.0
32.2	90	194.0	260.0	500	932.0	510.0	950	1742.0
33.3	92	197.6	265.6	510	950.0	515.6	960	1760.0
34.4	94	201.2	271.1	520	968.0	521.1	970	1778.0
35.6	96	204.8	276.7	530	986.0	526.7	980	1796.0
36.7	98	208.4	282.2	540	1004.0	532.2	990	1814.0
37.8	100	212.0	287.8	550	1022.0	537.8	1000	1832.0
43.3	110	230.0	293.3	560	1040.0	543.3	1010	1850.0
48.9	120	248.0	298.9	570	1058.0	548.9	1020	1868.0
54.4	130	266.0	304.4	580	1076.0	554.4	1030	1886.0
60.0	140	284.0	310.0	590	1094.0	560.0	1040	1904.0
65.6	150	302.0	315.6	600	1112.0	565.6	1050	1922.0
71.1	160	320.0	321.1	610	1130.0	571.1	1060	1940.0
76.7	170	338.0	326.7	620	1148.0	576.7	1070	1958.0
82.2	180	356.0	332.2	630	1166.0	582.2	1080	1976.0
87.8	190	374.0	337.8	640	1184.0	587.8	1090	1994.0
93.3	200	392.0	343.3	650	1202.0	593.3	1100	2012.0
98.9	210	410.0	348.9	660	1220.0	598.9	1110	2030.0
104.4	220	428.0	354.4	670	1238.0	604.4	1120	2048.0
110.0	230	446.0	360.0	680	1256.0	610.0	1130	2066.0
115.6	240	464.0	365.6	690	1274.0	615.6	1140	2084.0
121.1	250	482.0	371.1	700	1292.0	621.1	1150	2102.0
126.7	260	500.0	376.7	710	1310.0	626.7	1160	2120.0
132.2	270	518.0	382.2	720	1328.0	632.2	1170	2138.0
137.8	280	536.0	387.8	730	1346.0	637.8	1180	2156.0
143.3	290	554.0	393.3	740	1364.0	643.3	1190	2174.0
148.9	300	572.0	398.9	750	1382.0	648.9	1200	2192.0
154.4	310	590.0	404.4	760	1400.0	654.4	1210	2210.0
160.0	320	608.0	410.0	770	1418.0	660.0	1220	2228.0
165.6	330	626.0	415.6	780	1436.0	665.6	1230	2246.0
171.1	340	644.0	421.1	790	1454.0	671.1	1240	2264.0
176.7	350	662.0	426.7	800	1472.0	676.7	1250	2282.0
182.2	360	680.0	432.2	810	1490.0	682.2	1260	2300.0
187.8	370	698.0	437.8	820	1508.0	687.8	1270	2318.0
193.3	380	716.0	443.3	830	1526.0	693.3	1280	2336.0
198.9	390	734.0	448.9	840	1544.0	698.9	1290	2354.0

- Continued -

Temperature Conversions (Continued)

°C	Temp. in °C or °F to be Converted	°F	°C	Temp. in °C or °F to be Converted	°F	°C	Temp. in °C or °F to be Converted	°F
704.4	1300	2372.0	760.0	1400	2552.0	815.6	1500	2732.0
710.0	1310	2390.0	765.6	1410	2570.0			
715.6	1320	2408.0	771.1	1420	2588.0			
721.1	1330	2426.0	776.7	1430	2606.0			
726.7	1340	2444.0	782.2	1440	2624.0			
732.2	1350	2462.0	787.0	1450	2642.0			
737.8	1360	2480.0	793.3	1460	2660.0			
743.3	1370	2498.0	798.9	1470	2678.0			
748.9	1380	2516.0	804.4	1480	2696.0			
754.4	1390	2534.0	810.0	1490	2714.0			

A.P.I. and Baumé Gravity Tables and Weight Factors

A.P.I. Gravity	Baumé Gravity	Specific Gravity	Lb/ U.S. Gal	U.S. Gal/ Lb	A.P.I. Gravity	Baumé Gravity	Specific Gravity	Lb/ U.S. Gal	U.S. Gal/ Lb
0	10.247	1.0760	8.962	0.1116					
1	9.223	1.0679	8.895	0.1124	31	30.78	0.8708	7.251	0.1379
2	8.198	1.0599	8.828	0.1133	32	31.77	0.8654	7.206	0.1388
3	7.173	1.0520	8.762	0.1141	33	32.76	0.8602	7.163	0.1396
4	6.148	1.0443	8.698	0.1150	34	33.75	0.8550	7.119	0.1405
5	5.124	1.0366	8.634	0.1158	35	34.73	0.8498	7.076	0.1413
6	4.099	1.0291	8.571	0.1167	36	35.72	0.8448	7.034	0.1422
7	3.074	1.0217	8.509	0.1175	37	36.71	0.8398	6.993	0.1430
8	2.049	1.0143	8.448	0.1184	38	37.70	0.8348	6.951	0.1439
9	1.025	1.0071	8.388	0.1192	39	38.69	0.8299	6.910	0.1447
10	10.00	1.0000	8.328	0.1201	40	39.68	0.8251	6.870	0.1456
11	10.99	0.9930	8.270	0.1209	41	40.67	0.8203	6.830	0.1464
12	11.98	0.9861	8.212	0.1218	42	41.66	0.8155	6.790	0.1473
13	12.97	0.9792	8.155	0.1226	43	42.65	0.8109	6.752	0.1481
14	13.96	0.9725	8.099	0.1235	44	43.64	0.8063	6.713	0.1490
15	14.95	0.9659	8.044	0.1243	45	44.63	0.8017	6.675	0.1498
16	15.94	0.9593	7.989	0.1252	46	45.62	0.7972	6.637	0.1507
17	16.93	0.9529	7.935	0.1260	47	50.61	0.7927	6.600	0.1515
18	17.92	0.9465	7.882	0.1269	48	50.60	0.7883	6.563	0.1524
19	18.90	0.9402	7.830	0.1277	49	50.59	0.7839	6.526	0.1532
20	19.89	0.9340	7.778	0.1286	50	50.58	0.7796	6.490	0.1541
21	20.88	0.9279	7.727	0.1294	51	50.57	0.7753	6.455	0.1549
22	21.87	0.9218	7.676	0.1303	52	51.55	0.7711	6.420	0.1558
23	22.86	0.9159	7.627	0.1311	53	52.54	0.7669	6.385	0.1566
24	23.85	0.9100	7.578	0.1320	54	53.53	0.7628	6.350	0.1575
25	24.84	0.9042	7.529	0.1328	55	54.52	0.7587	6.316	0.1583
26	25.83	0.8984	7.481	0.1337	56	55.51	0.7547	6.283	0.1592
27	26.82	0.8927	7.434	0.1345	57	56.50	0.7507	6.249	0.1600
28	27.81	0.8871	7.387	0.1354	58	57.49	0.7467	6.216	0.1609
29	28.80	0.8816	7.341	0.1362	59	58.48	0.7428	6.184	0.1617
30	29.79	0.8762	7.296	0.1371	60	59.47	0.7389	6.151	0.1626

- Continued -

A.P.I. and Baumé Gravity Tables and Weight Factors (Continued)

A.P.I. Gravity	Baumé Gravity	Specific Gravity	Lb/ U.S. Gal	U.S. Gal/ Lb	A.P.I. Gravity	Baumé Gravity	Specific Gravity	Lb/ U.S. Gal	U.S. Gal/ Lb
61	60.46	0.7351	6.119	0.1634	81	80.25	0.6659	5.542	0.1804
62	61.45	0.7313	6.087	0.1643	82	81.24	0.6628	5.516	0.1813
63	62.44	0.7275	6.056	0.1651	83	82.23	0.6597	5.491	0.1821
64	63.43	0.7238	6.025	0.1660	84	83.22	0.6566	5.465	0.1830
65	64.42	0.7201	6.994	0.1668	85	84.20	0.6536	5.440	0.1838
66	65.41	0.7165	5.964	0.1677	86	85.19	0.6506	5.415	0.1847
67	66.40	0.7128	5.934	0.1685	87	86.18	0.6476	5.390	0.1855
68	67.39	0.7093	5.904	0.1694	88	87.17	0.6446	5.365	0.1864
69	68.37	0.7057	5.874	0.1702	89	88.16	0.6417	5.341	0.1872
70	69.36	0.7022	5.845	0.1711	90	89.15	0.6388	5.316	0.1881
71	70.35	0.6988	5.817	0.1719	91	90.14	0.6360	5.293	0.1889
72	71.34	0.6953	5.788	0.1728	92	91.13	0.6331	5.269	0.1898
73	72.33	0.6919	5.759	0.1736	93	92.12	0.6303	5.246	0.1906
74	73.32	0.6886	5.731	0.1745	94	93.11	0.6275	5.222	0.1915
75	74.31	0.6852	5.703	0.1753	95	94.10	0.6247	5.199	0.1924
76	75.30	0.6819	5.676	0.1762	96	95.09	0.6220	5.176	0.1932
77	76.29	0.6787	5.649	0.1770	97	96.08	0.6193	5.154	0.1940
78	77.28	0.6754	5.622	0.1779	98	97.07	0.6166	5.131	0.1949
79	78.27	0.6722	5.595	0.1787	99	98.06	0.6139	5.109	0.1957
80	79.26	0.6690	5.568	0.1796	100	99.05	0.6112	5.086	0.1966

The relation of Degrees Baumé or A.P.I. to Specific Gravity is expressed by the following formulas:

For liquids lighter than water:

$$\text{Degrees Baumé} = \frac{140}{G} - 130, \quad G = \frac{140}{130 + \text{Degrees Baumé}}$$

$$\text{Degrees A.P.I.} = \frac{141.5}{G} - 131.5, \quad G = \frac{141.5}{131.5 + \text{Degrees A.P.I.}}$$

For liquids heavier than water:

$$\text{Degrees Baumé} = 145 - \frac{145}{G}, \quad G = \frac{145}{145 - \text{Degrees Baumé}}$$

G = Specific Gravity = ratio of the weight of a given volume of oil at 60° Fahrenheit to the weight of the same volume of water at 60° Fahrenheit.

The above tables are based on the weight of 1 gallon (U.S.) of oil with a volume of 231 cubic inches at 60° Fahrenheit in air at 760 mm pressure and 50% humidity. Assumed weight of 1 gallon of water at 60° Fahrenheit in air is 8.32828 pounds.

To determine the resulting gravity by mixing oils of different gravities:

$$D = \frac{md_1 + nd_2}{m + n}$$

D = Density or Specific Gravity of mixture
m = Proportion of oil of d_1 density
n = Proportion of oil of d_2 density
d_1 = Specific Gravity of m oil
d_2 = Specific Gravity of n oil

Equivalent Volume and Weight Flow Rates of Compressible Fluids

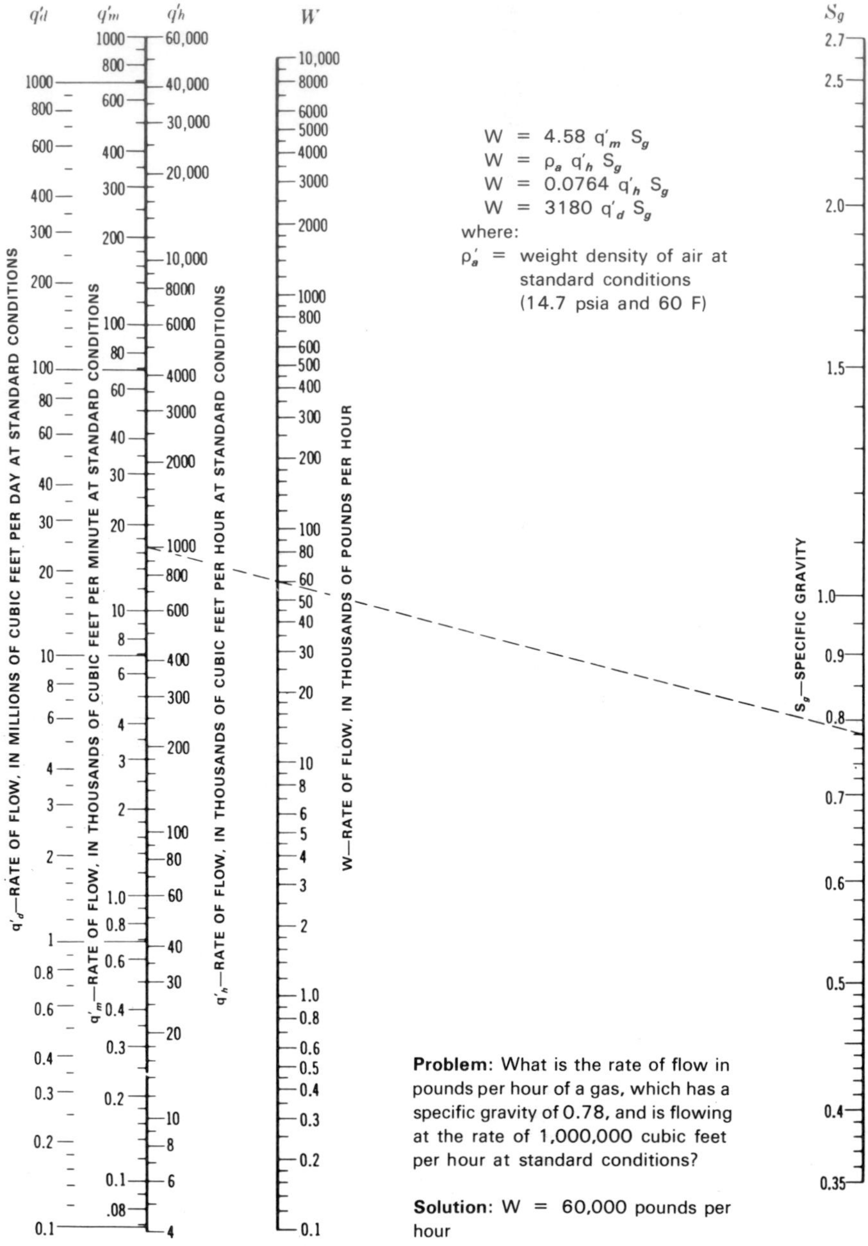

$W = 4.58\ q'_m\ S_g$

$W = \rho_a\ q'_h\ S_g$

$W = 0.0764\ q'_h\ S_g$

$W = 3180\ q'_d\ S_g$

where:

ρ'_a = weight density of air at standard conditions (14.7 psia and 60 F)

Problem: What is the rate of flow in pounds per hour of a gas, which has a specific gravity of 0.78, and is flowing at the rate of 1,000,000 cubic feet per hour at standard conditions?

Solution: W = 60,000 pounds per hour

Viscosity Conversion Nomograph

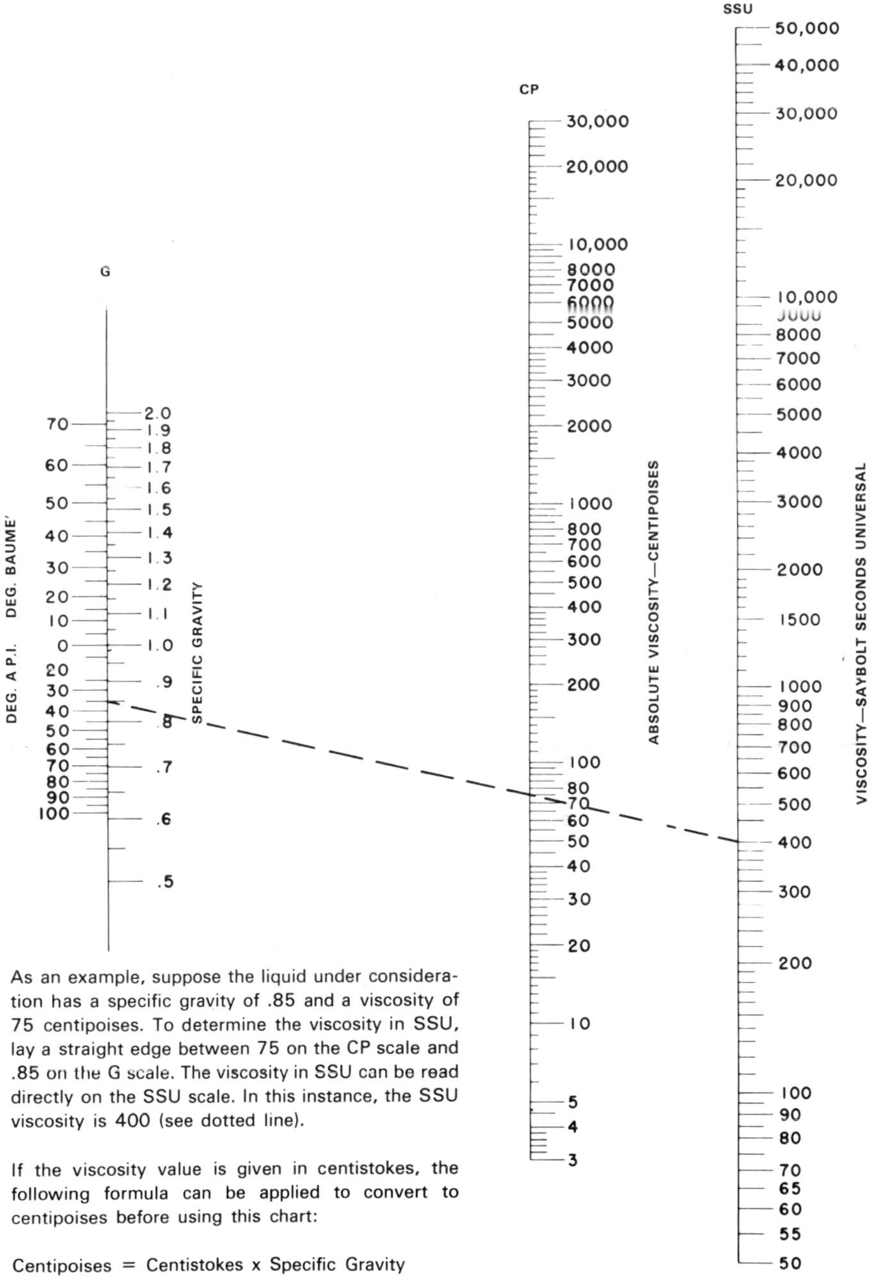

As an example, suppose the liquid under consideration has a specific gravity of .85 and a viscosity of 75 centipoises. To determine the viscosity in SSU, lay a straight edge between 75 on the CP scale and .85 on the G scale. The viscosity in SSU can be read directly on the SSU scale. In this instance, the SSU viscosity is 400 (see dotted line).

If the viscosity value is given in centistokes, the following formula can be applied to convert to centipoises before using this chart:

Centipoises = Centistokes x Specific Gravity

VISCOSITY CONVERSION NOMOGRAPH

Other Useful Conversions

To Convert From	To	Multiply By
Cu Ft (Methane)	B.T.U.	1000 (approx.)
Cu Ft of Water	Lbs of Water	62.4
Degrees	Radians	0.01745
Gals	Lbs of Water	8.336
Grams	Ounces	0.0352
Horsepower (mech.)	Ft Lbs per Min	33,000
Horsepower (elec.)	Watts	746
Kg	Lbs	2.205
Kg per Cu Meter	Lbs per Cu Ft	0.06243
Kilowatts	Horsepower	1.341
Lbs	Kg	0.4536
Lbs of Air (14.7 psia and 60°F)	Cu Ft of Air	13.1
Lbs per Cu Ft	Kg per Cu Meter	16.0184
Lbs per Hr (Gas)	Std Cu Ft per Hr	$\frac{13.1}{\text{Specific Gravity}}$
Lbs per Hr (Water)	Gals per Min	0.002
Lbs per Sec (Gas)	Std Cu Ft per Hr	$\frac{46{,}160}{\text{Specific Gravity}}$
Radians	Degrees	57.3
Scfh Air	Scfh Propane	0.81
Scfh Air	Scfh Butane	0.71
Scfh Air	Scfh 0.6 Natural Gas	1.29
Scfh	Cu Meters per Hr	0.028317

Section 7

Engineering Data

Characteristics of the Elements

Element	Symbol	Atomic Number	Mass Number*	Melting Point (°C)	Boiling Point (°C)
actinium	Ac	89	(227)	1600†	
aluminum	Al	13	27	659.7	2057
americium	Am	95	(243)		
antimony (stibium)	Sb	51	121	630.5	1380
argon	Ar	18	40	−189.2	−185.7
arsenic	As	33	75	sublimes at 615	
astatine	At	85	(210)		
barium	Ba	56	138	850	1140
berkelium	Bk	97	(247)		
beryllium	Be	4	9	1278±5	2970
bismuth	Bi	83	209	271.3	1560±5
boron	B	5	11	2300	2550
bromine	Br	35	79	−7.2	58.78
cadmium	Cd	48	114	320.9	767±2
calcium	Ca	20	40	842±8	1240
californium	Cf	98	(249)		
carbon	C	6	12	>3550	4200
cerium	Ce	58	140	804	1400
cesium	Cs	55	133	28.5	670
chlorine	Cl	17	35	−103±5	−34.6
chromium	Cr	24	52	1890	2480
cobalt	Co	27	59	1495	2900
copper	Cu	29	63	1083	2336
curium	Cm	96	(248)		
dysprosium	Dy	66	164		

*Mass number shown is that of the stable isotope most common in nature. Mass numbers shown in parentheses designate the isotope with the longest half-life (slowest rate of radio-active decay) for those elements having no stable isotope.
† Calculated.
> Greater than.

- Continued -

Characteristics of the Elements (Continued)

Element	Symbol	Atomic Number	Mass Number*	Melting Point (°C)	Boiling Point (°C)
einsteinium	Es	99	(254)		
erbium	Er	68	166		
europium	Eu	63	153	1150±50	
fermium	Fm	100	(252)		
fluorine	F	9	19	−223	−188
francium	Fr	87	(223)		
gadolinium	Gd	64	158		
gallium	Ga	31	69	29.78	1983
germanium	Ge	32	74	958.5	2700
gold	Au	79	197	1063	2600
hafnium	Hf	72	180	1700†	>3200
helium	He	2	4	−272	−268.9
holmium	Ho	67	165		
hydrogen	H	1	1	−259.14	−252.8
indium	In	49	115	156.4	2000±10
iodine	I	53	127	113.7	184.35
iridium	Ir	77	193	2454	>4800
iron	Fe	26	56	1535	3000
krypton	Kr	36	84	−156.6	−152.9
lanthanum	La	57	139	826	
lawrencium	Lw	103	(257)		
lead	Pb	82	208	327.43	1620
lithium	Li	3	7	186	1336±5
lutetium	Lu	71	175		
magnesium	Mg	12	24	651	1107
manganese	Mn	25	55	1260	1900
mendelevium	Mv	101	(256)		
mercury	Hg	80	202	−38.87	356.58
molybdenum	Mo	42	98	2620±10	4800
neodymium	Nd	60	142	840	
neon	Ne	10	20	−248.67	−245.9
neptunium	Np	93	(237)		
nickel	Ni	28	58	1455	2900
niobium	Nb	41	93	2500±50	3700
nitrogen	N	7	14	−209.86	−195.8
nobelium	No	102	(253)		
osmium	Os	76	192	2700	>5300
oxygen	O	8	16	−218.4	−182.86
palladium	Pd	46	106	1549.4	2000
phosphorus	P	15	31		
platinum	Pt	78	195	1773.5	4300
plutonium	Pu	94	(242)		
polonium	Po	84	(209)		
potassium	K	19	39	63.3	760
praseodymium	Pr	59	141	940	
promethium	Pm	61	(145)		
protactinium	Pa	91	(231)		
radium	Ra	88	(226)	700	1140
radon	Rn	86	(222)	−71	−61.8
rhenium	Re	75	187	3167±60	

*Mass number shown is that of the stable isotope most common in nature. Mass numbers shown in parentheses designate the isotope with the longest half-life (slowest rate of radio-active decay) for those elements having no stable isotope.
† Calculated.
>Greater than.

- Continued -

Characteristics of the Elements (Continued)

Element	Symbol	Atomic Number	Mass Number*	Melting Point (°C)	Boiling Point (°C)
rhodium	Rh	45	103	1966±3	>2500
rubidium	Rb	37	85	38.5	700
ruthenium	Ru	44	102	2450	2700
samarium	Sm	62	152	>1300	
scandium	Sc	21	45	1200	2400
selenium	Se	34	80	217	688
silicon	Si	14	28	1420	2355
silver	Ag	47	107	960.8	1950
sodium	Na	11	23	97.5	880
strontium	Sr	38	88	800	1150
sulfur	S	16	32		
tantalum	Ta	73	180	2996±50	c.4100
technetium	Tc	43	(99)		
tellurium	Te	52	130	452	1390
terbium	Tb	65	159	327±5	
thallium	Tl	81	205	302	1457±10
thorium	Th	90	232	1845	4500
thulium	Tm	69	169		
tin	Sn	50	120	231.89	2270
titanium	Ti	22	48	1800	>3000
tungsten (wolfram)	W	74	184	3370	5900
uranium	U	92	238	c.1133	
vanadium	V	23	51	1710	3000
xenon	Xe	54	132	−112	−107.1
ytterbium	Yb	70	174	1800	
yttrium	Y	39	89	1490	2500
zinc	Zn	30	64	419.47	907
zirconium	Zr	40	90	1857	>2900

*Mass number shown is that of the stable isotope most common in nature. Mass numbers shown in parentheses designate the isotope with the longest half-life (slowest rate of radio-active decay) for those elements having no stable isotope.
† Calculated.
> Greater than.

Recommended Standard Specifications for Valve Materials

Pressure-Containing Castings

(1) Carbon Steel
ASTM A216 Grade WCB

Temp. range = −20°F to 1000°F
Composition (Percent)
C 0.30 max
Mn 1.00 max
P 0.05 max
S 0.06 max
Si 0.60 max

(2) Carbon Steel
ASTM A352 Grade LCB

Temp. range = −50°F to 650°F
Composition: Same as ASTM A216 Grade WCB

(3) Chrome Moly Steel
ASTM A217 Grade C5

Temp. range = −20°F to 1100°F
Composition (Percent)
C 0.20 max
Mn 0.40 to 0.70
P 0.05 max
S 0.06 max
Si 0.75 max
Cr 4.00 to 6.50
Mo 0.45 to 0.65

Recommended Standard Specifications for Valve Materials

Pressure-Containing Castings (Continued)

(4) Carbon Moly Steel
ASTM A217 Grade WC1

Temp. range = −20°F to 850°F
Composition (Percent)
C 0.25 max
Mn 0.50 to 0.80
P 0.05 max
S 0.06 max
Si 0.60 max
Mo 0.45 to 0.65

(5) Chrome Moly Steel
ASTM A217 Grade WC6

Temp. range = −20°F to 1000°F
Composition (Percent)
C 0.20 max
Mn 0.50 to 0.80
P 0.05 max
S 0.06 max
Si 0.60 max
Cr 1.00 to 1.50
Mo 0.45 to 0.65

(6) Chrome Moly Steel
ASTM A217 Grade WC9

Temp. range = −20°F to 1050°F
Composition (Percent)
C 0.18 max
Mn 0.40 to 0.70
P 0.05 max
Si 0.60 max
Cr 2.00 to 2.75
Mo 0.90 to 1.20

(7) 3-1/2% Nickel Steel
ASTM A352 Grade LC3

Temp. range = −150°F to 650°F
Composition (Percent)
C 0.15 max
Mn 0.50 to 0.80
P 0.05 max
S 0.05 max
Si 0.60 max
Ni 3.00 to 4.00

(8) Chrome Moly Steel
ASTM A217 Grade C12

Temp. range = −20°F to 1100°F
Composition (Percent)
C 0.20 max
Si 1.00 max
Mn 0.35 to 0.65
Cr 8.00 to 10.00
Mo 0.90 to 1.20
P 0.05 max
S 0.06 max

(9) Type 304 Stainless Steel
ASTM A351 Grade CF-8

Temp. range = −425°F to 1500°F
Composition (Percent)
C 0.08 max
Mn 1.50 max
Si 2.00 max
S 0.04 max
P 0.04 max
Cr 18.00 to 21.00
Ni 8.00 to 11.00

(10) Type 316 Stainless Steel
ASTM A351 Grade CF-8M

Temp. range = −425°F to 1500°F
Composition (Percent)
C 0.08 max
Mn 1.50 max
Si 2.00 max
P 0.04 max
S 0.04 max
Cr 18.00 to 21.00
Ni 9.00 to 12.00
Mo 2.00 to 3.00

(11) Cast Iron
ASTM A126 Class B

Temp. range = −150°F to 450°F
Composition (Percent)
P 0.75 max
S 0.12 max

(12) Cast Iron
ASTM A126 Class C

Temp. range = −150°F to 450°F
Composition (Percent)
P 0.75 max
S 0.12 max

Recommended Standard Specifications for Valve Materials

Pressure-Containing Castings (Continued)

MAT'L. CODE	MINIMUM PHYSICAL PROPERTIES				MODULUS OF ELASTICITY AT 70°F (PSI x 10⁶)	APPROX. BRINELL HARDNESS
	Tensile (Psi)	Yield Point (Psi)	Elong. in 2" (%)	Reduction of Area (%)		
(1)	70,000	36,000	22	35	27.9	137-187
(2)	65,000	35,000	24	35	27.9	137-187
(3)	90,000	60,000	18	35	27.4	241 Max.
(4)	65,000	35,000	24	35	29.9	215 Max.
(5)	70,000	40,000	20	35	29.9	215 Max.
(6)	70,000	40,000	20	35	29.9	241 Max.
(7)	65,000	40,000	24	35	27.9	137
(8)	90,000	60,000	18	35	27.4	180-240
(9)	65,000	28,000	35	...	28.0	140
(10)	70,000	30,000	30	...	28.3	156-170
(11)	31,000	...	...	...	...	160-220
(12)	41,000	...	...	...	...	160-220
(13)	60,000	45,000	15	...	23-26	143-207
(14)	58,000	30,000	7	...	...	148-211
(15)	30,000	14,000	20	17	13.5	55-65*
(16)	40,000	18,000	20	20	15	75-85*
(17)	65,000	25,000	20	20	15.4	98*
(18)	75,000	30,000	12 min.	12	17	150
(19)	65,000	32,500	25	...	23	120-170
(20)	72,000	46,000	6	...	...	...
(21)	72,000	46,000	4	...	...	...
(22)	121,000	64,000	1-2	...	30.4	...

*500 kg load.

(13) Ductile Iron
ASTM A395 Type 60-45-15

Temp. range = −20°F to 650°F
Composition (Percent)
C 3.00 min
Si 2.75 max
P 0.08 max

(14) Ductile Ni-Resist* Iron
ASTM A439 Type D-2B

Temp. range = −20°F to 750°F
Composition (Percent)
C 3.00 max
Si 1.50 to 3.00
Mn 0.70 to 1.25
P 0.08 max
Ni 18.00 to 22.00
Cr 2.75 to 4.00

*Trademark of International Nickel Co.

(15) Standard Valve Bronze
ASTM B62

Temp. range = −325°F to 450°F
Composition (Percent)
Cu 84.00 to 86.00
Sn 4.00 to 6.00
Pb 4.00 to 6.00
Zn 4.00 to 6.00
Ni 1.00 max
Fe 0.30 max
P 0.05 max

Recommended Standard Specifications for Valve Materials

Pressure-Containing Castings
(Continued)

(16) Tin Bronze
ASTM B143 Alloy 1A

Temp. range = −325°F to 400°F
Composition (Percent)
Cu 86.00 to 89.00
Sn 9.00 to 11.00
Pb 0.30 max
Zn 1.00 to 3.00
Ni 1.00 max
Fe 0.15 max
P 0.05 max

(17) Manganese Bronze
ASTM B147 Alloy 8A

Temp. range = −325°F to 350°F
Composition (Percent)
Cu 55.00 to 60.00
Sn 1.00 max
Pb 0.40 max
Ni 0.50 max
Fe 0.40 to 2.00
Al 0.50 to 1.50
Mn 1.50 max
Zn Remainder

(18) Aluminum Bronze
ASTM B148 Alloy 9C

Temp. range = −325°F to 500°F
Composition (Percent)
Cu 83.00 min
Al 10.00 to 11.50
Fe 3.00 to 5.00
Mn 0.50
Ni 2.50 max
Min. total named elements = 99.5

(19) Monel* Alloy 411
(Weldable Grade)

Temp. range = −325°F to 900°F
Composition (Percent)
Ni 60.00 min
Cu 26.00 to 33.00
C 0.30 max
Mn 1.50 max
Fe 3.50 max
S 0.015 max
Si 1.00 to 2.00
Nb 1.00 to 3.00

(20) Nickel-Moly Alloy "B"
ASTM A494 (Hastelloy "B"†)

Temp. range = −325°F to 700°F
Composition (Percent)
Cr 1.00 max
Fe 4.00 to 6.00
C 0.12 max
Si 1.00 max
Co 2.50 max
Mn 1.00 max
V 0.20 to 0.60
Mo 26.00 to 30.00
P 0.04 max
S 0.03 max
Ni Remainder

(21) Nickel-Moly-Chrome Alloy "C"
ASTM A494 (Hastelloy "C"†)

Temp. range = −325°F to 1000°F
Composition (Percent)
Cr 15.50 to 17.50
Fe 4.50 to 7.50
W 3.75 to 5.25
C 0.12 max
Si 1.00 max
Co 2.50 max
Mn 1.00 max
V 0.20 to 0.40
Mo 16.00 to 18.00
P 0.04
S 0.03
Ni Remainder

(22) Cobalt-base Alloy No. 6
Stellite† No. 6

Composition (Percent)
C 0.90 to 1.40
Mn 1.00
W 3.00 to 6.00
Ni 3.00
Cr 26.00 to 32.00
Mo 1.00
Fe 3.00
Si 0.40 to 2.00
Co Remainder

*Trademark of International Nickel Co.
†Trademark of Stellite Div., Cabot Corp.

Bar Stock Materials

Frequently Used for Trim Parts of Valves

(23) Aluminum Bar
ASTM B211 Alloy 2011-T3

Composition (Percent)
Si 0.40 max
Fe 0.70 max
Cu 5.00 to 6.00
Zn 0.30 max
Bi 0.20 to 0.60
Pb 0.20 to 0.60
Other Elements 0.15 max
Al Remainder

(24) Yellow Brass Bar
ASTM B16 1/2 Hard

Composition (Percent)
Cu 60.00 to 63.00
Pb 2.50 to 3.70
Fe 0.35 max
Zn Remainder

(25) Naval Brass Bar
ASTM B21 Alloy 464

Composition (Percent)
Cu 59.00 to 62.00
Sn 0.50 to 1.00
Pb 0.20 max
Zn Remainder

(26) Leaded Steel Bar
AISI 12L14

Composition (Percent)
C 0.15 max
Mn 0.80 to 1.20
P 0.04 to 0.09
S 0.25 to 0.35
Pb 0.15 to 0.35

(27) Carbon Steel Bar
ASTM A108 Grade 1018

Composition (Percent)
C 0.15 to 0.20
Mn 0.60 to 0.90
P 0.04 max
S 0.05 max

(28) AISI 4140 Chrome-Moly Steel
(Suitable for ASTM A193 Grade B7 bolt material)

Composition (Percent)
C 0.38 to 0.43
Mn 0.75 to 1.00
P 0.035 max
S 0.040 max
Si 0.20 to 0.35
Cr 0.80 to 1.10
Mo 0.15 to 0.25
Fe Remainder

(29) Type 302 Stainless Steel
ASTM A276 Type 302

Composition (Percent)
C 0.15 max
Mn 2.00 max
P 0.045 max
S 0.030 max
Si 1.00 max
Cr 17.00 to 19.00
Ni 8.00 to 10.00

(30) Type 304 Stainless Steel
ASTM A276 Type 304

Composition (Percent)
C 0.08 max
Mn 2.00 max
P 0.045 max
S 0.030 max
Si 1.00 max
Cr 18.00 to 20.00
Ni 8.00 to 12.00

(31) Type 316 Stainless Steel
ASTM A276 Type 316

Composition (Percent)
C 0.08 max
Mn 2.00 max
P 0.045 max
S 0.030 max
Si 1.00 max
Cr 16.00 to 18.00
Ni 10.00 to 14.00
Mo 2.00 to 3.00

Bar Stock Material (Continued)
Frequently Used for Trim Parts of Valves

(32) Type 316L Stainless Steel
ASTM A276 Type 316L

Composition (Percent)
C 0.03 max
Mn 2.00 max
P 0.045 max
S 0.030 max
Si 1.00 max
Cr 16.00 to 18.00
Ni 10.00 to 14.00
Mo 2.00 to 3.00

(33) Type 410 Stainless Steel
ASTM A276 Type 410

Composition (Percent)
C 0.15 max
Mn 1.00 max
P 0.040 max
S 0.030 max
Si 1.00 max
Cr 11.50 to 13.50
Al 0.10 to 0.30

(34) Type 17-4PH Stainless Steel
ASTM A461 Grade 630

Composition (Percent)
C 0.07 max
Mn 1.00 max
Si 1.00 max
P 0.04 max
S 0.03 max
Cr 15.50 to 17.50
Nb 0.05 to 0.45
Cu 3.00 to 5.00
Ni 3.00 to 5.00
Fe Remainder

(35) Nickel-Copper Alloy Bar
Alloy K500 (K Monel*)

Composition (Percent)
Ni 63.00 to 70.00
Fe 2.00 max
Mn 1.50 max
Si 1.00 max
C 0.25 max
S 0.01 max
Al 2.00 to 4.00
Ti 0.25 to 1.00
Cu Remainder

*Trademark of International Nickel Co.
†Trademark of Stellite Div., Cabot Corp.

(36) Nickel-Moly Alloy "B" Bar
ASTM B335 (Hastelloy "B"†)

Composition (Percent)
Cr 1.00 max
Fe 4.00 to 6.00
C 0.05 max
Si 1.00 max
Co 2.50 max
Mn 1.00 max
V 0.20 to 0.40
Mo 26.00 to 30.00
P 0.025 max
S 0.030 max
Ni Remainder

(37) Nickel-Moly-Chrome Alloy "C" Bar
ASTM B336 (Hastelloy "C"†)

Composition (Percent)
Cr 14.50 to 16.50
Fe 4.00 to 7.00
W 3.00 to 4.50
C 0.08 max
Si 1.00 max
Co 2.50 max
Mn 1.00 max
Va 0.35 max
Mo 15.00 to 17.00
P 0.04
S 0.03
Ni Remainder

MAT'L. CODE	MINIMUM PHYSICAL PROPERTIES				MODULUS OF ELASTICITY AT 70°F (PSI x 10^6)	APPROX. BRINELL HARDNESS
	Tensile (Psi)	Yield Point (Psi)	Elong. in 2″ (%)	Reduction of Area (%)		
(23)	44,000	36,000	15	. . .	10.2	95
(24)	45,000	15,000	7	50	14	. . .
(25)	60,000	27,000	22	55	. . .	. . .
(26)	79,000	71,000	16	52	. . .	163
(27)	69,000	48,000	38	62	. . .	143
(28)	135,000	115,000	22	63	29.9	255
(29)	85,000	35,000	60	70	28	150
(30)	85,000	35,000	60	70	. . .	149
(31)	80,000	30,000	60	70	28	149
(32)	81000	34,000	55	. . .	. . .	146
(33)	75,000	40,000	35	70	29	155
(34)	135,000	105,000	16	50	29	275-345
(35)	100,000	70,000	35	. . .	26	175-260
(36)	100,000	46,000	30	. . .	. . .	. . .
(37)	100,000	46,000	20	. . .	. . .	. . .

Physical Constants of Hydrocarbons

NO.	COMPOUND	FORMULA	MOLECULAR WEIGHT	BOILING POINT AT 14.696 psia (°F)	VAPOR PRESSURE AT 100° F (psia)	FREEZING POINT AT 14.696 psia (°F)	CRITICAL CONSTANTS		SPECIFIC GRAVITY at 14.696 psia	
							Critical Temperature (°F)	Critical Pressure (psia)	Liquid,[3,4] 60° F/60° F	Gas at 60° F (Air = 1)[1]
1	Methane	CH_4	16.043	−258.69	(5000)[2]	−296.46[5]	−116.63	667.8	0.3[8]	0.5539
2	Ethane	C_2H_6	30.070	−127.48	(800)[2]	−297.89[5]	90.09	707.8	0.3564[7]	1.0382
3	Propane	C_3H_8	44.097	−43.67	190.	−305.84[5]	206.01	616.3	0.5077[7]	1.5225
4	n-Butane	C_4H_{10}	58.124	31.10	51.6	−217.05	305.65	550.7	0.5844[7]	2.0068
5	Isobutane	C_4H_{10}	58.124	10.90	72.2	−255.29	274.98	529.1	0.5631[7]	2.0068
6	n-Pentane	C_5H_{12}	72.151	96.92	15.570	−201.51	385.7	488.6	0.6310	2.4911
7	Isopentane	C_5H_{12}	72.151	82.12	20.44	−255.83	369.10	490.4	0.6247	2.4911
8	Neopentane	C_5H_{12}	72.151	49.10	35.9	2.17	321.13	464.0	0.5967[7]	2.4911
9	n-Hexane	C_6H_{14}	86.178	155.72	4.956	−139.58	453.7	436.9	0.6640	2.9753
10	2-Methylpentane	C_6H_{14}	86.178	140.47	6.767	−244.63	435.83	436.6	0.6579	2.9753
11	3-Methylpentane	C_6H_{14}	86.178	145.89	6.098	. . .	448.3	453.1	0.6689	2.9753
12	Neohexane	C_6H_{14}	86.178	121.52	9.856	−147.72	420.13	446.8	0.6540	2.9753
13	2,3-Dimethylbutane	C_6H_{14}	86.178	136.36	7.404	−199.38	440.29	453.5	0.6664	2.9753
14	n-Heptane	C_7H_{16}	100.205	209.17	1.620	−131.05	512.8	396.8	0.6882	3.4596
15	2-Methylhexane	C_7H_{16}	100.205	194.09	2.271	−180.89	495.00	396.5	0.6830	3.4596
16	3-Methylhexane	C_7H_{16}	100.205	197.32	2.130	. . .	503.78	408.1	0.6917	3.4596
17	3-Ethylpentane	C_7H_{16}	100.205	200.25	2.012	−181.48	513.48	419.3	0.7028	3.4596
18	2,2-Dimethylpentane	C_7H_{16}	100.205	174.54	3.492	−190.86	477.23	402.2	0.6782	3.4596
19	2,4-Dimethylpentane	C_7H_{16}	100.205	176.89	3.292	−182.63	475.95	396.9	0.6773	3.4596
20	3,3-Dimethylpentane	C_7H_{16}	100.205	186.91	2.773	−210.01	505.85	427.2	0.6976	3.4596
21	Triptane	C_7H_{16}	100.205	177.58	3.374	−12.82	496.44	428.4	0.6946	3.4596

- Continued -

22	n-Octane	C_8H_{18}	114.232	258.22	0.537	−70.18	564.22	360.6	0.7068	3.9439
23	Diisobutyl	C_8H_{18}	114.232	228.39	1.101	−132.07	530.44	360.6	0.6979	3.9439
24	Isooctane	C_8H_{18}	114.232	210.63	1.708	−161.27	519.46	372.4	0.6962	3.9439
25	n-Nonane	C_9H_{20}	128.259	303.47	0.179	−64.28	610.68	332.	0.7217	4.4282
26	n-Decane	$C_{10}H_{22}$	142.286	345.48	0.0597	−21.36	652.1	304.	0.7342	4.9125
27	Cyclopentane	C_5H_{10}	70.135	120.65	9.914	−136.91	461.5	653.8	0.7504	2.4215
28	Methylcyclopentane	C_6H_{12}	84.162	161.25	4.503	−224.44	499.35	548.9	0.7536	2.9057
29	Cyclohexane	C_6H_{12}	84.162	177.29	3.264	43.77	536.7	591.	0.7834	2.9057
30	Methylcyclohexane	C_7H_{14}	98.189	213.68	1.609	−195.87	570.27	503.5	0.7740	3.3900
31	Ethylene	C_2H_4	28.054	−154.62	...	−272.45[5]	48.58	729.8	...	0.9686
32	Propene	C_3H_6	42.081	−53.90	226.4	−301.45[5]	196.9	669.	0.5220[7]	1.4529
33	1-Butene	C_4H_8	56.108	20.75	63.05	−301.63[5]	295.6	583.	0.6013[7]	1.9372
34	Cis-2-Butene	C_4H_8	56.108	38.69	45.54	−218.06	324.37	610.	0.6271[7]	1.9372
35	Trans-2-Butene	C_4H_8	56.108	33.58	49.80	−157.96	311.86	595.	0.6100[7]	1.9372
36	Isobutene	C_4H_8	56.108	19.59	63.40	−220.61	292.55	580.	0.6004[7]	1.9372
37	1-Pentene	C_5H_{10}	70.135	85.93	19.115	−265.39	376.93	590.	0.6457	2.4215
38	1,2-Butadiene	C_4H_6	54.092	51.53	(20.)[2]	−213.16	(339.)[2]	(653.)[2]	0.658[7]	1.8676
39	1,3-Butadiene	C_4H_6	54.092	24.06	(60.)[2]	−164.02	306.	628.	0.6272[7]	1.8676
40	Isoprene	C_5H_8	68.119	93.30	16.672	−230.74	(412.)[2]	(558.4)[2]	0.6861	2.3519
41	Acetylene	C_2H_2	26.038	−119.[6]	...	−114.[5]	95.31	890.4	0.615[9]	0.8990
42	Benzene	C_6H_6	78.114	176.17	3.224	41.96	552.22	710.4	0.8844	2.6969
43	Toluene	C_7H_8	92.141	231.13	1.032	−138.94	605.55	595.9	0.8718	3.1812
44	Ethylbenzene	C_8H_{10}	106.168	277.16	0.371	−138.91	651.24	523.5	0.8718	3.6655
45	o-Xylene	C_8H_{10}	106.168	291.97	0.264	−13.30	675.0	541.4	0.8848	3.6655
46	m-Xylene	C_8H_{10}	106.168	282.41	0.326	−54.12	651.02	513.6	0.8687	3.6655
47	p-Xylene	C_8H_{10}	106.168	281.05	0.342	55.86	649.6	509.2	0.8657	3.6655
48	Styrene	C_8H_8	104.152	293.29	(0.24)[2]	−23.10	706.0	580.	0.9110	3.5959
49	Isopropylbenzene	C_9H_{12}	120.195	306.34	0.188	−140.82	676.4	465.4	0.8663	4.1498

1. Calculated values.
2. ( )-Estimated values.
3. Air saturated hydrocarbons.
4. Absolute values from weights in vacuum.
5. At saturation pressure (triple point).
6. Sublimation point.
7. Saturation pressure and 60°F.
8. Apparent value for methane at 60°F.
9. Specific gravity, 119°F/60°F (sublimation point).

Physical Constants of Various Fluids

FLUID	FORMULA	MOLECULAR WEIGHT	BOILING POINT (°F AT 14.696 PSIA)	VAPOR PRESSURE @ 70°F (PSIG)	CRITICAL TEMP. (°F)	CRITICAL PRESSURE (PSIA)	SPECIFIC GRAVITY	
							Liquid 60/60°F	Gas
Acetic Acid	$HC_2H_3O_2$	60.05	245				1.05	
Acetone	C_3H_6O	58.08	133		455	691	0.79	2.01
Air	N_2O_2	28.97	−317		−221	547	0.86‡	1.0
Alcohol, Ethyl	C_2H_6O	46.07	173	2.3†	470	925	0.794	1.59
Alcohol, Methyl	CH_4O	32.04	148	4.63†	463	1174	0.796	1.11
Ammonia	NH_3	17.03	−28	114	270	1636	0.62	0.59
Ammonium Chloride*	NH_4Cl						1.07	
Ammonium Hydroxide*	NH_4OH						0.91	
Ammonium Sulfate*	$(NH_4)_2SO_4$						1.15	
Aniline	C_6H_7N	93.12	365		798	770	1.02	
Argon	A	39.94	−302		−188	705	1.65	1.38
Beer							1.01	
Bromine	Br_2	159.84	138		575		2.93	5.52
Calcium Chloride*	$CaCl_2$						1.23	
Carbon Dioxide	CO_2	44.01	−109	839	88	1072	0.801‡	1.52
Carbon Disulfide	CS_2	76.1	115				1.29	2.63
Carbon Monoxide	CO	28.01	−314		−220	507	0.80	0.97
Carbon Tetrachloride	CCl_4	153.84	170		542	661	1.59	5.31
Chlorine	Cl_2	70.91	−30	85	291	1119	1.42	2.45
Chromic Acid	H_2CrO_4	118.03					1.21	
Citric Acid	$C_6H_8O_7$	192.12					1.54	
Copper Sulfate*	$CuSO_4$						1.17	

- Continued -

Ether	$(C_2H_5)_2O$	74.12	34				0.74	2.55
Ferric Chloride*	$FeCl_3$						1.23	
Fluorine	F_2	38.00	−305	300	−200	809	1.11	1.31
Formaldehyde	H_2CO	30.03	−6				0.82	1.08
Formic Acid	HCO_2H	46.03	214				1.23	
Furfural	$C_5H_4O_2$	96.08	324				1.16	
Glycerine	$C_3H_8O_3$	92.09	554				1.26	
Glycol	$C_2H_6O_2$	62.07	387				1.11	
Helium	He	4.003	−454		−450	33	0.18	0.14
Hydrochloric Acid	HCl	36.47	−115				1.64	
Hydrofluoric Acid	HF	20.01	66	0.9	446		0.92	
Hydrogen	H_2	2.016	−422		−400	188	0.07‡	0.07
Hyrogen Chloride	HCl	36.47	−115	613	125	1198	0.86	1.26
Hydrogen Sulfide	H_2S	34.07	−76	252	213	1307	0.79	1.17
Isopropyl Alcohol	C_3H_8O	60.09	180				0.78	2.08
Linseed Oil			538				0.93	
Magnesium Chloride*	$MgCl_2$						1.22	
Mercury	Hg	200.61	670				13.6	6.93
Methyl Bromide	CH_3Br	94.95	38	13	376		1.73	3.27
Methyl Chloride	CH_3Cl	50.49	−11	59	290	969	0.99	1.74
Naphthalene	$C_{10}H_8$	128.16	424				1.14	4.43
Nitric Acid	HNO_3	63.02	187				1.5	
Nitrogen	N_2	28.02	−320		−233	493	0.81‡	0.97
Oil, Vegetable							0.91 - 0.94	
Oxygen	O_2	32	−297		−181	737	1.14‡	1.105

*Aqueous Solution - 25% by weight of compound.
†Vapor pressure in psia at 100°F.
‡Density of liquid, gm/ml at normal boiling point.

- Continued -

Physical Constants of Various Fluids (Continued)

FLUID	FORMULA	MOLECULAR WEIGHT	BOILING POINT (°F AT 14.696 PSIA)	VAPOR PRESSURE @ 70°F (PSIG)	CRITICAL TEMP. (°F)	CRITICAL PRESSURE (PSIA)	SPECIFIC GRAVITY	
							Liquid 60/60°F	Gas
Phosgene	$COCl_2$	98.92	47	10.7	360	823	1.39	3.42
Phosphoric Acid	H_3PO_4	98.00	415				1.83	
Potassium Carbonate*	K_2CO_3						1.24	
Potassium Chloride*	KCl						1.16	
Potassium Hydroxide*	KOH						1.24	
Refrigerant 11	CCl_3F	137.38	75	13.4	388	635		5.04
Refrigerant 12	CCl_2F_2	120.93	−22	70.2	234	597		4.2
Refrigerant 13	$CClF_3$	104.47	−115	458.7	84	561		
Refrigerant 21	$CHCl_2F$	102.93	48	8.4	353	750		3.82
Refrigerant 22	$CHClF_2$	86.48	−41	122.5	205	716		
Refrigerant 23	CHF_3	70.02	−119	635	91	691		
Sodium Chloride*	NaCl						1.19	
Sodium Hydroxide*	NaOH						1.27	
Sodium Sulfate*	Na_2SO_4						1.24	
Sodium Thiosulfate*	$Na_2S_2O_3$						1.23	
Starch	$(C_6H_{10}O_5)x$						1.50	
Sugar Solutions*	$C_{12}H_{22}O_{11}$						1.10	
Sulfuric Acid	H_2SO_4	98.08	626				1.83	
Sulfur Dioxide	SO_2	64.6	14	34.4	316	1145	1.39	2.21
Turpentine			320				0.87	
Water	H_2O	18.016	212	0.9492†	706	3208	1.00	0.62
Zinc Chloride*	$ZnCl_2$						1.24	
Zinc Sulfate*	$ZnSO_4$						1.31	

*Aqueous Solution - 25% by weight of compound.
†Vapor pressure in psia at 100°F.

Properties of Water

Temperature of Water (°F)	Saturation Pressure (Pounds Per Square Inch Absolute)	Weight (Pounds Per Gallon)	Specific Gravity 60/60 F	Conversion Factor,* lbs./hr. to GPM
32	.0885	8.345	1.0013	.00199
40	.1217	8.345	1.0013	.00199
50	.1781	8.340	1.0007	.00199
60	.2653	8.334	1.0000	.00199
70	.3631	8.325	.9989	.00200
80	.5069	8.314	.9976	.00200
90	.6982	8.303	.9963	.00200
100	.9492	8.289	.9946	.00201
110	1.2748	8.267	.9919	.00201
120	1.6924	8.253	.9901	.00201
130	2.2225	8.227	.9872	.00202
140	2.8886	8.207	.9848	.00203
150	3.718	8.182	.9818	.00203
160	4.741	8.156	.9786	.00204
170	5.992	8.127	.9752	.00205
180	7.510	8.098	.9717	.00205
190	9.339	8.068	.9681	.00206
200	11.526	8.039	.9646	.00207
210	14.123	8.005	.9605	.00208
212	14.696	7.996	.9594	.00208
220	17.186	7.972	.9566	.00209
240	24.969	7.901	.9480	.00210
260	35.429	7.822	.9386	.00211
280	49.203	7.746	.9294	.00215
300	67.013	7.662	.9194	.00217
350	134.63	7.432	.8918	.00224
400	247.31	7.172	.8606	.00232
450	422.6	6.892	.8270	.00241
500	680.8	6.553	.7863	.00254
550	1045.2	6.132	.7358	.00271
600	1542.9	5.664	.6796	.00294
700	3093.7	3.623	.4347	.00460

*Multiply flow in pounds per hour by the factor to get equivalent flow in gallons per minute.

Weight per gallon is based on 7.48 gallons per cubic foot.

Properties of Saturated Steam

ABSOLUTE PRESSURE		VACUUM (INCHES OF Hg)	TEMPERATURE t (°F)	HEAT OF THE LIQUID (BTU/LB)	LATENT HEAT OF EVAPORATION (BTU/LB)	TOTAL HEAT OF STEAM H_g (BTU/LB)	SPECIFIC VOLUME $\overline{V}$ (CU FT PER LB)
Lbs Per Sq In. P′	Inches of Hg						
0.20	0.41	29.51	53.14	21.21	1063.8	1085.0	1526.0
0.25	0.51	29.41	59.30	27.36	1060.3	1087.7	1235.3
0.30	0.61	29.31	64.47	32.52	1057.4	1090.0	1039.5
0.35	0.71	29.21	68.93	36.97	1054.9	1091.9	898.5
0.40	0.81	29.11	72.86	40.89	1052.7	1093.6	791.9
0.45	0.92	29.00	76.38	44.41	1050.7	1095.1	708.5
0.50	1.02	28.90	79.58	47.60	1048.8	1096.4	641.4
0.60	1.22	28.70	85.21	53.21	1045.7	1098.9	540.0
0.70	1.43	28.49	90.08	58.07	1042.9	1101.0	466.9
0.80	1.63	28.29	94.38	62.36	1040.4	1102.8	411.7
0.90	1.83	28.09	98.24	66.21	1038.3	1104.5	368.4
1.0	2.04	27.88	101.74	69.70	1036.3	1106.0	333.6
1.2	2.44	27.48	107.92	75.87	1032.7	1108.6	280.9
1.4	2.85	27.07	113.26	81.20	1029.6	1110.8	243.0
1.6	3.26	26.66	117.99	85.91	1026.9	1112.8	214.3
1.8	3.66	26.26	122.23	90.14	1024.5	1114.6	191.8
2.0	4.07	25.85	126.08	93.99	1022.2	1116.2	173.73
2.2	4.48	25.44	129.62	97.52	1020.2	1117.7	158.85
2.4	4.89	25.03	132.89	100.79	1018.3	1119.1	146.38
2.6	5.29	24.63	135.94	103.83	1016.5	1120.3	135.78
2.8	5.70	24.22	138.79	106.68	1014.8	1121.5	126.65
3.0	6.11	23.81	141.48	109.37	1013.2	1122.6	118.71
3.5	7.13	22.79	147.57	115.46	1009.6	1125.1	102.72
4.0	8.14	21.78	152.97	120.86	1006.4	1127.3	90.63
4.5	9.16	20.76	157.83	125.71	1003.6	1129.3	81.16
5.0	10.18	19.74	162.24	130.13	1001.0	1131.1	73.52
5.5	11.20	18.72	166.30	134.19	998.5	1132.7	67.24
6.0	12.22	17.70	170.06	137.96	996.2	1134.2	61.98
6.5	13.23	16.69	173.56	141.47	994.1	1135.6	57.50
7.0	14.25	15.67	176.85	144.76	992.1	1136.9	53.64
7.5	15.27	14.65	179.94	147.86	990.2	1138.1	50.29
8.0	16.29	13.63	182.86	150.79	988.5	1139.3	47.34
8.5	17.31	12.61	185.64	153.57	986.8	1140.4	44.73
9.0	18.32	11.60	188.28	156.22	985.2	1141.4	42.40
9.5	19.34	10.58	190.80	158.75	983.6	1142.3	40.31
10.0	20.36	9.56	193.21	161.17	982.1	1143.3	38.42
11.0	22.40	7.52	197.75	165.73	979.3	1145.0	35.14
12.0	24.43	5.49	201.96	169.96	976.6	1146.6	32.40
13.0	26.47	3.45	205.88	173.91	974.2	1148.1	30.06
14.0	28.50	1.42	209.56	177.61	971.9	1149.5	28.04

Properties of Saturated Steam

PRESSURE (LBS PER SQ IN.) Absolute P′	Gauge P	TEMPERATURE t (°F)	HEAT OF THE LIQUID (BTU/LB)	LATENT HEAT OF EVAPORATION (BTU/LB)	TOTAL HEAT OF STEAM H_g (BTU/LB)	SPECIFIC VOLUME $\overline{V}$ (CU FT PER LB)
14.696	0.0	212.00	180.07	970.3	1150.4	26.80
15.0	0.3	213.03	181.11	969.7	1150.8	26.29
16.0	1.3	216.32	184.42	967.6	1152.0	24.75
17.0	2.3	219.44	187.56	965.5	1153.1	23.39
18.0	3.3	222.41	190.56	963.6	1154.2	22.17
19.0	4.3	225.24	193.42	961.9	1155.3	21.08
20.0	5.3	227.96	196.16	960.1	1156.3	20.089
21.0	6.3	230.57	198.79	958.4	1157.2	19.192
22.0	7.3	233.07	201.33	956.8	1158.1	18.375
23.0	8.3	235.49	203.78	955.2	1159.0	17.627
24.0	9.3	237.82	206.14	953.7	1159.8	16.938
25.0	10.3	240.07	208.42	952.1	1160.6	16.303
26.0	11.3	242.25	210.62	950.7	1161.3	15.715
27.0	12.3	244.36	212.75	949.3	1162.0	15.170
28.0	13.3	246.41	214.83	947.9	1162.7	14.663
29.0	14.3	248.40	216.86	946.5	1163.4	14.189
30.0	15.3	250.33	218.82	945.3	1164.1	13.746
31.0	16.3	252.22	220.73	944.0	1164.7	13.330
32.0	17.3	254.05	222.59	942.8	1165.4	12.940
33.0	18.3	255.84	224.41	941.6	1166.0	12.572
34.0	19.3	257.58	226.18	940.3	1166.5	12.226
35.0	20.3	259.28	227.91	939.2	1167.1	11.898
36.0	21.3	260.95	229.60	938.0	1167.6	11.588
37.0	22.3	262.57	231.26	936.9	1168.2	11.294
38.0	23.3	264.16	232.89	935.8	1168.7	11.015
39.0	24.3	265.72	234.48	934.7	1169.2	10.750
40.0	25.3	267.25	236.03	933.7	1169.7	10.498
41.0	26.3	268.74	237.55	932.6	1170.2	10.258
42.0	27.3	270.21	239.04	931.6	1170.7	10.029
43.0	28.3	271.64	240.51	930.6	1171.1	9.810
44.0	29.3	273.05	241.95	929.6	1171.6	9.601
45.0	30.3	274.44	243.36	928.6	1172.0	9.401
46.0	31.3	275.80	244.75	927.7	1172.4	9.209
47.0	32.3	277.13	246.12	926.7	1172.9	9.025
48.0	33.3	278.45	247.47	925.8	1173.3	8.848
49.0	34.3	279.74	248.79	924.9	1173.7	8.678
50.0	35.3	281.01	250.09	924.0	1174.1	8.515
51.0	36.3	282.26	251.37	923.0	1174.4	8.359
52.0	37.3	283.49	252.63	922.2	1174.8	8.208
53.0	38.3	284.70	253.87	921.3	1175.2	8.062
54.0	39.3	285.90	255.09	920.5	1175.6	7.922

- Continued -

Properties of Saturated Steam (Continued)

PRESSURE (LBS PER SQ IN.)		TEMPERATURE t (°F)	HEAT OF THE LIQUID (BTU/LB)	LATENT HEAT OF EVAPORATION (BTU/LB)	TOTAL HEAT OF STEAM H_g (BTU/LB)	SPECIFIC VOLUME $\overline{V}$ (CU FT PER LB)
Absolute P′	Gauge P					
55.0	40.3	287.07	256.30	919.6	1175.9	7.787
56.0	41.3	288.23	257.50	918.8	1176.3	7.656
57.0	42.3	289.37	258.67	917.9	1176.6	7.529
58.0	43.3	290.50	259.82	917.1	1176.9	7.407
59.0	44.3	291.61	260.96	916.3	1177.3	7.289
60.0	45.3	292.71	262.09	915.5	1177.6	7.175
61.0	46.3	293.79	263.20	914.7	1177.9	7.064
62.0	47.3	294.85	264.30	913.9	1178.2	6.957
63.0	48.3	295.90	265.38	913.1	1178.5	6.853
64.0	49.3	296.94	266.45	912.3	1178.8	6.752
65.0	50.3	297.97	267.50	911.6	1179.1	6.655
66.0	51.3	298.99	268.55	910.8	1179.4	6.560
67.0	52.3	299.99	269.58	910.1	1179.7	6.468
68.0	53.3	300.98	270.60	909.4	1180.0	6.378
69.0	54.3	301.96	291.61	908.7	1180.3	6.291
70.0	55.3	302.92	272.61	907.9	1180.6	6.206
71.0	56.3	303.88	273.60	907.2	1180.8	6.124
72.0	57.3	304.83	274.57	906.5	1181.1	6.044
73.0	58.3	305.76	275.54	905.8	1181.3	5.966
74.0	59.3	306.68	276.49	905.1	1181.6	5.890
75.0	60.3	307.60	277.43	904.5	1181.9	5.816
76.0	61.3	308.50	278.37	903.7	1182.1	5.743
77.0	62.3	309.40	279.30	903.1	1182.4	5.673
78.0	63.3	310.29	280.21	902.4	1182.6	5.604
79.0	64.3	311.16	281.12	901.7	1182.8	5.537
80.0	65.3	312.03	282.02	901.1	1183.1	5.472
81.0	66.3	312.89	282.91	900.4	1183.3	5.408
82.0	67.3	313.74	283.79	899.7	1183.5	5.346
83.0	68.3	314.59	284.66	899.1	1183.8	5.285
84.0	69.3	315.42	285.53	898.5	1184.0	5.226
85.0	70.3	316.25	286.39	897.8	1184.2	5.168
86.0	71.3	317.07	287.24	897.2	1184.4	5.111
87.0	72.3	317.88	288.08	896.5	1184.6	5.055
88.0	73.3	318.68	288.91	895.9	1184.8	5.001
89.0	74.3	319.48	289.74	895.3	1185.1	4.948
90.0	75.3	320.27	290.56	894.7	1185.3	4.896
91.0	76.3	321.06	291.38	894.1	1185.5	4.845
92.0	77.3	321.83	292.18	893.5	1185.7	4.796
93.0	78.3	322.60	292.98	892.9	1185.9	4.747
94.0	79.3	323.36	293.78	892.3	1186.1	4.699
95.0	80.3	324.12	294.56	891.7	1186.2	4.652
96.0	81.3	324.87	295.34	891.1	1186.4	4.606
97.0	82.3	325.61	296.12	890.5	1186.6	4.561
98.0	83.3	326.35	296.89	889.9	1186.8	4.517
99.0	84.3	327.08	297.65	889.4	1187.0	4.474

- Continued -

Properties of Saturated Steam (Continued)

PRESSURE (LBS PER SQ IN.)		TEMPER-ATURE t (°F)	HEAT OF THE LIQUID (BTU/LB)	LATENT HEAT OF EVAPORATION (BTU/LB)	TOTAL HEAT OF STEAM H_g (BTU/LB)	SPECIFIC VOLUME $\bar{V}$ (CU FT PER LB)
Absolute P′	Gauge P					
100.0	85.3	327.81	298.40	888.8	1187.2	4.432
101.0	86.3	328.53	299.15	888.2	1187.4	4.391
102.0	87.3	329.25	299.90	887.6	1187.5	4.350
103.0	88.3	329.96	300.64	887.1	1187.7	4.310
104.0	89.3	330.66	301.37	886.5	1187.9	4.271
105.0	90.3	331.36	302.10	886.0	1188.1	4.232
106.0	91.3	332.05	302.82	885.4	1188.2	4.194
107.0	92.3	332.74	303.54	884.9	1188.4	4.157
108.0	93.3	333.42	304.26	884.3	1188.6	4.120
109.0	94.3	334.10	304.97	883.7	1188.7	4.084
110.0	95.3	334.77	305.66	883.2	1188.9	4.049
111.0	96.3	335.44	306.37	882.6	1189.0	4.015
112.0	97.3	336.11	307.06	882.1	1189.2	3.981
113.0	98.3	336.77	307.75	881.6	1189.4	3.947
114.0	99.3	337.42	308.43	881.1	1189.5	3.914
115.0	100.3	338.07	309.11	880.6	1189.7	3.882
116.0	101.3	338.72	309.79	880.0	1189.8	3.850
117.0	102.3	339.36	310.46	879.5	1190.0	3.819
118.0	103.3	339.99	311.12	879.0	1190.1	3.788
119.0	104.3	340.62	311.78	878.4	1190.2	3.758
120.0	105.3	341.25	312.44	877.9	1190.4	3.728
121.0	106.3	341.88	313.10	877.4	1190.5	3.699
122.0	107.3	342.50	313.75	876.9	1190.7	3.670
123.0	108.3	343.11	314.40	876.4	1190.8	3.642
124.0	109.3	343.72	315.04	875.9	1190.9	3.614
125.0	110.3	344.33	315.68	875.4	1191.1	3.587
126.0	111.3	344.94	316.31	874.9	1191.2	3.560
127.0	112.3	345.54	316.94	874.4	1191.3	3.533
128.0	113.3	346.13	317.57	873.9	1191.5	3.507
129.0	114.3	346.73	318.19	873.4	1191.6	3.481
130.0	115.3	347.32	318.81	872.9	1191.7	3.455
131.0	116.3	347.90	319.43	872.5	1191.9	3.430
132.0	117.3	348.48	320.04	872.0	1192.0	3.405
133.0	118.3	349.06	320.65	871.5	1192.1	3.381
134.0	119.3	349.64	321.25	871.0	1192.2	3.357
135.0	120.3	350.21	321.85	870.6	1192.4	3.333
136.0	121.3	350.78	322.45	870.1	1192.5	3.310
137.0	122.3	351.35	323.05	869.6	1192.6	3.287
138.0	123.3	351.91	323.64	869.1	1192.7	3.264
139.0	124.3	352.47	324.23	868.7	1192.9	3.242
140.0	125.3	353.02	324.82	868.2	1193.0	3.220
141.0	126.3	353.57	325.40	867.7	1193.1	3.198
142.0	127.3	354.12	325.98	867.2	1193.2	3.177
143.0	128.3	354.67	326.56	866.7	1193.3	3.155
144.0	129.3	355.21	327.13	866.3	1193.4	3.134

- Continued -

Properties of Saturated Steam (Continued)

PRESSURE (LBS PER SQ IN.)		TEMPERATURE t (°F)	HEAT OF THE LIQUID (BTU/LB)	LATENT HEAT OF EVAPORATION (BTU/LB)	TOTAL HEAT OF STEAM H_g (BTU/LB)	SPECIFIC VOLUME $\overline{V}$ (CU FT PER LB)
Absolute P′	Gauge P					
145.0	130.3	355.76	327.70	865.8	1193.5	3.114
146.0	131.3	356.29	328.27	865.3	1193.6	3.094
147.0	132.3	356.83	328.83	864.9	1193.8	3.074
148.0	133.3	357.36	329.39	864.5	1193.9	3.054
149.0	134.3	357.89	329.95	864.0	1194.0	3.034
150.0	135.3	358.42	330.51	863.6	1194.1	3.015
152.0	137.3	359.46	331.61	862.7	1194.3	2.977
154.0	139.3	360.49	332.70	861.8	1194.5	2.940
156.0	141.3	361.52	333.79	860.9	1194.7	2.904
158.0	143.3	362.53	334.86	860.0	1194.9	2.869
160.0	145.3	363.53	335.93	859.2	1195.1	2.834
162.0	147.3	364.53	336.98	858.3	1195.3	2.801
164.0	149.3	365.51	338.02	857.5	1195.5	2.768
166.0	151.3	366.48	339.05	856.6	1195.7	2.736
168.0	153.3	367.45	340.07	855.7	1195.8	2.705
170.0	155.3	368.41	341.09	854.9	1196.0	2.675
172.0	157.3	369.35	342.10	854.1	1196.2	2.645
174.0	159.3	370.29	343.10	853.3	1196.4	2.616
176.0	161.3	371.22	344.09	852.4	1196.5	2.587
178.0	163.3	372.14	345.06	851.6	1196.7	2.559
180.0	165.3	373.06	346.03	850.8	1196.9	2.532
182.0	167.3	373.96	347.00	850.0	1197.0	2.505
184.0	169.3	374.86	347.96	849.2	1197.2	2.479
186.0	171.3	375.75	348.92	848.4	1197.3	2.454
188.0	173.3	376.64	349.86	847.6	1197.5	2.429
190.0	175.3	377.51	350.79	846.8	1197.6	2.404
192.0	177.3	378.38	351.72	846.1	1197.8	2.380
194.0	179.3	379.24	352.64	845.3	1197.9	2.356
196.0	181.3	380.10	353.55	844.5	1198.1	2.333
198.0	183.3	380.95	354.46	843.7	1198.2	2.310
200.0	185.3	381.79	355.36	843.0	1198.4	2.288
205.0	190.3	383.86	357.58	841.1	1198.7	2.234
210.0	195.3	385.90	359.77	839.2	1199.0	2.183
215.0	200.3	387.89	361.91	837.4	1199.3	2.134
220.0	205.3	389.86	364.02	835.6	1199.6	2.087
225.0	210.3	391.79	366.09	833.8	1199.9	2.0422
230.0	215.3	393.68	368.13	832.0	1200.1	1.9992
235.0	220.3	395.54	370.14	830.3	1200.4	1.9579
240.0	225.3	397.37	372.12	828.5	1200.6	1.9183
245.0	230.3	399.18	374.08	826.8	1200.9	1.8803
250.0	235.3	400.95	376.00	825.1	1201.1	1.8438
255.0	240.3	402.70	377.89	823.4	1201.3	1.8086
260.0	245.3	404.42	379.76	821.8	1201.5	1.7748
265.0	250.3	406.11	381.60	820.1	1201.7	1.7422
270.0	255.3	407.78	383.42	818.5	1201.9	1.7107

- Continued -

Properties of Saturated Steam (Continued)

PRESSURE (LBS PER SQ IN.)		TEMPERATURE	HEAT OF THE LIQUID (BTU/LB)	LATENT HEAT OF EVAPORATION (BTU/LB)	TOTAL HEAT OF STEAM H_g (BTU/LB)	SPECIFIC VOLUME $\overline{V}$ (CU FT PER LB)
Absolute P′	Gauge P	t (°F)				
275.0	260.3	409.43	385.21	816.9	1202.1	1.6804
280.0	265.3	411.05	386.98	815.3	1202.3	1.6511
285.0	270.3	412.65	388.73	813.7	1202.4	1.6228
290.0	275.3	414.23	390.46	812.1	1202.6	1.5954
295.0	280.3	415.79	392.16	810.5	1202.7	1.5689
300.0	285.3	417.33	393.84	809.0	1202.8	1.5433
320.0	305.3	[illegible]	[illegible]	803.0	1203.4	1.4485
340.0	325.3	428.97	406.66	797.1	1203.7	1.3645
360.0	345.3	434.40	412.67	791.4	1204.1	1.2895
380.0	365.3	439.60	418.45	785.8	1204.3	1.2222
400.0	385.3	444.59	424.0	780.5	1204.5	1.1613
420.0	405.3	449.39	429.4	775.2	1204.6	1.1061
440.0	425.3	454.02	434.6	770.0	1204.6	1.0556
460.0	445.3	458.50	439.7	764.9	1204.6	1.0094
480.0	465.3	462.82	444.6	759.9	1204.5	0.9670
500.0	485.3	467.01	449.4	755.0	1204.4	0.9278
520.0	505.3	471.07	454.1	750.1	1204.2	0.8915
540.0	525.3	475.01	458.6	745.4	1204.0	0.8578
560.0	545.3	478.85	463.0	740.8	1203.8	0.8265
580.0	565.3	482.58	467.4	736.1	1203.5	0.7973
600.0	585.3	486.21	471.6	731.6	1203.2	0.7698
620.0	605.3	489.75	475.7	727.2	1202.9	0.7440
640.0	625.3	493.21	479.8	722.7	1202.5	0.7198
660.0	645.3	496.58	483.8	718.3	1202.1	0.6971
680.0	665.3	499.88	487.7	714.0	1201.7	0.6757
700.0	685.3	503.10	491.5	709.7	1201.2	0.6554
720.0	705.3	506.25	495.3	705.4	1200.7	0.6362
740.0	725.3	509.34	499.0	701.2	1200.2	0.6180
760.0	745.3	512.36	502.6	697.1	1199.7	0.6007
780.0	765.3	515.33	506.2	692.9	1199.1	0.5843
800.0	785.3	518.23	509.7	688.9	1198.6	0.5687
820.0	805.3	521.08	513.2	684.8	1198.0	0.5538
840.0	825.3	523.88	516.6	680.8	1197.4	0.5396
860.0	845.3	526.63	520.0	676.8	1196.8	0.5260
880.0	865.3	529.33	523.3	672.8	1196.1	0.5130
900.0	885.3	531.98	526.6	668.8	1195.4	0.5006
920.0	905.3	534.59	529.8	664.9	1194.7	0.4886
940.0	925.3	537.16	533.0	661.0	1194.0	0.4772
960.0	945.3	539.68	536.2	657.1	1193.3	0.4663
980.0	965.3	542.17	539.3	653.3	1192.6	0.4557
1000.0	985.3	544.61	542.4	649.4	1191.8	0.4456
1050.0	1035.3	550.57	550.0	639.9	1189.9	0.4218
1100.0	1085.3	556.31	557.4	630.4	1187.8	0.4001
1150.0	1135.3	561.86	564.6	621.0	1185.6	0.3802
1200.0	1185.3	567.22	571.7	611.7	1183.4	0.3619

- Continued -

Properties of Saturated Steam (Continued)

PRESSURE (LBS PER SQ IN.)		TEMPERATURE t (°F)	HEAT OF THE LIQUID (BTU/LB)	LATENT HEAT OF EVAPORATION (BTU/LB)	TOTAL HEAT OF STEAM H_g (BTU/LB)	SPECIFIC VOLUME $\overline{V}$ (CU FT PER LB)
Absolute P′	Gauge P					
1250.0	1235.3	572.42	578.6	602.4	1181.0	0.3450
1300.0	1285.3	577.46	585.4	593.2	1178.6	0.3293
1350.0	1335.3	582.35	592.1	584.0	1176.1	0.3148
1400.0	1385.3	587.10	598.7	574.7	1173.4	0.3012
1450.0	1435.3	591.73	605.2	565.5	1170.7	0.2884
1500.0	1485.3	596.23	611.6	556.3	1167.9	0.2765
1600.0	1585.3	604.90	624.1	538.0	1162.1	0.2548
1700.0	1685.3	613.15	636.3	519.6	1155.9	0.2354
1800.0	1785.3	621.03	648.3	501.1	1149.4	0.2179
1900.0	1885.3	628.58	660.1	482.4	1142.4	0.2021
2000.0	1985.3	635.82	671.7	463.4	1135.1	0.1878
2100.0	2085.3	642.77	683.3	444.1	1127.4	0.1746
2200.0	2185.3	649.46	694.8	424.4	1119.2	0.1625
2300.0	2285.3	655.91	706.5	403.9	1110.4	0.1513
2400.0	2385.3	662.12	718.4	382.7	1101.1	0.1407
2500.0	2485.3	668.13	730.6	360.5	1091.1	0.1307
2600.0	2585.3	673.94	743.0	337.2	1080.2	0.1213
2700.0	2685.3	679.55	756.2	312.1	1068.3	0.1123
2800.0	2785.3	684.99	770.1	284.7	1054.8	0.1035
2900.0	2885.3	690.26	785.4	253.6	1039.0	0.0947
3000.0	2985.3	695.36	802.5	217.8	1020.3	0.0858
3100.0	3085.3	700.31	825.0	168.1	993.1	0.0753
3200.0	3185.3	705.11	872.4	62.0	934.4	0.0580
3206.2	3191.5	705.40	902.7	0.0	902.7	0.0503

Refrigerant 717 (Ammonia)
Properties of Liquid and Saturated Vapor

TEMP. (°F)	PRESSURE		VOLUME (CU. FT./LB.)	DENSITY (LB./CU. FT.)	ENTHALPY† (BTU/LB.)		ENTROPY† BTU/(LB.)(°R)	
	psia	psig	Vapor V_g	Liquid l/v_f	Liquid h_f	Vapor h_g	Liquid s_f	Vapor s_g
−105	0.996	27.9*	223.2	45.71	−68.5	570.3	−0.1774	1.6243
−104	1.041	27.8*	214.2	45.67	−67.5	570.7	− .1744	1.6205
−103	1.087	27.7*	205.7	45.63	−66.4	571.2	− .1714	1.6167
−102	1.135	27.6*	197.6	45.59	−65.4	571.6	− .1685	1.6129
−101	1.184	27.5*	189.8	45.55	−64.3	572.1	− .1655	1.6092
−100	1.24	27.4*	182.4	45.52	−63.3	572.5	−0.1626	1.6055
−99	1.29	27.3*	175.3	45.47	−62.2	572.9	− .1597	1.6018
−98	1.34	27.2*	168.5	45.43	−61.2	573.4	− .1568	1.5982
−97	1.40	27.1*	162.1	45.40	−60.1	573.8	− .1539	1.5945
−96	1.46	26.9*	155.9	45.36	−59.1	574.3	− .1510	1.5910
−95	1.52	26.8*	150.0	45.32	−58.0	574.7	−0.1481	1.5874
−94	1.59	26.7*	144.3	45.28	−57.0	575.1	− .1452	1.5838
−93	1.65	26.6*	138.9	45.24	−55.9	575.6	− .1423	1.5803
−92	1.72	26.4*	133.8	45.20	−54.9	576.0	− .1395	1.5768
−91	1.79	26.3*	128.9	45.16	−53.8	576.5	− .1366	1.5734
−90	1.86	26.1*	124.1	45.12	−52.8	576.9	−0.1338	1.5699
−89	1.94	26.0*	119.6	45.08	−51.7	577.3	− .1309	1.5665
−88	2.02	25.8*	115.3	45.04	−50.7	577.8	− .1281	1.5631
−87	2.10	25.6*	111.1	45.00	−49.6	578.2	− .1253	1.5597
−86	2.18	25.5*	107.1	44.96	−48.6	578.6	− .1225	1.5564
−85	2.27	25.3*	103.3	44.92	−47.5	579.1	−0.1197	1.5531
−84	2.35	25.1*	99.68	44.88	−46.5	579.5	− .1169	1.5498
−83	2.45	24.9*	96.17	44.84	−45.4	579.9	− .1141	1.5465
−82	2.54	24.7*	92.81	44.80	−44.4	580.4	− .1113	1.5432
−81	2.64	24.5*	89.59	44.76	−43.3	580.8	− .1085	1.5400
−80	2.74	24.3*	86.50	44.73	−42.2	581.2	0.1057	1.5368
−79	2.84	24.1*	83.54	44.68	−41.2	581.6	− .1030	1.5336
−78	2.95	23.9*	80.69	44.64	−40.1	582.1	− .1002	1.5304
−77	3.06	23.7*	77.96	44.60	−39.1	582.5	− .0975	1.5273
−76	3.18	23.5*	75.33	44.56	−38.0	582.9	− .0947	1.5242
−75	3.29	23.2*	72.81	44.52	−37.0	583.3	−0.0920	1.5211
−74	3.42	23.0*	70.39	44.48	−35.9	583.8	− .0892	1.5180
−73	3.54	22.7*	68.06	44.44	−34.9	584.2	− .0865	1.5149
−72	3.67	22.4*	65.82	44.40	−33.8	584.6	− .0838	1.5119
−71	3.80	22.2*	63.67	44.36	−32.8	585.0	− .0811	1.5089
−70	3.94	21.9*	61.60	44.32	−31.7	585.5	−0.0784	1.5059
−69	4.08	21.6*	59.61	44.28	−30.7	585.9	− .0757	1.5029
−68	4.23	21.3*	57.69	44.24	−29.6	586.3	− .0730	1.4999
−67	4.38	21.0*	55.85	44.19	−28.6	586.7	− .0703	1.4970
−66	4.53	20.7*	54.08	44.15	−27.5	587.1	− .0676	1.4940
−65	4.69	20.4*	52.37	44.11	−26.5	587.5	−0.0650	1.4911
−64	4.85	20.0*	50.73	44.07	−25.4	588.0	− .0623	1.4883
−63	5.02	19.7*	49.14	44.03	−24.4	588.4	− .0596	1.4854
−62	5.19	19.4*	47.62	43.99	−23.3	588.8	− .0570	1.4826
−61	5.37	19.0*	46.15	43.95	−22.2	589.2	− .0543	1.4797
−60	5.55	18.6*	44.73	43.91	−21.2	589.6	− .0517	1.4769

*Inches of mercury below one standard atmosphere.
† Based on 0 for the saturated liquid at −40°F.

Refrigerant 717 (Ammonia)
Properties of Liquid and Saturated Vapor (Continued)

TEMP. (°F)	PRESSURE		VOLUME (CU. FT./LB.)	DENSITY (LB./CU. FT.)	ENTHALPY† (BTU/LB.)		ENTROPY† BTU/(LB.)(°R)	
	psia	psig	Vapor V_g	Liquid $1/v_f$	Liquid h_f	Vapor h_g	Liquid s_f	Vapor s_g
−59	5.74	18.2*	43.37	43.87	−20.1	590.0	−0.0490	1.4741
−58	5.93	17.8*	42.05	43.83	−19.1	590.4	− .0464	1.4713
−57	6.13	17.4*	40.79	43.78	−18.0	590.8	− .0438	1.4686
−56	6.33	17.0*	39.56	43.74	−17.0	591.2	− .0412	1.4658
−55	6.54	16.6*	38.38	43.70	−15.9	591.6	− .0386	1.4631
−54	6.75	16.2*	37.24	43.66	−14.8	592.1	−0.0360	1.4604
−53	6.97	15.7*	36.15	43.62	−13.8	592.4	− .0334	1.4577
−52	7.20	15.3*	35.09	43.58	−12.7	592.9	− .0307	1.4551
−51	7.43	14.8*	34.06	43.54	−11.7	593.2	− .0281	1.4524
−50	7.67	14.3*	33.08	43.49	−10.6	593.7	− .0256	1.4497
−49	7.91	13.8*	32.12	43.45	−9.6	594.0	−0.0230	1.4471
−48	8.16	13.3*	31.20	43.41	−8.5	594.4	− .0204	1.4445
−47	8.42	12.8*	30.31	43.37	−7.4	594.9	− .0179	1.4419
−46	8.68	12.2*	29.45	43.33	−6.4	595.2	− .0153	1.4393
−45	8.95	11.7*	28.62	43.28	−5.3	595.6	− .0127	1.4368
−44	9.23	11.1*	27.82	43.24	−4.3	596.0	−0.0102	1.4342
−43	9.51	10.6*	27.04	43.20	−3.2	596.4	− .0076	1.4317
−42	9.81	10.0*	26.29	43.16	−2.1	596.8	− .0051	1.4292
−41	10.10	9.3*	25.56	43.12	−1.1	597.2	− .0025	1.4267
−40	10.41	8.7*	24.86	43.08	0.0	597.6	.0000	1.4242
−39	10.72	8.1*	24.18	43.04	1.1	598.0	0.0025	1.4217
−38	11.04	7.4*	23.53	42.99	2.1	598.3	.0051	1.4193
−37	11.37	6.8*	22.89	42.95	3.2	598.7	.0076	1.4169
−36	11.71	6.1*	22.27	42.90	4.3	599.1	.0101	1.4144
−35	12.05	5.4*	21.68	42.86	5.3	599.5	.0126	1.4120
−34	12.41	4.7*	21.10	42.82	6.4	599.9	0.0151	1.4096
−33	12.77	3.9*	20.54	42.78	7.4	600.2	.0176	1.4072
−32	13.14	3.2*	20.00	42.73	8.5	600.6	.0201	1.4048
−31	13.52	2.4*	19.48	42.69	9.6	601.0	.0226	1.4025
−30	13.90	1.6*	18.97	42.65	10.7	601.4	.0250	1.4001
−29	14.30	0.8*	18.48	42.61	11.7	601.7	0.0275	1.3978
−28	14.71	0.0	18.00	42.57	12.8	602.1	.0300	1.3955
−27	15.12	0.4	17.54	42.54	13.9	602.5	.0325	1.3932
−26	15.55	0.8	17.09	42.48	14.9	602.8	.0350	1.3909
−25	15.98	1.3	16.66	42.44	16.0	603.2	.0374	1.3886
−24	16.24	1.7	16.24	42.40	17.1	603.6	0.0399	1.3863
−23	16.88	2.2	15.83	42.35	18.1	603.9	.0423	1.3840
−22	17.34	2.6	15.43	42.31	19.2	604.3	.0448	1.3818
−21	17.81	3.1	15.05	42.26	20.3	604.6	.0472	1.3796
−20	18.30	3.6	14.68	42.22	21.4	605.0	.0497	1.3774
−19	18.79	4.1	14.32	42.18	22.4	605.3	0.0521	1.3752
−18	19.30	4.6	13.97	42.13	23.5	605.7	.0545	1.3729
−17	19.81	5.1	13.62	42.09	24.6	606.1	.0570	1.3708
−16	20.34	5.6	13.29	42.04	25.6	606.4	.0594	1.3686
−15	20.88	6.2	12.97	42.00	26.7	606.7	.0618	1.3664
−14	21.43	6.7	12.66	41.96	27.8	607.1	.0642	1.3642

*Inches of mercury below one standard atmosphere.
† Based on 0 for the saturated liquid at −40°F.

Refrigerant 717 (Ammonia)
Properties of Liquid and Saturated Vapor (Continued)

TEMP. (°F)	PRESSURE		VOLUME (CU. FT./LB.)	DENSITY (LB./CU. FT.)	ENTHALPY† (BTU/LB.)		ENTROPY† BTU/(LB.)(°R)	
	psia	psig	Vapor V_g	Liquid l/v_f	Liquid h_f	Vapor h_g	Liquid s_f	Vapor s_g
−13	21.99	7.3	12.36	41.91	28.9	607.5	0.0666	1.3624
−12	22.56	7.9	12.06	41.87	30.0	607.8	.0690	1.3600
−11	23.15	8.5	11.78	41.82	31.0	608.1	.0714	1.3579
−10	23.74	9.0	11.50	41.78	32.1	608.5	.0738	1.3558
−9	24.35	9.7	11.23	41.74	33.2	608.8	.0762	1.3537
−8	24.97	10.3	10.97	41.69	34.3	609.2	0.0786	1.3516
−7	25.61	10.9	10.71	41.65	35.4	609.5	.0809	1.3493
−6	26.26	11.6	10.47	41.60	36.4	609.8	.0833	1.3474
−5	26.92	12.2	10.23	41.56	37.5	610.1	.0857	1.3454
−4	27.59	12.9	9.991	41.52	38.6	610.5	.0880	1.3433
−3	28.28	13.6	9.763	41.47	39.7	610.8	0.0909	1.3413
−2	28.98	14.3	9.541	41.43	40.7	611.1	.0928	1.3393
−1	29.69	15.0	9.326	41.38	41.8	611.4	.0951	1.3372
0	30.42	15.7	9.116	41.34	42.9	611.8	.0975	1.3352
1	31.16	16.5	8.912	41.29	44.0	612.1	.0998	1.3332
2	31.92	17.2	8.714	41.25	45.1	612.4	0.1022	1.3312
3	32.69	18.0	8.521	41.20	46.2	612.7	.1045	1.3292
4	33.47	18.8	8.333	41.16	47.2	613.0	.1069	1.3273
5‡	34.27	19.6	8.150	41.11	48.3	613.3	.1092	1.3253
6	35.09	20.4	7.971	41.07	49.4	613.6	.1115	1.3234
7	35.92	21.2	7.798	41.01	50.5	613.9	0.1138	1.3214
8	36.77	22.1	7.629	40.98	51.6	614.3	.1162	1.3195
9	37.63	22.9	7.464	40.93	52.7	614.6	.1185	1.3176
10	38.51	23.8	7.304	40.89	53.8	614.9	.1208	1.3157
11	39.40	24.7	7.148	40.84	54.9	615.2	.1231	1.3137
12	40.31	25.6	6.996	40.80	56.0	615.5	0.1254	1.3118
13	41.24	26.5	6.847	40.75	57.1	615.8	.1277	1.3099
14	42.18	27.5	6.703	40.71	58.2	616.1	.1300	1.3081
15	43.14	28.4	6.562	40.66	59.2	616.3	.1323	1.3062
16	44.12	29.4	6.425	40.61	60.3	616.6	.1346	1.3043
17	45.12	30.4	6.291	40.57	61.4	616.9	0.1369	1.3025
18	46.13	31.4	6.161	40.52	62.5	617.2	.1392	1.3006
19	47.16	32.5	6.034	40.48	63.6	617.5	.1415	1.2988
20	48.21	33.5	5.910	40.43	64.7	617.8	.1437	1.2969
21	49.28	34.6	5.789	40.38	65.8	618.0	.1460	1.2951
22	50.36	35.7	5.671	40.34	66.9	618.3	0.1483	1.2933
23	51.47	36.8	5.556	40.29	68.0	618.6	.1505	1.2915
24	52.59	37.9	5.443	40.25	69.1	618.9	.1528	1.2897
25	53.73	39.0	5.334	40.20	70.2	619.1	.1551	1.2879
26	54.90	40.2	5.227	40.15	71.3	619.4	.1573	1.2861
27	56.08	41.4	5.123	40.10	72.4	619.7	0.1596	1.2843
28	57.28	42.6	5.021	40.06	73.5	619.9	.1618	1.2823
29	58.50	43.8	4.922	40.01	74.6	620.2	.1641	1,2809
30	59.74	45.0	4.825	39.96	75.7	620.5	.1663	1.2790
31	61.00	46.3	4.730	39.91	76.8	620.7	.1686	1.2773
32	62.29	47.6	4.637	39.86	77.9	621.0	.1708	1.2755

*Inches of mercury below one standard atmosphere.
† Based on 0 for the saturated liquid at −40°F.
‡ Standard cycle temperatures.

Refrigerant 717 (Ammonia)
Properties of Liquid and Saturated Vapor (Continued)

TEMP. (°F)	PRESSURE		VOLUME (CU. FT./LB.)	DENSITY (LB./CU. FT.)	ENTHALPY† (BTU/LB.)		ENTROPY† BTU/(LB.)(°R)	
	psia	psig	Vapor V_g	Liquid $1/v_f$	Liquid h_f	Vapor h_g	Liquid s_f	Vapor s_g
33	63.59	48.9	4.547	39.82	79.0	621.2	0.1730	1.2738
34	64.91	50.2	4.459	39.77	80.1	621.5	.1753	1.2721
35	66.26	51.6	4.373	39.72	81.2	621.7	.1775	1.2704
36	67.63	52.9	4.289	39.67	82.3	622.0	.1797	1.2686
37	69.02	54.3	4.207	39.63	83.4	622.2	.1819	1.2669
38	70.43	55.7	4.126	39.58	84.6	622.5	0.1841	1.2652
39	71.87	57.2	4.048	39.54	85.7	622.7	.1863	1.2635
40	73.32	58.6	3.971	39.49	86.8	623.0	.1885	1.2618
41	74.80	60.1	3.897	39.44	87.9	623.2	.1908	1.2602
42	76.31	61.6	3.823	39.39	89.0	623.4	.1930	1.2585
43	77.83	63.1	3.752	39.34	90.1	623.7	0.1952	1.2568
44	79.38	64.7	3.682	39.29	91.2	623.9	.1974	1.2552
45	80.96	66.3	3.614	39.24	92.3	624.1	.1996	1.2535
46	82.55	67.9	3.547	39.19	93.5	624.4	.2018	1.2518
47	84.18	69.5	3.481	39.14	94.6	624.6	.2040	1.2492
48	85.82	71.1	3.418	39.10	95.7	624.8	0.2062	1.2484
49	87.49	72.8	3.355	39.05	96.8	625.0	.2083	1.2469
50	89.19	74.5	3.294	39.00	97.9	625.2	.2105	1.2453
51	90.91	76.2	3.234	38.95	99.1	625.5	.2127	1.2437
52	92.66	78.0	3.176	38.90	100.2	625.7	.2149	1.2421
53	94.43	79.7	3.119	38.85	101.3	625.9	0.2171	1.2405
54	96.23	81.5	3.063	38.80	102.4	626.1	.2192	1.2382
55	98.06	83.4	3.008	38.75	103.5	626.3	.2214	1.2372
56	99.91	85.2	2.954	38.70	104.7	626.5	.2236	1.2357
57	101.8	87.1	2.902	38.65	105.8	626.7	.2257	1.2341
58	103.7	89.0	2.851	38.60	106.9	626.9	0.2279	1.2325
59	105.6	90.9	2.800	38.55	108.1	627.1	.2301	1.2310
60	107.6	92.9	2.751	38.50	109.2	627.3	.2322	1.2294
61	109.6	94.9	2.703	38.45	110.3	627.5	.2344	1.2273
62	111.6	96.9	2.656	38.40	111.5	627.7	.2365	1.2263
63	113.6	98.9	2.610	38.35	112.6	627.9	0.2387	1.2247
64	115.7	101.0	2.565	38.30	113.7	628.0	.2408	1.2231
65	117.8	103.1	2.520	38.25	114.8	628.2	.2430	1.2213
66	120.0	105.3	2.477	38.20	116.0	628.4	.2451	1.2201
67	122.1	107.4	2.435	38.15	117.1	628.6	.2473	1.2183
68	124.3	109.6	2.393	38.10	118.3	628.8	0.2494	1.2179
69	126.5	111.8	2.352	38.05	119.4	628.9	.2515	1.2155
70	128.8	114.1	2.312	38.00	120.5	629.1	.2537	1.2140
71	131.1	116.4	2.273	37.95	121.7	629.3	.2558	1.2125
72	133.4	118.7	2.235	37.90	122.8	629.4	.2579	1.2110
73	135.7	121.0	2.197	37.84	124.0	629.6	0.2601	1.2095
74	138.1	123.4	2.161	37.79	125.1	629.8	.2622	1.2080
75	140.5	125.8	2.125	37.74	126.2	629.9	.2643	1.2065
76	143.0	128.3	2.089	37.69	127.4	630.1	.2664	1.2050
77	145.4	130.7	2.055	37.64	128.5	630.2	.2685	1.2035
78	147.9	133.2	2.021	37.58	129.7	630.4	.2706	1.2020

*Inches of mercury below one standard atmosphere.
† Based on 0 for the saturated liquid at −40°F.

Refrigerant 717 (Ammonia)
Properties of Liquid and Saturated Vapor (Continued)

TEMP. (°F)	PRESSURE		VOLUME (CU. FT./LB.)	DENSITY (LB./CU. FT.)	ENTHALPY† (BTU/LB.)		ENTROPY† BTU/(LB.)(°R)	
	psia	psig	Vapor V_g	Liquid $1/v_f$	Liquid h_f	Vapor h_g	Liquid s_f	Vapor s_g
79	150.5	135.8	1.988	37.53	130.8	630.5	0.2728	1.2006
80	153.0	138.3	1.955	37.48	132.0	630.7	.2749	1.1991
81	155.6	140.9	1.923	37.43	133.1	630.8	.2769	1.1976
82	158.3	143.6	1.892	37.37	134.3	631.0	.2791	1.1962
83	161.0	146.3	1.861	37.32	135.4	631.1	.2812	1.1947
84	163.7	149.0	1.831	37.26	136.6	631.3	0.2833	1.1933
85	166.4	151.7	1.801	37.21	137.8	631.4	.2854	1.1918
86‡	169.2	154.5	1.772	37.16	138.9	631.5	.2875	1.1904
87	172.0	157.3	1.744	37.11	140.1	631.7	.2895	1.1889
88	174.8	160.1	1.716	37.05	141.2	631.8	.2917	1.1875
89	177.7	163.0	1.688	37.00	142.4	631.9	0.2937	1.1860
90	180.6	165.9	1.661	36.95	143.5	632.0	.2958	1.1846
91	183.6	168.9	1.635	36.89	144.7	632.1	.2979	1.1832
92	186.6	171.9	1.609	36.84	145.8	632.2	.3000	1.1818
93	189.6	174.9	1.584	36.78	147.0	632.3	.3021	1.1804
94	192.7	178.0	1.559	36.73	148.2	632.5	0.3041	1.1789
95	195.8	181.1	1.534	36.67	149.4	632.6	.3062	1.1775
96	198.9	184.2	1.510	36.62	150.5	632.6	.3083	1.1761
97	202.1	187.4	1.487	36.56	151.7	632.8	.3104	1.1747
98	205.3	190.6	1.464	36.51	152.9	632.9	.3125	1.1733
99	208.6	193.9	1.441	36.45	154.0	632.9	0.3145	1.1719
100	211.9	197.2	1.419	36.40	155.2	633.0	.3166	1.1705
101	215.2	200.5	1.397	36.34	156.4	633.1	.3187	1.1691
102	218.6	203.9	1.375	36.29	157.6	633.2	.3207	1.1677
103	222.0	207.3	1.354	36.23	158.7	633.3	.3228	1.1663
104	225.4	210.7	1.334	36.18	159.9	633.4	0.3248	1.1649
105	228.9	214.2	1.313	36.12	161.1	633.4	.3269	1.1635
106	232.5	217.8	1.293	36.06	162.3	633.5	.3289	1.1621
107	236.0	221.3	1.274	36.01	163.5	633.6	.3310	1.1607
108	239.7	225.0	1.254	35.95	164.6	633.6	.3330	1.1593
109	243.3	228.6	1.235	35.90	165.8	633.7	0.3351	1.1580
110	247.0	232.3	1.217	35.84	167.0	633.7	.3372	1.1566
111	250.8	236.1	1.198	35.78	168.2	633.8	.3392	1.1552
112	254.5	239.8	1.180	35.72	169.4	633.8	.3413	1.1538
113	258.4	243.7	1.163	35.67	170.6	633.9	.3433	1.1524
114	262.2	247.5	1.145	35.61	171.8	633.9	0.3453	1.1510
115	266.2	251.5	1.128	35.55	173.0	633.9	.3474	1.1497
116	270.1	255.4	1.112	35.49	174.2	634.0	.3495	1.1483
117	274.1	259.4	1.095	35.43	175.4	634.0	.3515	1.1469
118	278.2	263.5	1.079	35.38	176.6	634.0	.3535	1.1455
119	282.3	267.6	1.063	35.32	177.8	634.0	.3556	1.1441
120	286.4	271.7	1.047	35.26	179.0	634.0	0.3576	1.1427
121	290.6	275.9	1.032	35.20	180.2	634.0	.3597	1.1414
122	294.8	280.1	1.017	35.14	181.4	634.0	.3618	1.1400
123	299.1	284.4	1.002	35.08	182.6	634.0	.3638	1.1386
124	303.4	288.7	0.987	35.02	183.9	634.0	.3659	1.1372
125	307.8	293.1	0.973	34.96	185.1	634.0	.3679	1.1358

*Inches of mercury below one standard atmosphere.
† Based on 0 for the saturated liquid at −40°F.
‡ Standard cycle temperatures.

Properties of Superheated Steam

$\overline{V}$ = specific volume, cubic feet per pound

h_g = total heat of steam, Btu per pound

PRESSURE (LBS PER SQ IN.) Absolute P′	Gauge P	SAT. TEMP. t		TOTAL TEMPERATURE—DEGREES FAHRENHEIT (t) 360°	400°	440°	480°	500°	600°	700°	800°	900°	1000°	1200°
14.696	0.0	212.00	$\overline{V}$	33.03	34.68	36.32	37.96	38.78	42.86	46.94	51.00	55.07	59.13	67.25
			h_g	1221.1	1239.9	1258.8	1277.6	1287.1	1334.8	1383.2	1432.3	1482.3	1533.1	1637.5
20.0	5.3	227.96	$\overline{V}$	24.21	25.43	26.65	27.86	28.46	31.47	34.47	37.46	40.45	43.44	49.41
			h_g	1220.3	1239.2	1258.2	1277.1	1286.6	1334.4	1382.9	1432.1	1482.1	1533.0	1637.4
30.0	15.3	250.33	$\overline{V}$	16.072	16.897	17.714	18.528	18.933	20.95	22.96	24.96	26.95	28.95	32.93
			h_g	1218.6	1237.9	1257.0	1276.2	1285.7	1333.8	1382.4	1431.7	1481.8	1532.7	1637.2
40.0	25.3	267.25	$\overline{V}$	12.001	12.628	13.247	13.862	14.168	15.688	17.198	18.702	20.20	21.70	24.69
			h_g	1216.9	1236.5	1255.9	1275.2	1284.8	1333.1	1381.9	1431.3	1481.4	1532.4	1637.0
50.0	35.3	281.01	$\overline{V}$	9.557	10.065	10.567	11.062	11.309	12.532	13.744	14.950	16.152	17.352	19.747
			h_g	1215.2	1235.1	1254.7	1274.2	1283.9	1332.5	1381.4	1430.9	1481.1	1532.1	1636.8
60.0	45.3	292.71	$\overline{V}$	7.927	8.357	8.779	9.196	9.403	10.427	11.441	12.449	13.452	14.454	16.451
			h_g	1213.4	1233.6	1253.5	1273.2	1283.0	1331.8	1380.9	1430.5	1480.8	1531.9	1636.6
70.0	55.3	302.92	$\overline{V}$	6.762	7.136	7.502	7.863	8.041	8.924	9.796	10.662	11.524	12.383	14.097
			h_g	1211.5	1232.1	1252.3	1272.2	1282.0	1331.1	1380.4	1430.1	1480.5	1531.6	1636.3
80.0	65.3	312.03	$\overline{V}$	5.888	6.220	6.544	6.862	7.020	7.797	8.562	9.322	10.077	10.830	12.332
			h_g	1209.7	1230.7	1251.1	1271.1	1281.1	1330.5	1379.9	1429.7	1480.1	1531.3	1636.2
90.0	75.3	320.27	$\overline{V}$	5.208	5.508	5.799	6.084	6.225	6.920	7.603	8.279	8.952	9.623	10.959
			h_g	1207.7	1229.1	1249.8	1270.1	1280.1	1329.8	1379.4	1429.3	1479.8	1531.0	1635.9
100.0	85.3	327.81	$\overline{V}$	4.663	4.937	5.202	5.462	5.589	6.218	6.835	7.446	8.052	8.656	9.860
			h_g	1205.7	1227.6	1248.6	1269.0	1279.1	1329.1	1378.9	1428.9	1479.5	1530.8	1635.7
120.0	105.3	341.25	$\overline{V}$	3.844	4.081	4.307	4.527	4.636	5.165	5.683	6.195	6.702	7.207	8.212
			h_g	1201.6	1224.4	1246.0	1266.9	1277.2	1327.7	1377.8	1428.1	1478.8	1530.2	1635.3

- Continued -

140.0	125.3	353.02	$\overline{V}$ h_g	3.258 1197.3	3.468 1221.1	3.667 1243.3	3.860 1264.7	3.954 1275.2	4.413 1326.4	4.861 1376.8	5.3[illegible]1 142[illegible].3	5.738 1478.2	6.172 1529.7	7.035 1634.9
160.0	145.3	363.53	$\overline{V}$ h_g	. . . . . .	3.008 1217.6	3.187 1240.6	3.359 1262.4	3.443 1273.1	3.849 1325.0	4.244 1375.7	4.6[illegible]1 142[illegible].4	5.015 1477.5	5.396 1529.1	6.152 1634.5
180.0	165.3	373.06	$\overline{V}$ h_g	. . . . . .	2.649 1214.0	2.813 1237.8	2.969 1260.2	3.044 1271.0	3.411 1323.5	3.764 1374.7	4.1[illegible]0 142[illegible].6	4.452 1476.8	4.792 1528.6	5.466 1634.1
200.0	185.3	381.79	$\overline{V}$ h_g	. . . . . .	2.361 1210.3	2.513 1234.9	2.656 1257.8	2.726 1268.9	3.060 1322.1	3.380 1373.6	3.6[illegible]3 142[illegible].8	4.002 1476.2	4.309 1528.0	4.917 1633.7
220.0	205.3	389.86	$\overline{V}$ h_g	. . . . . .	2.125 1206.5	2.267 1231.9	2.400 1255.4	2.465 1266.7	2.772 1320.7	3.066 1372.6	3.3[illegible]2 142[illegible].0	3.634 1475.5	3.913 1527.5	4.467 1633.3
240.0	225.3	397.37	$\overline{V}$ h_g	. . . . . .	1.9276 1202.5	2.062 1228.8	2.187 1253.0	2.247 1264.5	2.533 1319.2	2.804 1371.5	3.0[illegible]8 142[illegible].2	3.327 1474.8	3.584 1526.9	4.093 1632.9
260.0	245.3	404.42	$\overline{V}$ h_g	. . . . . .	. . . . . .	1.8882 1225.7	2.006 1250.5	2.063 1262.3	2.330 1317.7	2.582 1370.4	2.8[illegible]7 142[illegible].3	3.067 1474.2	3.305 1526.3	3.776 1632.5
280.0	265.3	411.05	$\overline{V}$ h_g	. . . . . .	. . . . . .	1.7388 1222.4	1.8512 1247.9	1.9047 1260.0	2.156 1316.2	2.392 1369.4	2.6[illegible]1 142[illegible].5	2.845 1473.5	3.066 1525.8	3.504 1632.1
300.0	285.3	417.33	$\overline{V}$ h_g	. . . . . .	. . . . . .	1.6090 1219.1	1.7165 1245.3	1.7675 1257.6	2.005 1314.7	2.227 1368.3	2.4[illegible]2 142[illegible]6	2.652 1472.8	2.859 1525.2	3.269 1631.7
320.0	305.3	423.29	$\overline{V}$ h_g	. . . . . .	. . . . . .	1.4950 1215.6	1.5985 1242.6	1.6472 1255.2	1.8734 1313.2	2.083 1367.2	2.28[illegible] 141[illegible]8	2.483 1472.1	2.678 1524.7	3.063 1631.3
340.0	325.3	428.97	$\overline{V}$ h_g	. . . . . .	. . . . . .	1.3941 1212.1	1.4941 1239.9	1.5410 1252.8	1.7569 1311.6	1.9562 1366.1	2.1[illegible] 141[illegible]0	2.334 1471.5	2.518 1524.1	2.881 1630.9
360.0	345.3	434.40	$\overline{V}$ h_g	. . . . . .	. . . . . .	1.3041 1208.4	1.4012 1237.1	1.4464 1250.3	1.6533 1310.1	1.8431 1365.0	2.02[illegible] 141[illegible]1	2.202 1470.8	2.376 1523.5	2.719 1630.5

- Continued -

Properties of Superheated Steam (Continued)

$\overline{V}$ = specific volume, cubic feet per pound

h_g = total heat of steam, Btu per pound

PRESSURE (LBS PER SQ IN.) Absolute P′	Gauge P	SAT. TEMP. t		500°	540°	600°	640°	660°	700°	740°	800°	900°	1000°	1200°
380.0	365.3	439.60	$\overline{V}$	1.3616	1.4444	1.5605	1.6345	1.6707	1.7419	1.8118	1.9149	2.083	2.249	2.575
			h_g	1247.7	1273.1	1308.5	1331.0	1342.0	1363.8	1385.3	1417.3	1470.1	1523.0	1630.0
400.0	385.3	444.59	$\overline{V}$	1.2851	1.3652	1.4770	1.5480	1.5827	1.6508	1.7177	1.8161	1.9767	2.134	2.445
			h_g	1245.1	1271.0	1306.9	1329.6	1340.8	1362.7	1384.3	1416.4	1469.4	1522.4	1629.6
420.0	405.3	449.39	$\overline{V}$	1.2158	1.2935	1.4014	1.4697	1.5030	1.5684	1.6324	1.7267	1.8802	2.031	2.327
			h_g	1242.5	1268.9	1305.3	1328.3	1339.5	1361.6	1383.3	1415.5	1468.7	1521.9	1629.2
440.0	425.3	454.02	$\overline{V}$	1.1526	1.2282	1.3327	1.3984	1.4306	1.4934	1.5549	1.6454	1.7925	1.9368	2.220
			h_g	1239.8	1266.7	1303.6	1326.9	1338.2	1360.4	1382.3	1414.7	1468.1	1521.3	1628.8
460.0	445.3	458.50	$\overline{V}$	1.0948	1.1685	1.2698	1.3334	1.3644	1.4250	1.4842	1.5711	1.7124	1.8508	2.122
			h_g	1237.0	1264.5	1302.0	1325.4	1336.9	1359.3	1381.3	1413.8	1467.4	1520.7	1628.4
480.0	465.3	462.82	$\overline{V}$	1.0417	1.1138	1.2122	1.2737	1.3038	1.3622	1.4193	1.5031	1.6390	1.7720	2.033
			h_g	1234.2	1262.3	1300.3	1324.0	1335.6	1358.2	1380.3	1412.9	1466.7	1520.2	1628.0
500.0	485.3	467.01	$\overline{V}$	0.9927	1.0633	1.1591	1.2188	1.2478	1.3044	1.3596	1.4405	1.5715	1.6996	1.9504
			h_g	1231.3	1260.0	1298.6	1322.6	1334.2	1357.0	1379.3	1412.1	1466.0	1519.6	1627.6
520.0	505.3	471.07	$\overline{V}$	0.9473	1.0166	1.1101	1.1681	1.1962	1.2511	1.3045	1.3826	1.5091	1.6326	1.8743
			h_g	1228.3	1257.7	1296.9	1321.1	1332.9	1355.8	1378.2	1411.2	1465.3	1519.0	1627.2
540.0	525.3	475.01	$\overline{V}$	0.9052	0.9733	1.0646	1.1211	1.1485	1.2017	1.2535	1.3291	1.4514	1.5707	1.8039
			h_g	1225.3	1255.4	1295.2	1319.7	1331.5	1354.6	1377.2	1410.3	1464.6	1518.5	1626.8
560.0	545.3	478.85	$\overline{V}$	0.8659	0.9330	1.0224	1.0775	1.1041	1.1558	1.2060	1.2794	1.3978	1.5132	1.7385
			h_g	1222.2	1253.0	1293.4	1318.2	1330.2	1353.5	1376.1	1409.4	1463.9	1517.9	1626.4
580.0	565.3	482.58	$\overline{V}$	0.8291	0.8954	0.9830	1.0368	1.0627	1.1331	1.1619	1.2331	1.3479	1.4596	1.6776
			h_g	1219.0	1250.5	1291.7	1316.7	1328.8	1352.3	1375.1	1408.6	1463.2	1517.3	1626.0

- Continued -

600.0	585.3	486.21	$\overline{V}$ h_g	0.7947 1215.7	0.8602 1248.1	0.9463 1289.9	0.9988 1315.2	1.0241 1327.4	1.0732 1351.1	1.1207 1374.0	1.1[illegible]9 140[illegible].7	1.3013 1462.5	1.4096 1516.7	1.6208 1625.5
620.0	605.3	489.75	$\overline{V}$ h_g	0.7624 1212.4	0.8272 1245.5	0.9118 1288.1	0.9633 1313.7	0.9880 1326.0	1.0358 1349.9	1.0821 1373.0	1.14[illegible]4 140[illegible].8	1.2577 1461.8	1.3628 1516.2	1.5676 1625.1
640.0	625.3	493.21	$\overline{V}$ h_g	0.7319 1209.0	0.7963 1243.0	0.8795 1286.2	0.9299 1312.2	0.9541 1324.6	1.0008 1348.6	1.0459 1371.9	1.11[illegible]5 140[illegible].9	1.2168 1461.1	1.3190 1515.6	1.5178 1624.7
660.0	645.3	496.58	$\overline{V}$ h_g	0.7032 1205.4	0.7670 1240.4	0.8491 1284.4	0.8985 1310.6	0.9222 1323.2	0.9679 1347.4	1.0119 1370.8	1.07[illegible]9 140[illegible].0	1.1784 1460.4	1.2778 1515.0	1.4709 1624.3
680.0	665.3	499.88	$\overline{V}$ h_g	0.6759 1201.8	0.7395 1237.7	0.8205 1282.5	0.8690 1309.1	0.8922 1321.7	0.9369 1346.2	0.9800 1369.8	1.04[illegible]4 140[illegible].1	1.1423 1459.7	1.2390 1514.5	1.4269 1623.9
700.0	685.3	503.10	$\overline{V}$ h_g	. . . . . .	0.7134 1235.0	0.7934 1280.6	0.8411 1307.5	0.8639 1320.3	0.9077 1345.0	0.9498 1368.7	1.01[illegible]8 140[illegible].2	1.1082 1459.0	1.2024 1513.9	1.3853 1623.5
750.0	735.3	510.86	$\overline{V}$ h_g	. . . . . .	0.6540 1227.9	0.7319 1275.7	0.7778 1303.5	0.7996 1316.6	0.8414 1341.8	0.8813 1366.0	0.93[illegible]1 140[illegible].9	1.0310 1457.2	1.1196 1512.4	1.2912 1622.4
800.0	785.3	518.23	$\overline{V}$ h_g	. . . . . .	0.6015 1220.5	0.6779 1270.7	0.7223 1299.4	0.7433 1312.9	0.7833 1338.6	0.8215 1363.2	0.87[illegible]3 139[illegible].6	0.9633 1455.4	1.0470 1511.0	1.2088 1621.4
850.0	835.3	525.26	$\overline{V}$ h_g	. . . . . .	0.5546 1212.7	0.6301 1265.5	0.6732 1295.2	0.6934 1309.0	0.7320 1335.4	0.7685 1360.4	0.82[illegible]9 139[illegible].3	0.9037 1453.6	0.9830 1509.5	1.1360 1620.4
900.0	885.3	531.98	$\overline{V}$ h_g	. . . . . .	0.5124 1204.4	0.5873 1260.1	0.6294 1290.9	0.6491 1305.1	0.6863 1332.1	0.7215 1357.5	0.77[illegible]6 139[illegible].9	0.8506 1451.8	0.9262 1508.1	1.0714 1619.3
950.0	935.3	538.42	$\overline{V}$ h_g	. . . . . .	0.4740 1195.5	0.5489 1254.6	0.5901 1286.4	0.6092 1301.1	0.6453 1328.7	0.6793 1354.7	0.72[illegible]5 139[illegible].6	0.8031 1450.0	0.8753 1506.6	1.0136 1618.3
1000.0	985.3	544.61	$\overline{V}$ h_g	. . . . . .	. . . . . .	0.5140 1248.8	0.5546 1281.9	0.5733 1297.0	0.6084 1325.3	0.6413 1351.7	0.68[illegible]8 138[illegible].2	0.7604 1448.2	0.8294 1505.1	0.9615 1617.3

- Continued -

Properties of Superheated Steam (Continued)

$\overline{V}$ = specific volume, cubic feet per pound

h_g = total heat of steam, Btu per pound

PRESSURE (LBS PER SQ IN.) Absolute P′	Gauge P	SAT. TEMP. t		TOTAL TEMPERATURE—DEGREES FAHRENHEIT (t) 660°	700°	740°	760°	780°	800°	860°	900°	1000°	1100°	1200°
1100.0	1085.3	556.31	$\overline{V}$	0.5110	0.5445	0.5755	0.5904	0.6049	0.6191	0.6601	0.6866	0.7503	0.8117	0.8716
			h_g	1288.5	1318.3	1345.8	1358.9	1371.7	1384.3	1420.8	1444.5	1502.2	1558.8	1615.2
1200.0	1185.3	567.22	$\overline{V}$	0.4586	0.4909	0.5206	0.5347	0.5484	0.5617	0.6003	0.6250	0.6843	0.7412	0.7967
			h_g	1279.6	1311.0	1339.6	1353.2	1366.4	1379.3	1416.7	1440.7	1499.2	1556.4	1613.1
1300.0	1285.3	577.46	$\overline{V}$	0.4139	0.4454	0.4739	0.4874	0.5004	0.5131	0.5496	0.5728	0.6284	0.6816	0.7333
			h_g	1270.2	1303.4	1333.3	1347.3	1361.0	1374.3	1412.5	1437.0	1496.2	1553.9	1611.0
1400.0	1385.3	587.10	$\overline{V}$	0.3753	0.4062	0.4338	0.4468	0.4593	0.4714	0.5061	0.5281	0.5805	0.6305	0.6789
			h_g	1260.3	1295.5	1326.7	1341.3	1355.4	1369.1	1408.2	1433.1	1493.2	1551.4	1608.9
1500.0	1485.3	596.23	$\overline{V}$	0.3413	0.3719	0.3989	0.4114	0.4235	0.4352	0.4684	0.4893	0.5390	0.5862	0.6318
			h_g	1249.8	1287.2	1320.0	1335.2	1349.7	1363.8	1403.9	1429.3	1490.1	1548.9	1606.8
1600.0	1585.3	604.90	$\overline{V}$	0.3112	0.3417	0.3682	0.3804	0.3921	0.4034	0.4353	0.4553	0.5027	0.5474	0.5906
			h_g	1238.7	1278.7	1313.0	1328.8	1343.9	1358.4	1399.5	1425.3	1487.0	1546.4	1604.6
1700.0	1685.3	613.15	$\overline{V}$	0.2842	0.3148	0.3410	0.3529	0.3643	0.3753	0.4061	0.4253	0.4706	0.5132	0.5542
			h_g	1226.8	1269.7	1305.8	1322.3	1337.9	1352.9	1395.0	1421.4	1484.0	1543.8	1602.5
1800.0	1785.3	621.03	$\overline{V}$	0.2597	0.2907	0.3166	0.3284	0.3395	0.3502	0.3801	0.3986	0.4421	0.4828	0.5218
			h_g	1214.0	1260.3	1298.4	1315.5	1331.8	1347.2	1390.4	1417.4	1480.8	1541.3	1600.4
1900.0	1885.3	628.58	$\overline{V}$	0.2371	0.2688	0.2947	0.3063	0.3173	0.3277	0.3568	0.3747	0.4165	0.4556	0.4929
			h_g	1200.2	1250.4	1290.6	1308.6	1325.4	1341.5	1385.8	1413.3	1477.7	1538.8	1598.2
2000.0	1985.3	635.82	$\overline{V}$	0.2161	0.2489	0.2748	0.2863	0.2972	0.3074	0.3358	0.3532	0.3935	0.4311	0.4668
			h_g	1184.9	1240.0	1282.6	1301.4	1319.0	1335.5	1381.2	1409.2	1474.5	1536.2	1596.1
2100.0	2085.3	642.77	$\overline{V}$	0.1962	0.2306	0.2567	0.2682	0.2789	0.2890	0.3167	0.3337	0.3727	0.4089	0.4433
			h_g	1167.7	1229.0	1274.3	1294.0	1312.3	1329.5	1376.4	1405.0	1471.4	1533.6	1593.9

- Continued -

2200.0	2185.3	649.46	$\bar{V}$	0.1768	0.2135	0.2400	0.2514	0.2621	0.2721	0.2994	0.3[illegible]9	0.3538	0.3887	0.4218
			h_g	1147.8	1217.4	1265.7	1286.3	1305.4	1323.3	1371.5	140[illegible].8	1468.2	1531.1	1591.8
2300.0	2285.3	655.91	$\bar{V}$	0.1575	0.1978	0.2247	0.2362	0.2468	0.2567	0.2835	0.2[illegible]7	0.3365	0.3703	0.4023
			h_g	1123.8	1204.9	1256.7	1278.4	1298.4	1316.9	1366.6	139[illegible].5	1464.9	1528.5	1589.6
2400.0	2385.3	662.12	$\bar{V}$	...	0.1828	0.2105	0.2221	0.2327	0.2425	0.2689	0.28[illegible]8	0.3207	0.3534	0.3843
			h_g	...	1191.5	1247.3	1270.2	1291.1	1310.3	1361.6	139[illegible].2	1461.7	1525.9	1587.4
2500.0	2485.3	668.13	$\bar{V}$	...	0.1686	0.1973	0.2090	0.2196	0.2294	0.2555	0.27[illegible]0	0.3061	0.3379	0.3678
			h_g	...	1176.8	12-7.6	1261.8	1283.6	1303.6	1356.5	138[illegible].8	1458.4	1523.2	1585.3
2600.0	2585.3	673.94	$\bar{V}$	...	0.1549	0.1849	0.1967	0.2074	0.2172	0.2431	0.25[illegible]4	0.2926	0.3236	0.3526
			h_g	...	1160.6	1227.3	1252.9	1275.8	1296.8	1351.4	138[illegible].4	1455.1	1520.6	1583.1
2700.0	2685.3	679.55	$\bar{V}$	...	0.1415	0.1732	0.1853	0.1960	0.2059	0.2315	0.24[illegible]6	0.2801	0.3103	0.3385
			h_g	...	1142.5	1216.5	1243.8	1267.9	1289.7	1346.1	137[illegible].9	1451.8	1518.0	1580.9
2800.0	2785.3	684.99	$\bar{V}$	...	0.1281	0.1622	0.1745	0.1854	0.1953	0.2208	0.23[illegible]6	0.2685	0.2979	0.3254
			h_g	...	1121.4	1205.1	1234.2	1259.6	1282.4	1340.8	137[illegible].3	1448.5	1515.4	1578.7
2900.0	2885.3	690.26	$\bar{V}$	...	0.1143	0.1517	0.1644	0.1754	0.1853	0.2108	0.22[illegible]4	0.2577	0.2864	0.3132
			h_g	...	1095.9	1193.0	1224.3	1251.1	1274.9	1335.3	136[illegible].7	1445.1	1512.7	1576.5
3000.0	2985.3	695.36	$\bar{V}$	...	0.0984	0.1416	0.1548	0.1660	0.1760	0.2014	0.21[illegible]9	0.2476	0.2757	0.3018
			h_g	...	1060.7	1180.1	1213.8	1242.2	1267.2	1329.7	136[illegible]0	1441.8	1510.0	1574.3
3100.0	3085.3	700.31	$\bar{V}$	...	...	0.1320	0.1456	0.1571	0.1672	0.1926	0.20[illegible]0	0.2382	0.2657	0.2911
			h_g	...	...	1166.2	1202.9	1233.0	1259.3	1324.1	136[illegible]3	1438.4	1507.4	1572.1
3200.0	3185.3	705.11	$\bar{V}$	...	...	0.1226	0.1369	0.1486	0.1589	0.1843	0.19[illegible]6	0.2293	0.2563	0.2811
			h_g	...	...	1151.1	1191.4	1223.5	1251.1	1318.3	135[illegible]5	1434.9	1504.7	1569.9
3206.2	3191.5	705.40	$\bar{V}$	...	...	0.1220	0.1363	0.1480	0.1583	0.1838	0.19[illegible]1	0.2288	0.2557	0.2806
			h_g	...	...	1150.2	1190.6	1222.9	1250.5	1317.9	135[illegible]2	1434.7	1504.5	1569.8

Velocity of Liquids in Pipe

The mean velocity of any flowing liquid can be calculated from the following formula, or, from the nomograph on the opposite page. The nomograph is a graphical solution of the formula.

$$v = 183.3 \frac{q}{d^2} = 0.408 \frac{Q}{d^2} = 0.0509 \frac{W}{d^2 \rho}$$

(For values of d, see pages 166-174.)

The pressure drop per 100 feet and the velocity in Schedule 40 pipe, for water at 60°F, have been calculated for commonly used flow rates for pipe sizes of 1/8 to 24-inch; these values are tabulated on pages 156-159.

Example 1

Given: No. 3 Fuel Oil of 0.898 specific gravity at 60°F flows through a 2-inch Schedule 40 pipe at the rate of 45,000 pounds per hour.

Find: The rate of flow in gallons per minute and the mean velocity in the pipe.

Solution:

1. ρ = 56.02 = weight density in pounds per cubic foot (specific gravity of fluid times weight density of water at same temperature.)

	Connect		Read
2.	W = 45,000	ρ = 56.02	Q = **100**
3.	Q = 100	2″ Sched 40	v = **10**

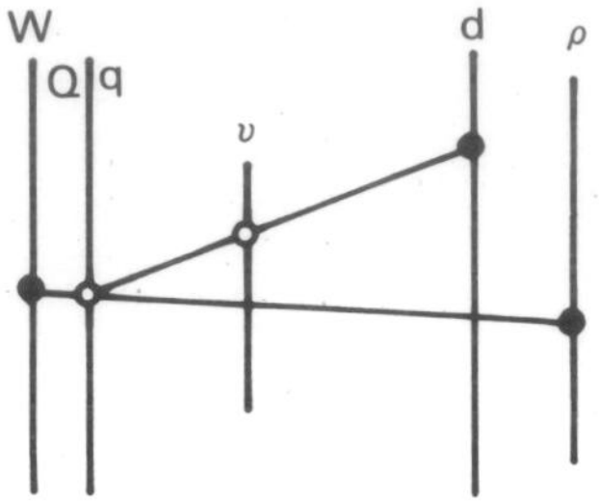

Example 2

Given: Maximum flow rate of a liquid will be 300 gallons per minute with maximum velocity limited to 12 feet per second through Schedule 40 pipe.

Find: The smallest suitable pipe size and the velocity through the pipe.

Solution:

	Connect		Read
1.	Q = 300	v = 12	d = 3.2
2.	**3-1/2″** Schedule 40 pipe suitable		
3.	Q = 300	3-1/2″ Sched 40	v = **10**

Reasonable Velocities For the Flow of Water through Pipe

Service Condition	Reasonable Velocity (feet per second)
Boiler Feed	8 to 15
Pump Suction and Drain Lines	4 to 7
General Service	4 to 10
City	to 7

Extracted from Technical Paper No. 410, *Flow of Fluids,* with permission of Crane Co.

Velocity of Liquids in Pipe (Continued)

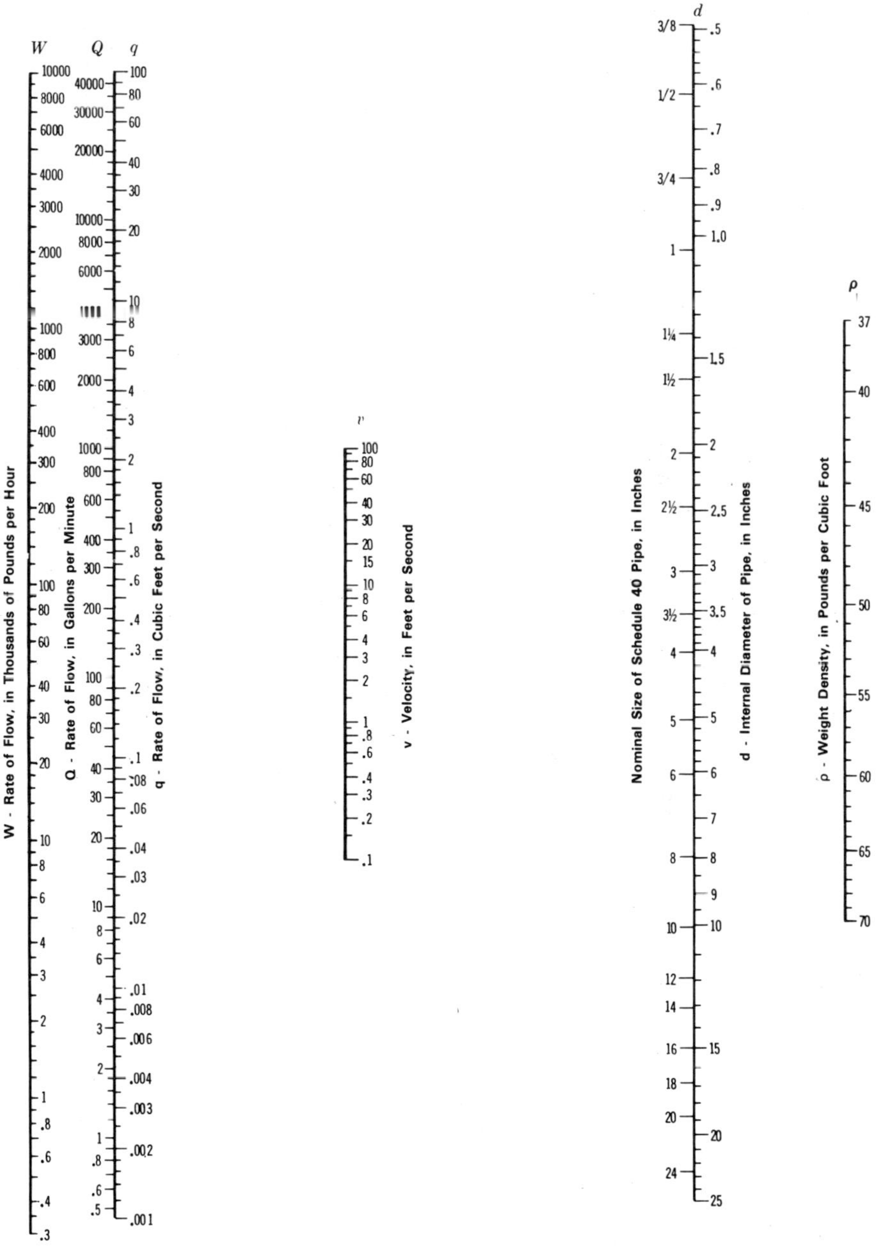

Flow of Water Through Schedule 40 Steel Pipe

DISCHARGE		PRESSURE DROP PER 100 FEET AND VELOCITY IN SCHEDULE 40 PIPE FOR WATER AT 60 F															
Gallons per Minute	Cubic Ft. per Second	Velocity (Feet per Sec.)	Press. Drop (PSI)	Velocity (Feet per Sec.)	Press. Drop (PSI)	Velocity (Feet per Sec.)	Press. Drop (PSI)	Velocity (Feet per Sec.)	Press. Drop (PSI)	Velocity (Feet per Sec.)	Press. Drop (PSI)	Velocity (Feet per Sec.)	Press. Drop (PSI)	Velocity (Feet per Sec.)	Press. Drop (PSI)	Velocity (Feet per Sec.)	Press. Drop (PSI)
		1/8"		1/4"		3/8"		1/2"									
.2	0.000446	1.13	1.86	0.616	0.359												
										3/4"							
.3	0.000668	1.69	4.22	0.924	0.903	0.504	0.159	0.317	0.061								
.4	0.000891	2.26	6.98	1.23	1.61	0.672	0.345	0.422	0.086								
.5	0.00111	2.82	10.5	1.54	2.39	0.840	0.539	0.528	0.167	0.301	0.033						
.6	0.00134	3.39	14.7	1.85	3.29	1.01	0.751	0.633	0.240	0.361	0.041						
												1"					
.8	0.00178	4.52	25.0	2.46	5.44	1.34	1.25	0.844	0.408	0.481	0.102						
														1-1/4"			
1	0.00223	5.65	37.2	3.08	8.28	1.68	1.85	1.06	0.600	0.602	0.155	0.371	0.048				
																1-1/2"	
2	0.00446	11.29	134.4	6.16	30.1	3.36	6.58	2.11	2.10	1.20	0.526	0.743	0.164	0.429	0.044		
3	0.00668			9.25	64.1	5.04	13.9	3.17	4.33	1.81	1.09	1.114	0.336	0.644	0.090	0.473	0.043
4	0.00891			12.33	111.2	6.72	23.9	4.22	7.42	2.41	1.83	1.49	0.565	0.858	0.150	0.630	0.071
		2"															
5	0.01114					8.40	36.7	5.28	11.2	3.01	2.75	1.86	0.835	1.073	0.223	0.788	0.104
				2-1/2"													
6	0.01337	0.574	0.044			10.08	51.9	6.33	15.8	3.61	3.84	2.23	1.17	1.29	0.309	0.946	0.145
8	0.01782	0.765	0.073			13.44	91.1	8.45	27.7	4.81	6.60	2.97	1.99	1.72	0.518	1.26	0.241
						3"											
10	0.02228	0.956	0.108	0.670	0.046			10.56	42.4	6.02	9.99	3.71	2.99	2.15	0.774	1.58	0.361
15	0.03342	1.43	0.224	1.01	0.094					9.03	21.6	5.57	6.36	3.22	1.63	2.37	0.755
20	0.04456	1.91	0.375	1.34	0.158	0.868	0.056			12.03	37.8	7.43	10.9	4.29	2.78	3.16	1.28
								3-1/2"		4"							
25	0.05570	2.39	0.561	1.68	0.234	1.09	0.083	0.812	0.041			9.28	16.7	5.37	4.22	3.94	1.93
30	0.06684	2.87	0.786	2.01	0.327	1.30	0.114	0.974	0.056			11.14	23.8	6.44	5.92	4.73	2.72
35	0.07798	3.35	1.05	2.35	0.436	1.52	0.151	1.14	0.071	0.882	0.041	12.99	32.2	7.51	7.90	5.52	3.64
40	0.08912	3.83	1.35	2.68	0.556	1.74	0.192	1.30	0.095	1.01	0.052	14.85	41.5	8.59	10.24	6.30	4.65
45	0.1003	4.30	1.67	3.02	0.668	1.95	0.239	1.46	0.117	1.13	0.064			9.67	12.80	7.09	5.85

- Continued -

(Continued from facing page.)

		(2″)		(2-1/2″)		(3″)		(3-1/2″)		(4″)				(1-1/4″)		(1-1/2″)	
50	**0.1114**	4.78	**2.03**	3.35	**0.839**	2.17	**0.288**	1.62	**0.142**	1.26	**0.076**	**5″**		10.74	**15.66**	7.88	**7.15**
60	**0.1337**	5.74	**2.87**	4.02	**1.18**	2.60	**0.46**	1.95	**0.204**	1.51	**0.107**			12.89	**22.2**	9.47	**10.21**
70	**0.1560**	6.70	**3.84**	4.69	**1.59**	3.04	**0.540**	2.27	**0.261**	1.76	**0.143**	1.12	**0.[illegible]47**			11.05	**13.71**
80	**0.1782**	7.65	**4.97**	5.36	**2.03**	3.47	**0.687**	2.60	**0.334**	2.02	**0.180**	1.28	**0.[illegible]60**			12.62	**17.59**
90	**0.2005**	8.60	**6.20**	6.03	**2.53**	3.91	**0.861**	2.92	**0.416**	2.27	**0.224**	1.44	**0.[illegible]74**			14.20	**22.0**
														6″			
100	**0.2228**	9.56	**7.59**	6.70	**3.09**	4.34	**1.05**	3.25	**0.509**	2.52	**0.272**	1.60	**0.[illegible]90**	1.11	**0.036**	15.78	**26.9**
125	**0.2785**	11.97	**11.76**	8.38	**4.71**	5.43	**1.61**	4.06	**0.769**	3.15	**0.415**	2.01	**0.[illegible]35**	1.39	**0.055**	19.72	**41.4**
150	**0.3342**	14.36	**16.70**	10.05	**6.69**	6.51	**2.24**	4.87	**1.08**	3.78	**0.580**	2.41	**0.[illegible]90**	1.67	**0.077**		
175	**0.3899**	16.75	**22.3**	11.73	**8.97**	7.60	**3.00**	5.68	**1.44**	4.41	**0.774**	2.81	**0.[illegible]53**	1.94	**0.102**		
200	**0.4456**	19.14	**28.8**	13.42	**11.68**	8.68	**3.87**	6.49	**1.85**	5.04	**0.985**	3.21	**0.[illegible]23**	2.22	**0.130**		
																8″	
225	**0.5013**	. . .	. . .	15.09	**14.63**	9.77	**4.83**	7.30	**2.32**	5.67	**1.23**	3.61	**0.[illegible]01**	2.50	**0.162**	1.44	**0.043**
250	**0.557**	. . .	. . .	. . .	. . .	10.85	**5.93**	8.12	**2.84**	6.30	**1.46**	4.01	**0.[illegible]95**	2.78	**0.195**	1.60	**0.051**
275	**0.6127**	. . .	. . .	. . .	. . .	11.94	**7.14**	8.93	**3.40**	6.93	**1.79**	4.41	**0.[illegible]83**	3.05	**0.234**	1.76	**0.061**
300	**0.6684**	. . .	. . .	. . .	. . .	13.00	**8.36**	9.74	**4.02**	7.56	**2.11**	4.81	**0.[illegible]83**	3.33	**0.275**	1.92	**0.072**
325	**0.7241**	. . .	. . .	. . .	. . .	14.12	**9.89**	10.53	**4.09**	8.19	**2.47**	5.21	**0.[illegible]97**	3.61	**0.320**	2.08	**0.083**
350	**0.7798**			. . .	. . .	. . .	. . .	11.36	**5.41**	8.82	**2.84**	5.62	**0.[illegible]19**	3.89	**0.367**	2.24	**0.095**
375	**0.8355**			. . .	. . .	. . .	. . .	12.17	**6.18**	9.45	**3.25**	6.02	**1.[illegible]5**	4.16	**0.416**	2.40	**0.108**
400	**0.8912**			. . .	. . .	. . .	. . .	12.98	**7.03**	10.08	**3.68**	6.42	**1.[illegible]9**	4.44	**0.471**	2.56	**0.121**
425	**0.9469**			. . .	. . .	. . .	. . .	13.80	**7.89**	10.71	**4.12**	6.82	**1.[illegible]3**	4.72	**0.529**	2.73	**0.136**
450	**1.003**	**10″**		. . .	. . .	. . .	. . .	14.61	**8.80**	11.34	**4.60**	7.22	**1.[illegible]3**	5.00	**0.590**	2.89	**0.151**
475	**1.059**	1.93	**0.054**			. . .	. . .	. . .	. . .	11.97	**5.12**	7.62	**1.[illegible]4**	5.27	**0.653**	3.04	**0.166**
500	**1.114**	2.03	**0.059**			. . .	. . .	. . .	. . .	12.60	**5.65**	8.02	**1.[illegible]**	5.55	**0.720**	3.21	**0.182**
550	**1.225**	2.24	**0.071**			. . .	. . .	. . .	. . .	13.85	**6.79**	8.82	**2.[illegible]7**	6.11	**0.861**	3.53	**0.219**
600	**1.337**	2.44	**0.083**			. . .	. . .	. . .	. . .	15.12	**8.04**	9.63	**2.[illegible]5**	6.66	**1.02**	3.85	**0.258**
650	**1.448**	2.64	**0.097**			. . .	. . .	. . .	. . .	. . .	. . .	10.43	**2.[illegible]3**	7.22	**1.18**	4.17	**0.301**

- Continued

Extracted from Technical Paper No. 410, *Flow of Fluids,* with permission of Crane Co.

Flow of Water Through Schedule 40 Steel Pipe (Continued)

DISCHARGE		PRESSURE DROP PER 100 FEET AND VELOCITY IN SCHEDULE 40 PIPE FOR WATER AT 60 F															
Gallons per Minute	Cubic Ft. per Second	Velocity (Feet per Sec.)	Press. Drop (PSI)	Velocity (Feet per Sec.)	Press. Drop (PSI)	Velocity (Feet per Sec.)	Press. Drop (PSI)	Velocity (Feet per Sec.)	Press. Drop (PSI)	Velocity (Feet per Sec.)	Press. Drop (PSI)	Velocity (Feet per Sec.)	Press. Drop (PSI)	Velocity (Feet per Sec.)	Press. Drop (PSI)	Velocity (Feet per Sec.)	Press. Drop (PSI)
		10″		12″								5″		6″		8″	
700	1.560	2.85	**0.112**	2.01	**0.047**			...	...	...	...	11.23	**3.43**	7.78	**1.35**	4.49	**0.343**
750	1.671	3.05	**0.127**	2.15	**0.054**	14″		...	...	...	...	12.03	**3.92**	8.33	**1.55**	4.81	**0.392**
800	1.782	3.25	**0.143**	2.29	**0.061**			...	...	...	...	12.83	**4.43**	8.88	**1.75**	5.13	**0.443**
850	1.894	3.46	**0.160**	2.44	**0.068**	2.02	**0.042**	...	...	...	...	13.64	**5.00**	9.44	**1.96**	5.45	**0.497**
900	2.005	3.66	**0.179**	2.58	**0.075**	2.13	**0.047**	...	...	...	...	14.44	**5.58**	9.99	**2.18**	5.77	**0.554**
950	2.117	3.86	**0.198**	2.72	**0.083**	2.25	**0.052**			...	...	15.24	**6.21**	10.55	**2.42**	6.09	**0.613**
1000	2.228	4.07	**0.218**	2.87	**0.091**	2.37	**0.057**			...	...	16.04	**6.84**	11.10	**2.68**	6.41	**0.675**
1100	2.451	4.48	**0.260**	3.15	**0.110**	2.61	**0.068**	16″		...	...	17.65	**8.23**	12.22	**3.22**	7.05	**0.807**
1200	2.674	4.88	**0.306**	3.44	**0.128**	2.85	**0.080**	2.18	**0.042**	...	...	...	...	13.33	**3.81**	7.70	**.948**
1300	2.896	5.29	**0.355**	3.73	**0.150**	3.08	**0.093**	2.36	**0.048**	...	...	...	...	14.43	**4.45**	8.33	**1.11**
1400	3.119	5.70	**0.409**	4.01	**0.171**	3.32	**0.107**	2.54	**0.055**					15.55	**5.13**	8.98	**1.28**
1500	3.342	6.10	**0.466**	4.30	**0.195**	3.56	**0.122**	2.72	**0.063**	18″				16.66	**5.85**	9.62	**1.46**
1600	3.565	6.51	**0.527**	4.59	**0.219**	3.79	**0.138**	2.90	**0.071**					17.77	**6.61**	10.26	**1.65**
1800	4.010	7.32	**0.663**	5.16	**0.276**	4.27	**0.172**	3.27	**0.088**	2.58	**0.050**			19.99	**8.37**	11.54	**2.08**
2000	4.456	8.14	**0.808**	5.73	**0.339**	4.74	**0.209**	3.63	**0.107**	2.87	**0.060**			22.21	**10.3**	12.82	**2.55**
												20″					
2500	5.570	10.17	**1.24**	7.17	**0.515**	5.93	**0.321**	4.54	**0.163**	3.59	**0.091**					16.03	**3.94**
3000	6.684	12.20	**1.76**	8.60	**0.731**	7.11	**0.451**	5.45	**0.232**	4.30	**0.129**	3.46	**0.075**	24″		19.24	**5.59**
3500	7.798	14.24	**2.38**	10.03	**0.982**	8.30	**0.607**	6.35	**0.312**	5.02	**0.173**	4.04	**0.101**			22.44	**7.56**
4000	8.912	16.27	**3.08**	11.47	**1.27**	9.48	**0.787**	7.26	**0.401**	5.74	**0.222**	4.62	**0.129**	3.19	**0.052**	25.65	**9.80**
4500	10.03	18.31	**3.87**	12.90	**1.60**	10.67	**0.990**	8.17	**0.503**	6.46	**0.280**	5.20	**0.162**	3.59	**0.065**	28.87	**12.2**

- Continued -

(Continued from facing page.)

		(10″)		(12″)		(14″)		(16″)		(18″)		(20″)		(24″)			
5000	**11.14**	20.35	**4.71**	14.33	**1.95**	11.85	**1.21**	9.08	**0.617**	7.17	**0.340**	5.77	**0.199**	3.99	**0.079**	...	...
6000	**13.37**	24.41	**6.74**	17.20	**2.77**	14.23	**1.71**	10.89	**0.877**	8.61	**0.483**	6.93	**0.280**	4.79	**0.111**	...	...
7000	**15.60**	28.49	**9.11**	20.07	**3.74**	16.60	**2.31**	12.71	**1.18**	10.04	**0.652**	8.08	**0.376**	5.59	**0.150**	...	...
8000	**17.82**	...	...	22.93	**4.84**	18.96	**2.99**	14.52	**1.51**	11.47	**0.839**	9.23	**0.488**	6.38	**0.192**	...	...
9000	**20.05**	...	...	25.79	**6.09**	21.34	**3.76**	16.34	**1.90**	12.91	**1.05**	10.39	**0.608**	7.18	**0.242**	...	...
10,000	**22.28**	...	...	28.66	**7.46**	23.71	**4.61**	18.15	**2.34**	14.34	**1.28**	11.54	**0.739**	7.98	**0.294**	...	...
12,000	**26.74**	...	...	34.40	**10.7**	28.45	**6.59**	21.79	**3.33**	17.21	**1.83**	13.85	**1.06**	9.58	**0.416**	...	...
14,000	**31.19**	...	...	...	...	33.19	**8.89**	25.42	**4.49**	20.08	**2.45**	16.16	**1.43**	11.17	**0.562**	...	...
16,000	**35.65**	...	...	...	...	...	...	29.05	**5.83**	22.95	**3.18**	18.47	**1.85**	12.77	**0.723**	...	...
18,000	**40.10**	...	...	...	...	...	...	32.68	**7.31**	25.82	**4.03**	20.77	**2.32**	14.36	**0.907**	...	...
20,000	**44.56**	...	...	...	...	...	...	36.31	**9.03**	28.69	**4.93**	23.08	**2.86**	15.96	**1.12**	...	...

For pipe lengths other than 100 feet, the pressure drop is proportional to the length. Thus, for 50 feet of pipe, the pressure drop is approximately one-half the value given in the table . . . for 300 feet, three times the given value, etc.

Velocity is a function of the cross sectional flow area; thus, it is constant for a given flow rate and is independent of pipe length.

For calculations for pipe other than Schedule 40, see explanation on page 161.

For lengths of pipe other than 100 feet, the pressure drop is proportional to the length. Thus, for 50 feet of pipe, the pressure drop is approximately one-half the value given in the table . . . for 300 feet, three times the given value, etc.

The pressure drop is also inversely proportional to the absolute pressure and directly proportional to the absolute temperature.

Therefore, to determine the pressure drop for inlet or average pressures other than 100 psi and at temperatures other than 60°F, multiply the values given in the table by the ratio:

$$\left(\frac{100 + 14.7}{P + 14.7}\right) \left(\frac{460 + t}{520}\right)$$

where:

"P" is the inlet or average gauge pressure in pounds per square inch, and,

"t" is the temperature in degrees Fahrenheit under consideration.

The cubic feet per minute of compressed air at any pressure is inversely proportional to the absolute pressure and directly proportional to the absolute temperature.

Flow of Air Through Schedule 40 Steel Pipe

FREE AIR q'm Cubic Feet Per Minute at 60°F and 14.7 psia	COMPRESSED AIR Cubic Feet Per Minute at 60°F and 100 psig	PRESSURE DROP OF AIR IN POUNDS PER SQUARE INCH PER 100 FEET OF SCHEDULE 40 PIPE FOR AIR AT 100 POUNDS PER SQUARE INCH GAUGE PRESSURE AND 60°F TEMPERATURE								
		1/8″	1/4″	3/8″	1/2″	3/4″	1″	1-1/4″	1-1/2″	2″
1	**0.128**	0.361	0.083	0.018						
2	**0.256**	1.31	0.285	0.064	0.020					
3	**0.384**	3.06	0.605	0.133	0.042					
4	**0.513**	4.83	1.04	0.226	0.071					
5	**0.641**	7.45	1.58	0.343	0.106	0.027				
6	**0.769**	10.6	2.23	0.408	0.148	0.037				
8	**1.025**	18.6	3.89	0.848	0.255	0.062	0.019			
10	**1.282**	28.7	5.96	1.26	0.356	0.094	0.029			
15	**1.922**	. . .	13.0	2.73	0.834	0.201	0.062			
20	**2.563**	. . .	22.8	4.76	1.43	0.345	0.102	0.026		
25	**3.204**	. . .	35.6	7.34	2.21	0.526	0.156	0.039	0.019	
30	**3.845**	. . .	. . .	10.5	3.15	0.748	0.219	0.055	0.026	
35	**4.486**	. . .	. . .	14.2	4.24	1.00	0.293	0.073	0.035	
40	**5.126**	. . .	. . .	18.4	5.49	1.30	0.379	0.095	0.044	
45	**5.767**	. . .	. . .	23.1	6.90	1.62	0.474	0.116	0.055	
50	**6.408**			28.5	8.49	1.99	0.578	0.149	0.067	0.019
60	**7.690**	2-1/2″		40.7	12.2	2.85	0.819	0.200	0.094	0.027
70	**8.971**			. . .	16.5	3.83	1.10	0.270	0.126	0.036
80	**10.25**	0.019		. . .	21.4	4.96	1.43	0.350	0.162	0.046
90	**11.53**	0.023		. . .	27.0	6.25	1.80	0.437	0.203	0.058

(Continued on facing page.)

To determine the cubic feet per minute of compressed air at any temperature and pressure other than standard conditions, multiply the value of cubic feet per minute of free air by the ratio:

$$\left(\frac{14.7}{14.7 + P}\right)\left(\frac{460 + t}{520}\right)$$

Calculations for Pipe Other than Schedule 40

To determine the velocity of water, or the pressure drop of water or air, through pipe other than Schedule 40, use the following formulas:

$$v_a = v_{40}\left(\frac{d_{40}}{d_a}\right)^2$$

$$\Delta P_a = \Delta P_{40}\left(\frac{d_{40}}{d_a}\right)^5$$

Subscript "*a*" refers to the Schedule of pipe through which velocity or pressure drop is desired.

Subscript "40" refers to the velocity or pressure drop through Schedule 40 pipe, as given in the tables on pages 156 through 163.

Extracted from Technical Paper No. 410, *Flow of Fluids*, with permission of Crane Co.

		(2-1/2")			(1/2")	(3/4")	(1")	(1-1/4")	(1-1/2")	(2")
100	12.82	0.029			33.2	7.6[illegible]	2.21	0.534	0.247	0.070
			3"							
125	16.02	0.044			...	11.9	3.39	0.825	0.380	0.107
150	19.22	0.062	0.021		...	17.0	4.87	1.17	0.537	0.151
175	22.43	0.083	0.028		...	23.1	6.60	1.58	0.727	0.205
200	25.63	0.107	0.036		...	30.0	8.54	2.05	0.937	0.264
				3-1/2"						
225	28.84	0.134	0.045	0.022		37.9	10.8	2.59	1.19	0.331
250	32.04	0.164	0.055	0.027		...	13.3	3.18	1.45	0.404
275	35.24	0.191	0.066	0.032		...	16.0	3.83	1.75	0.484
300	38.45	0.232	0.078	0.037		...	19.0	4.56	2.07	0.573
325	41.65	0.270	0.090	0.043		...	22.3	5.32	2.42	0.673
					4"					
350	44.87	0.313	0.104	0.050		...	25.8	6.17	2.80	0.776
375	48.06	0.356	0.119	0.057	0.030	...	29.6	7.05	3.20	0.887
400	51.26	0.402	0.134	0.064	0.034	...	33.6	8.02	3.64	1.00
425	54.47	0.452	0.151	0.072	0.038	...	37.9	9.01	4.09	1.13
450	57.67	0.507	0.168	0.081	0.042	...	...	10.2	4.59	1.26
475	60.88	0.562	0.187	0.089	0.047		...	11.3	5.09	1.40
500	64.08	0.623	0.206	0.099	0.052		...	12.5	5.61	1.55
550	70.49	0.749	0.248	0.118	0.062		...	15.1	6.79	1.87
600	76.90	0.887	0.293	0.139	0.073		...	18.0	8.04	2.21
650	83.30	1.04	0.342	0.163	0.086		...	21.1	9.43	2.60
						5"				
700	89.71	1.19	0.395	0.188	0.099	0.03[illegible]		24.3	10.9	3.00
750	96.12	1.36	0.451	0.214	0.113	0.03[illegible]		27.9	12.6	3.44
800	102.5	1.55	0.513	0.244	0.127	0.04[illegible]		31.8	14.2	3.90
850	108.9	1.74	0.576	0.274	0.144	0.04[illegible]		35.9	16.0	4.40
900	115.3	1.95	0.642	0.305	0.160	0.05[illegible]		40.2	18.0	4.91
							6"			
950	121.8	2.18	0.715	0.340	0.178	0.05[illegible]	0.023	...	20.0	5.47
1,000	128.2	2.40	0.788	0.375	0.197	0.06[illegible]	0.025	...	22.1	6.06
1,100	141.0	2.89	0.948	0.451	0.236	0.07[illegible]	0.030	...	26.7	7.29
1,200	153.8	3.44	1.13	0.533	0.279	0.08[illegible]	0.035	...	31.8	8.63
1,300	166.6	4.01	1.32	0.626	0.327	0.10[illegible]	0.041	...	37.3	10.1

- Continued -

Flow of Air Through Schedule 40 Steel Pipe (Continued)

FREE AIR q′m	COMPRESSED AIR	PRESSURE DROP OF AIR IN POUNDS PER SQUARE INCH PER 100 FEET OF SCHEDULE 40 PIPE FOR AIR AT 100 POUNDS PER SQUARE INCH GAUGE PRESSURE AND 60°F TEMPERATURE								
Cubic Feet Per Minute at 60°F and 14.7 psia	Cubic Feet Per Minute at 60°F and 100 psig	2-1/2″	3″	3-1/2″	4″	5″	6″	8″	10″	2″
1,400	179.4	4.65	1.52	0.718	0.377	0.119	0.047			11.8
1,500	192.2	5.31	1.74	0.824	0.431	0.136	0.054			13.5
1,600	205.1	6.04	1.97	0.932	0.490	0.154	0.061			15.3
1,800	230.7	7.65	2.50	1.18	0.616	0.193	0.075			19.3
2,000	256.3	9.44	3.06	1.45	0.757	0.237	0.094	0.023		23.9
2,500	320.4	14.7	4.76	2.25	1.17	0.366	0.143	0.035		37.3
3,000	384.5	21.1	6.82	3.20	1.67	0.524	0.204	0.051	0.016	
3,500	448.6	28.8	9.23	4.33	2.26	0.709	0.276	0.068	0.022	
4,000	512.6	37.6	12.1	5.66	2.94	0.919	0.358	0.088	0.028	
4,500	576.7	47.6	15.3	7.16	3.69	1.16	0.450	0.111	0.035	
										12″
5,000	640.8	...	18.8	8.85	4.56	1.42	0.552	0.136	0.043	0.018
6,000	769.0	...	27.1	12.7	6.57	2.03	0.794	0.195	0.061	0.025
7,000	897.1	...	36.9	17.2	8.94	2.76	1.07	0.262	0.082	0.034
8,000	1025	...	...	22.5	11.7	3.59	1.39	0.339	0.107	0.044
9,000	1153	...	...	28.5	14.9	4.54	1.76	0.427	0.134	0.055
10,000	1282	...	...	35.2	18.4	5.60	2.16	0.526	0.164	0.067
11,000	1410	...	...	...	22.2	6.78	2.62	0.633	0.197	0.081
12,000	1538	...	...	...	26.4	8.07	3.09	0.753	0.234	0.096
13,000	1666	...	...	...	31.0	9.47	3.63	0.884	0.273	0.112
14,000	1794	...	...	...	36.0	11.0	4.21	1.02	0.316	0.129

- Continued -

(Continued from facing page.)

						(5″)	(6″)	(8″)	(10″)	(12″)
15,000	**1922**	...	...	...	...	12.6	4.84	1.17	0.3[illegible]4	0.148
16,000	**2051**	...	...	...	...	14.3	5.50	1.33	0.4[illegible]1	0.167
18,000	**2307**	...	...	...	...	18.2	6.96	1.68	0.5[illegible]0	0.213
20,000	**2563**	...	...	...	...	22.4	8.60	2.01	0.6[illegible]2	0.260
22,000	**2820**	...	...	...	...	27.1	10.4	2.50	0.7[illegible]1	0.314
24,000	**3076**	...	...	...	...	32.3	12.4	2.97	0.9[illegible]8	0.371
26,000	**3332**	...	...	...	...	37.9	14.5	3.49	1.1[illegible]	0.435
28,000	**3588**	...	...	...	...	...	16.9	4.04	1.2[illegible]	0.505
30,000	**3845**	...	...	...	...	...	19.3	4.64	1.4[illegible]	0.520

Extracted from Technical Paper No. 410, *Flow of Fluids,* with permission of Crane Co.

Section 8

Pipe Data

Pipe Engagement
Length of Thread on Pipe to Make a Tight Joint

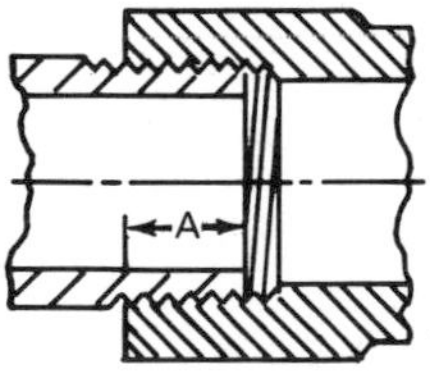

Nominal Pipe Size (Inches)	Dimension A (Inches)	Nominal Pipe Size (Inches)	Dimension A (Inches)
1/8	1/4	1-1/2	11/16
1/4	3/8	2	3/4
3/8	3/8	2-1/2	15/16
1/2	1/2	3	1
3/4	9/16	4	1-1/8
1	11/16	5	1-1/4
1-1/4	11/16	6	1-5/16

Dimensions do not allow for variation in tapping or threading.

Drill Sizes for Pipe Taps

Nominal Pipe Size (Inches)	Tap Drill Size (Inches)	Nominal Pipe Size (Inches)	Tap Drill Size (Inches)
1/8	11/32	1-1/2	1-23/32
1/4	7/16	2	2-3/16
3/8	19/32	2-1/2	2-9/16
1/2	23/32	3	3-3/16
3/4	15/16	4	4-3/16
1	1-5/32	5	5-5/16
1-1/4	1-1/2	6	6-5/16

Pipe Data

Carbon and Alloy Steel—Stainless Steel

Identification, wall thickness and weights are extracted from ANSI B36.10 and B39.19. The notations STD, XS, and XXS indicate Standard, Extra Strong, and Double Extra Strong pipe respectively.

Transverse internal area values listed in "square feet" also represent volume in cubic feet per foot of pipe length.

NOMINAL PIPE SIZE (INCHES)	OUTSIDE DIAM. (INCHES)	IDENTIFICATION			WALL THICK-NESS (t) (INCHES)	INSIDE DIAM-ETER (d) (INCHES)	AREA OF METAL (SQUARE INCHES)	TRANSVERSE INTERNAL AREA		WEIGHT PIPE (POUNDS PER FOOT)	WEIGHT WATER (POUNDS PER FOOT OF PIPE)
		Steel		Stainless Steel Sched. No.				(a) (Square Inches)	(A) (Square Feet)		
		Iron Pipe Size	Sched. No.								
1/8	0.405	...	...	10S	0.049	0.307	0.0548	0.0740	0.00051	0.19	0.032
		STD	40	40S	0.068	0.269	0.0720	0.0568	0.00040	0.24	0.025
		XS	80	80S	0.095	0.215	0.0925	0.0364	0.00025	0.31	0.016
1/4	0.540	...	...	10S	0.065	0.410	0.0970	0.1320	0.00091	0.33	0.057
		STD	40	40S	0.088	0.364	0.1250	0.1041	0.00072	0.42	0.045
		XS	80	80S	0.119	0.302	0.1574	0.0716	0.00050	0.54	0.031
3/8	0.675	...	...	10S	0.065	0.545	0.1246	0.2333	0.00162	0.42	0.101
		STD	40	40S	0.091	0.493	0.1670	0.1910	0.00133	0.57	0.083
		XS	80	80S	0.126	0.423	0.2173	0.1405	0.00098	0.74	0.061
1/2	0.840	...	...	5S	0.065	0.710	0.1583	0.3959	0.00275	0.54	0.172
		...	...	10S	0.083	0.674	0.1974	0.3568	0.00248	0.67	0.155
		STD	40	40S	0.109	0.622	0.2503	0.3040	0.00211	0.85	0.132
		XS	80	80S	0.147	0.546	0.3200	0.2340	0.00163	1.09	0.102
		...	160	...	0.187	0.466	0.3836	0.1706	0.00118	1.31	0.074
		XXS	...	...	0.294	0.252	0.5043	0.050	0.00035	1.71	0.022

3/4	1.050	...	...	5S	0.065	0.920	0.2011	0.6648	0.00462	0.69	0.288
		...	...	10S	0.083	0.884	0.2521	0.6138	0.00426	0.86	0.266
		STD	40	40S	0.113	0.824	0.3326	0.5330	0.00371	1.13	0.231
		XS	80	80S	0.154	0.742	0.4335	0.4330	0.00300	1.47	0.188
		...	160	...	0.219	0.612	0.5698	0.2961	0.00206	1.94	0.128
		XXS	...	...	0.308	0.434	0.7180	0.148	0.00103	2.44	0.064
1	1.315	...	...	5S	0.065	1.185	0.2553	1.1029	0.00766	0.87	0.478
		...	...	10S	0.109	1.097	0.4130	0.9452	0.00656	1.40	0.409
		STD	40	40S	0.133	1.049	0.4939	0.8640	0.00600	1.68	0.375
		XS	80	80S	0.179	0.957	0.6388	0.7190	0.00499	2.17	0.312
		...	160	...	0.250	0.815	0.8365	0.5217	0.00362	2.84	0.230
		XXS	...	...	0.358	0.599	1.0760	0.282	0.00196	3.66	0.122
1-1/4	1.660	...	...	5S	0.065	1.530	0.3257	1.839	0.01277	1.11	0.797
		...	...	10S	0.109	1.442	0.4717	1.633	0.01134	1.81	0.708
		STD	40	40S	0.140	1.380	0.6685	1.495	0.01040	2.27	0.649
		XS	80	80S	0.191	1.278	0.8815	1.283	0.00891	3.00	0.555
		...	160	...	0.250	1.160	1.1070	1.057	0.00734	3.76	0.458
		XXS	...	...	0.382	0.896	1.534	0.630	0.00438	5.21	0.273
1-1/2	1.900	...	...	5S	0.065	1.770	0.3747	2.461	0.01709	1.28	1.066
		...	...	10S	0.109	1.682	0.6133	2.222	0.01543	2.09	0.963
		STD	40	40S	0.145	1.610	0.7995	2.036	0.01414	2.72	0.882
		XS	80	80S	0.200	1.500	1.068	1.767	0.01225	3.63	0.765
		...	160	...	0.281	1.338	1.429	1.406	0.00976	4.86	0.608
		XXS	...	...	0.400	1.100	1.885	0.950	0.00660	6.41	0.42
2	2.375	...	...	5S	0.065	2.245	0.4717	3.958	0.02749	1.61	1.72
		...	...	10S	0.109	2.157	0.7760	3.654	0.02538	2.64	1.58
		STD	40	40S	0.154	2.067	1.075	3.355	0.02330	3.65	1.45
		XS	80	80S	0.218	1.939	1.477	2.953	0.02050	5.02	1.28
		...	160	...	0.344	1.687	2.190	2.241	0.01556	7.46	0.97
		XXS	...	...	0.436	1.503	2.656	1.774	0.01232	9.03	0.77

- Continued -

Extracted from Technical Paper No. 410, *Flow of Fluids,* with permission of Crane Co.

Pipe Data

Carbon and Alloy Steel—Stainless Steel

NOMINAL PIPE SIZE (INCHES)	OUTSIDE DIAM. (INCHES)	IDENTIFICATION			WALL THICKNESS (t) (INCHES)	INSIDE DIAMETER (d) (INCHES)	AREA OF METAL (SQUARE INCHES)	TRANSVERSE INTERNAL AREA		WEIGHT PIPE (POUNDS PER FOOT)	WEIGHT WATER (POUNDS PER FOOT OF PIPE)
		Steel		Stainless Steel Sched. No.				(a) (Square Inches)	(A) (Square Feet)		
		Iron Pipe Size	Sched. No.								
2-1/2	2.875	...	...	5S	0.083	2.709	0.7280	5.764	0.04002	2.48	2.50
		...	...	10S	0.120	2.635	1.039	5.453	0.03787	3.53	2.36
		STD	40	40S	0.203	2.469	1.704	4.788	0.03322	5.79	2.07
		XS	80	80S	0.276	2.323	2.254	4.238	0.02942	7.66	1.87
		...	160	...	0.375	2.125	2.945	3.546	0.02463	10.01	1.54
		XXS	...	...	0.552	1.771	4.028	2.464	0.01710	13.69	1.07
3	3.500	...	...	5S	0.083	3.334	0.8910	8.730	0.06063	3.03	3.78
		...	...	10S	0.120	3.260	1.274	8.347	0.05796	4.33	3.62
		STD	40	40S	0.216	3.068	2.228	7.393	0.05130	7.58	3.20
		XS	80	80S	0.300	2.900	3.016	6.605	0.04587	10.25	2.86
		...	160	...	0.438	2.624	4.205	5.408	0.03755	14.32	2.35
		XXS	...	...	0.600	2.300	5.466	4.155	0.02885	18.58	1.80
3-1/2	4.000	...	...	5S	0.083	3.834	1.021	11.545	0.08017	3.48	5.00
		...	...	10S	0.120	3.760	1.463	11.104	0.07711	4.97	4.81
		STD	40	40S	0.226	3.548	2.680	9.886	0.06870	9.11	4.29
		XS	80	80S	0.318	3.364	3.678	8.888	0.06170	12.50	3.84
4	4.500	...	...	5S	0.083	4.334	1.152	14.75	0.10245	3.92	6.39
		...	...	10S	0.120	4.260	1.651	14.25	0.09898	5.61	6.18
		STD	40	40S	0.237	4.026	3.174	12.73	0.08840	10.79	5.50
		XS	80	80S	0.337	3.826	4.407	11.50	0.07986	14.98	4.98
		...	120	...	0.438	3.624	5.595	10.31	0.0716	19.00	4.47
		...	160	...	0.531	3.438	6.621	9.28	0.0645	22.51	4.02
		XXS	...	...	0.674	3.152	8.101	7.80	0.0542	27.54	3.38

5	5.563	. . .	. . .	5S	0.109	5.345	1.868	22.44	0.1558	6.36	9.72
		. . .	. . .	10S	0.134	5.295	2.285	22.02	0.1529	7.77	9.54
		STD	40	40S	0.258	5.047	4.300	20.01	0.1390	14.62	8.67
		XS	80	80S	0.375	4.813	6.112	18.19	0.1263	20.78	7.88
		. . .	120	. . .	0.500	4.563	7.953	16.35	0.1136	27.04	7.09
		. . .	160	. . .	0.625	4.313	9.696	14.61	0.1015	32.96	6.33
		XXS	. . .	. . .	0.750	4.063	11.340	12.97	0.0901	38.55	5.61
6	6.625	. . .	. . .	5S	0.109	6.407	2.231	32.24	0.2239	7.60	13.97
		. . .	. . .	10S	0.134	6.357	2.733	31.74	0.2204	9.29	13.75
		STD	40	40S	0.280	6.065	5.581	28.89	0.2006	18.97	12.51
		XS	80	80S	0.432	5.761	8.405	26.07	0.1810	28.57	11.29
		. . .	120	. . .	0.562	5.501	10.70	23.77	0.1650	36.39	10.30
		. . .	160	. . .	0.719	5.187	13.32	21.15	0.1469	45.35	9.16
		XXS	. . .	. . .	0.864	4.897	15.64	18.84	0.1308	53.16	8.16
8	8.625	. . .	. . .	5S	0.109	8.407	2.916	55.51	0.3855	9.93	24.06
		. . .	. . .	10S	0.148	8.329	3.941	54.48	0.3784	13.40	23.61
		. . .	20	. . .	0.250	8.125	6.57	51.85	0.3601	22.36	22.47
		. . .	30	. . .	0.277	8.071	7.26	51.16	0.3553	24.70	22.17
		STD	40	40S	0.322	7.981	8.40	50.03	0.3474	28.55	21.70
		. . .	60	. . .	0.406	7.813	10.48	47.94	0.3329	35.64	20.77
		XS	80	80S	0.500	7.625	12.76	45.66	0.3171	43.39	19.78
		. . .	100	. . .	0.594	7.437	14.96	43.46	0.3018	50.95	18.83
		. . .	120	. . .	0.719	7.187	17.84	40.59	0.2819	60.71	17.59
		. . .	140	. . .	0.812	7.001	19.93	38.50	0.2673	67.76	16.68
		XXS	. . .	. . .	0.875	6.875	21.30	37.12	0.2578	72.42	16.10
		. . .	160	. . .	0.906	6.813	21.97	36.46	0.2532	74.69	15.80
10 (Cont.)	10.750	. . .	. . .	5S	0.134	10.482	4.36	86.29	0.5992	15.19	37.39
		. . .	. . .	10S	0.165	10.420	5.49	85.28	0.5922	18.65	36.95
		. . .	20	. . .	0.250	10.250	8.24	82.52	0.5731	28.04	35.76
		. . .	30	. . .	0.307	10.136	10.07	80.69	0.5603	34.24	34.96
		STD	40	40S	0.365	10.020	11.90	78.86	0.5475	40.48	34.20

- Continued -

Extracted from Technical Paper No. 410, *Flow of Fluids,* with permission of Crane Co.

Pipe Data

Carbon and Alloy Steel—Stainless Steel

NOMINAL PIPE SIZE (INCHES)	OUTSIDE DIAM. (INCHES)	IDENTIFICATION			WALL THICK-NESS (t) (INCHES)	INSIDE DIAM-ETER (d) (INCHES)	AREA OF METAL (SQUARE INCHES)	TRANSVERSE INTERNAL AREA		WEIGHT PIPE (POUNDS PER FOOT)	WEIGHT WATER (POUNDS PER FOOT OF PIPE)
		Steel		Stainless Steel Sched. No.				(a) (Square Inches)	(A) (Square Feet)		
		Iron Pipe Size	Sched. No.								
10 (Cont.)	10.750	XS	60	80S	0.500	9.750	16.10	74.66	0.5185	54.74	32.35
		. . .	80	. . .	0.594	9.562	18.92	71.84	0.4989	64.43	31.13
		. . .	100	. . .	0.719	9.312	22.63	68.13	0.4732	77.03	29.53
		. . .	120	. . .	0.844	9.062	26.24	64.53	0.4481	89.29	27.96
		XXS	140	. . .	1.000	8.750	30.63	60.13	0.4176	104.13	26.06
		. . .	160	. . .	1.125	8.500	34.02	56.75	0.3941	115.64	24.59
12	12.75	. . .	. . .	5S	0.156	12.438	6.17	121.50	0.8438	20.98	52.65
		. . .	. . .	10S	0.180	12.390	7.11	120.57	0.8373	24.17	52.25
		. . .	20	. . .	0.250	12.250	9.82	117.86	0.8185	33.38	51.07
		. . .	30	. . .	0.330	12.090	12.87	114.80	0.7972	43.77	49.74
		STD	. . .	40S	0.375	12.000	14.58	113.10	0.7854	49.56	49.00
		. . .	40	. . .	0.406	11.938	15.77	111.93	0.7773	53.52	48.50
		XS	. . .	80S	0.500	11.750	19.24	108.43	0.7528	65.42	46.92
		. . .	60	. . .	0.562	11.626	21.52	106.16	0.7372	73.15	46.00
		. . .	80	. . .	0.688	11.374	26.03	101.64	0.7058	88.63	44.04
		. . .	100	. . .	0.844	11.062	31.53	96.14	0.6677	107.32	41.66
		XXS	120	. . .	1.000	10.750	36.91	90.76	0.6303	125.49	39.33
		. . .	140	. . .	1.125	10.500	41.08	86.59	0.6013	139.67	37.52
		. . .	160	. . .	1.312	10.126	47.14	80.53	0.5592	160.27	34.89
14 (Cont.)	14.00	. . .	. . .	5S	0.156	13.688	6.78	147.15	1.0219	23.07	63.77
		. . .	. . .	10S	0.188	13.624	8.16	145.78	1.0124	27.73	63.17
		. . .	10	. . .	0.250	13.500	10.80	143.14	0.9940	36.71	62.03
		. . .	20	. . .	0.312	13.376	13.42	140.52	0.9758	45.61	60.89
		STD	30	. . .	0.375	13.250	16.05	137.88	0.9575	54.57	59.75
		. . .	40	. . .	0.438	13.124	18.66	135.28	0.9394	63.44	58.64

14 (Cont.)	14.00	XS	...	...	0.500	13.000	21.21	132.73	0.[illegible]217	72.09	57.46
		...	60	...	0.594	12.812	24.98	128.96	0.[illegible]956	85.05	55.86
		...	80	...	0.750	12.500	31.22	122.72	0.[illegible]522	106.13	53.18
		...	100	...	0.938	12.124	38.45	115.49	0.[illegible]020	130.85	50.04
		...	120	...	1.094	11.812	44.32	109.62	0.[illegible]612	150.79	47.45
		...	140	...	1.250	11.500	50.07	103.87	0.[illegible]213	170.28	45.01
		...	160	...	1.406	11.188	55.63	98.31	0.[illegible]827	189.11	42.60
16	16.00	...	...	5S	0.165	15.670	8.21	192.85	1.[illegible]393	27.90	83.57
		...	...	10S	0.188	15.624	9.34	191.72	1.[illegible]314	31.75	83.08
		...	10	...	0.250	15.500	12.37	188.69	1.[illegible]103	42.05	81.74
		...	20	...	0.312	15.376	15.38	185.69	1.[illegible]895	52.27	80.50
		STD	30	...	0.375	15.250	18.41	182.65	1.[illegible]684	62.58	79.12
		XS	40	...	0.500	15.000	24.35	176.72	1.[illegible]272	82.77	76.58
		...	60	...	0.656	14.688	31.62	169.44	1.[illegible]766	107.50	73.42
		...	80	...	0.844	14.312	40.14	160.92	1.[illegible]175	136.61	69.73
		...	100	...	1.031	13.938	48.48	152.58	1.[illegible]596	164.82	66.12
		...	120	...	1.219	13.562	56.56	144.50	1.[illegible]035	192.43	62.62
		...	140	...	1.438	13.124	65.78	135.28	0.[illegible]394	223.64	58.64
		...	160	...	1.594	12.812	72.10	128.96	0.[illegible]956	245.25	55.83
18	18.00	...	...	5S	0.165	17.670	9.25	245.22	1.[illegible]029	31.43	106.26
		...	...	10S	0.188	17.624	10.52	243.95	1.[illegible]941	35.76	105.71
		...	10	...	0.250	17.500	13.94	240.53	1.[illegible]703	47.39	104.21
		...	20	...	0.312	17.376	17.34	237.13	1.[illegible]467	58.94	102.77
		STD	...	...	0.375	17.250	20.76	233.71	1.[illegible]230	70.59	101.18
		...	30	...	0.438	17.124	24.17	230.30	1.[illegible]990	82.15	99.84
		XS	...	...	0.500	17.000	27.49	226.98	1.[illegible]763	93.45	98.27
		...	40	...	0.562	16.876	30.79	223.68	1.[illegible]533	104.67	96.93
		...	60	...	0.750	16.500	40.64	213.83	1.[illegible]849	138.17	92.57
		...	80	...	0.938	16.124	50.23	204.24	1.[illegible]183	170.92	88.50
		...	100	...	1.156	15.688	61.17	193.30	1.[illegible]423	207.96	83.76
		...	120	...	1.375	15.250	71.81	182.66	1.[illegible]684	244.14	79.07
		...	140	...	1.562	14.876	80.66	173.80	1.[illegible]070	274.22	75.32
		...	160	...	1.781	14.438	90.75	163.72	1.[illegible]369	308.50	70.88

- Continued -

Extracted from Technical Paper No. 410, *Flow of Fluids,* with permission of Crane Co.

Pipe Data

Carbon and Alloy Steel—Stainless Steel

NOMINAL PIPE SIZE (INCHES)	OUTSIDE DIAM. (INCHES)	IDENTIFICATION			WALL THICK-NESS (t) (INCHES)	INSIDE DIAM-ETER (d) (INCHES)	AREA OF METAL (SQUARE INCHES)	TRANSVERSE INTERNAL AREA		WEIGHT PIPE (POUNDS PER FOOT)	WEIGHT WATER (POUNDS PER FOOT OF PIPE)
		Steel		Stainless Steel Sched. No.				(a) (Square Inches)	(A) (Square Feet)		
		Iron Pipe Size	Sched. No.								
20	20.00	...	...	5S	0.188	19.624	11.70	302.46	2.1004	39.78	131.06
		...	...	10S	0.218	19.564	13.55	300.61	2.0876	46.06	130.27
		...	10	...	0.250	19.500	15.51	298.65	2.0740	52.73	129.42
		STD	20	...	0.375	19.250	23.12	290.04	2.0142	78.60	125.67
		XS	30	...	0.500	19.000	30.63	283.53	1.9690	104.13	122.87
		...	40	...	0.594	18.812	36.15	278.00	1.9305	123.11	120.46
		...	60	...	0.812	18.376	48.95	265.21	1.8417	166.40	114.92
		...	80	...	1.031	17.938	61.44	252.72	1.7550	208.87	109.51
		...	100	...	1.281	17.438	75.33	238.83	1.6585	256.10	103.39
		...	120	...	1.500	17.000	87.18	226.98	1.5762	296.37	98.35
		...	140	...	1.750	16.500	100.33	213.82	1.4849	341.09	92.66
		...	160	...	1.969	16.062	111.49	202.67	1.4074	379.17	87.74
22	22.00	...	...	5S	0.188	21.624	12.88	367.25	2.5503	43.80	159.14
		...	...	10S	0.218	21.564	14.92	365.21	2.5362	50.71	158.26
		...	10	...	0.250	21.500	17.08	363.05	2.5212	58.07	157.32
		STD	20	...	0.375	21.250	25.48	354.66	2.4629	86.61	153.68
		XS	30	...	0.500	21.000	33.77	346.36	2.4053	114.81	150.09
		...	60	...	0.875	20.250	58.07	322.06	2.2365	197.41	139.56
		...	80	...	1.125	19.75	73.78	306.35	2.1275	250.81	132.76
		...	100	...	1.375	19.25	89.09	291.04	2.0211	302.88	126.12
		...	120	...	1.625	18.75	104.02	276.12	1.9175	353.61	119.65
		...	140	...	1.875	18.25	118.55	261.59	1.8166	403.00	113.36
		...	160	...	2.125	17.75	132.68	247.45	1.7184	451.06	107.23

24	24.00	. . .	. . .	5S	0.218	23.564	16.29	436.10	3.0285	55.37	188.98
		. . .	10	10S	0.250	23.500	18.65	433.74	3.0121	63.41	187.95
		STD	20	. . .	0.375	23.250	27.83	424.56	2.9483	94.62	183.95
		XS	. . .	. . .	0.500	23.000	36.91	415.48	2.8853	125.49	179.87
		. . .	30	. . .	0.562	22.876	41.39	411.00	2.8542	140.68	178.09
		. . .	40	. . .	0.688	22.624	50.31	402.07	2.7921	171.29	174.23
		. . .	60	. . .	0.969	22.062	70.04	382.35	2.6552	238.35	165.52
		. . .	80	. . .	1.219	21.562	87.17	365.22	2.5362	296.58	158.26
		. . .	100	. . .	1.531	20.938	108.07	344.32	2.3911	367.39	149.06
		. . .	120	. . .	1.812	20.376	126.31	326.08	2.2645	429.39	141.17
		. . .	140	. . .	2.062	19.876	142.11	310.28	2.1547	483.12	134.45
		. . .	160	. . .	2.344	19.312	159.41	292.98	2.0346	542.13	126.84
26	26.00	. . .	10	. . .	0.312	25.376	25.18	505.75	3.5122	85.60	219.16
		STD	. . .	. . .	0.375	25.250	30.19	500.74	3.4774	102.63	216.99
		XS	20	. . .	0.500	25.000	40.06	490.87	3.4088	136.17	212.71
28	28.00	. . .	10	. . .	0.312	27.376	27.14	588.61	4.0876	92.26	255.07
		STD	. . .	. . .	0.375	27.250	32.54	583.21	4.0501	110.64	252.73
		XS	20	. . .	0.500	27.000	43.20	572.56	3.9761	146.85	248.11
		. . .	30	. . .	0.625	26.750	53.75	562.00	3.9028	182.73	243.53
30	30.00	. . .	. . .	5S	0.250	29.500	23.37	683.49	4.7465	79.43	296.18
		. . .	10	10S	0.312	29.376	29.10	677.76	4.7067	98.93	293.70
		STD	. . .	. . .	0.375	29.250	34.90	671.96	4.6664	118.65	291.18
		XS	20	. . .	0.500	29.000	46.34	660.52	4.5869	157.53	286.22
		. . .	30	. . .	0.625	28.750	57.68	649.18	4.5082	196.08	281.31
32	32.00	. . .	10	. . .	0.312	31.376	31.06	773.19	5.3694	105.59	335.05
		STD	. . .	. . .	0.375	31.250	37.26	766.99	5.3263	126.66	332.36
		XS	20	. . .	0.500	31.000	49.48	754.77	5.2414	168.21	327.06
		. . .	30	. . .	0.625	30.750	61.60	742.64	5.1572	209.43	321.81
		. . .	40	. . .	0.688	30.624	67.68	736.57	5.1151	230.08	319.18

- Continued -

Extracted from Technical Paper No. 410, *Flow of Fluids,* with permission of Crane Co.

Pipe Data

Carbon and Alloy Steel—Stainless Steel

NOMINAL PIPE SIZE (INCHES)	OUTSIDE DIAM. (INCHES)	IDENTIFICATION			WALL THICK-NESS (t) (INCHES)	INSIDE DIAM-ETER (d) (INCHES)	AREA OF METAL (SQUARE INCHES)	TRANSVERSE INTERNAL AREA		WEIGHT PIPE (POUNDS PER FOOT)	WEIGHT WATER (POUNDS PER FOOT OF PIPE)
		Steel		Stainless Steel Sched. No.				(a) (Square Inches)	(A) (Square Feet)		
		Iron Pipe Size	Sched. No.								
34	34.00	. . .	10	. . .	0.344	33.312	36.37	871.55	6.0524	123.65	377.67
		STD	. . .	. . .	0.375	33.250	39.61	868.31	6.0299	134.67	376.27
		XS	20	. . .	0.500	33.000	52.62	855.30	5.9396	178.89	370.63
		. . .	30	. . .	0.625	32.750	65.53	842.39	5.8499	222.78	365.03
		. . .	40	. . .	0.688	32.624	72.00	835.92	5.8050	244.77	362.23
36	36.00	. . .	10	. . .	0.312	35.376	34.98	982.90	6.8257	118.92	425.92
		STD	. . .	. . .	0.375	35.250	41.97	975.91	6.7771	142.68	422.89
		XS	20	. . .	0.500	35.000	55.76	962.11	6.6813	189.57	416.91
		. . .	30	. . .	0.625	34.750	69.46	948.42	6.5862	236.13	417.22
		. . .	40	. . .	0.750	34.500	83.06	934.82	6.4918	282.35	405.09

Extracted from Technical Paper No. 410, *Flow of Fluids,* with permission of Crane Co.

American Pipe Flange Dimensions
Diameter of Bolt Circle—Inches
Per ANSI B16.1, B16.5, and B16.24

Nominal Pipe Size (Inches)	ANSI Class* 125 (Cast Iron) or Class 150 (Steel)	ANSI Class† 250 (Cast Iron) or Class 300 (Steel)	ANSI Class 600	ANSI Class 900	ANSI Class 1500	ANSI Class 2500
1	3.12	3.50	3.50	4.00	4.00	4.25
1-1/4	3.50	3.88	3.88	4.38	4.38	5.12
1-1/2	3.88	4.50	4.50	4.88	4.88	5.75
2	4.75	5.00	5.00	6.50	6.50	6.75
2-1/2	5.50	5.88	5.88	7.50	7.50	7.75
3	6.00	6.62	6.62	7.50	8.00	9.00
4	7.50	7.88	8.50	9.25	9.50	10.75
5	8.50	9.25	10.50	11.00	11.50	12.75
6	9.50	10.62	11.50	12.50	12.50	14.50
8	11.75	13.00	13.75	15.50	15.50	17.25
10	14.25	15.25	17.00	18.50	19.00	21.75
12	17.00	17.75	19.25	21.00	22.50	24.38
14	18.75	20.25	20.75	22.00	25.00	...
16	21.25	22.50	23.75	24.25	27.75	...
18	22.75	24.75	25.75	27.00	30.50	...
20	25.00	27.00	28.50	29.50	32.75	...
24	29.50	32.00	33.00	35.50	39.00	...
30	36.00	39.25	...	...	...	...
36	42.75	46.00	...	...	...	...
42	49.50	52.75	...	...	...	...
48	56.00	60.75	...	...	...	...

*Sizes 1-inch through 12-inch also apply to ANSI Class 150 bronze flanges.
†Sizes 1-inch through 8-inch also apply to ANSI Class 300 bronze flanges.

American Pipe Flange Dimensions

Number of Stud Bolts and Diameter in Inches
Per ANSI B16.1, B16.5, and B16.24

NOMINAL PIPE SIZE (INCHES)	ANSI CLASS* 125 (CAST IRON) OR CLASS 150 (STEEL)		ANSI CLASS† 250 (CAST IRON) OR CLASS 300 (STEEL)		ANSI CLASS 600		ANSI CLASS 900		ANSI CLASS 1500		ANSI CLASS 2500	
	No.	Dia.	No.	Dia.	No.	Dia.	No.	Dia.	No.	Dia.	No.	Dia.
1	4	0.50	4	0.62	4	0.62	4	0.88	4	0.88	4	0.88
1-1/4	4	0.50	4	0.62	4	0.62	4	0.88	4	0.88	4	1.00
1-1/2	4	0.50	4	0.75	4	0.75	4	1.00	4	1.00	4	1.12
2	4	0.62	8	0.62	8	0.62	8	0.88	8	0.88	8	1.00
2-1/2	4	0.62	8	0.75	8	0.75	8	1.00	8	1.00	8	1.12
3	4	0.62	8	0.75	8	0.75	8	0.88	8	1.12	8	1.25
4	8	0.62	8	0.75	8	0.75	8	1.12	8	1.25	8	1.50
5	8	0.75	8	0.75	8	1.00	8	1.25	8	1.50	8	1.75
6	8	0.75	12	0.75	12	1.00	12	1.12	12	1.38	8	2.00
8	8	0.75	12	0.88	12	1.12	12	1.38	12	1.62	12	2.00
10	12	0.88	16	1.00	16	1.25	16	1.38	12	1.88	12	2.50
12	12	0.88	16	1.12	20	1.25	20	1.38	16	2.00	12	2.75
14	12	1.00	20	1.12	20	1.38	20	1.50	16	2.25	...	...
16	16	1.00	20	1.25	20	1.50	20	1.62	16	2.50	...	...
18	16	1.12	24	1.25	20	1.62	20	1.88	16	2.75	...	...
20	20	1.12	24	1.25	24	1.62	20	2.00	16	3.00	...	...
24	20	1.25	24	1.50	24	1.88	20	2.50	16	3.50	...	...
30	28	1.25	28	1.75	...	...	...	...	...	...	...	...
36	32	1.50	32	2.00	...	...	...	...	...	...	...	...
42	36	1.50	36	2.00	...	...	...	...	...	...	...	...
48	44	1.50	40	2.00	...	...	...	...	...	...	...	...

* Sizes 1-inch through 12-inch also apply to ANSI Class 150 bronze flanges.
† Sizes 1-inch through 8-inch also apply to ANSI Class 300 bronze flanges.

American Pipe Flange Dimensions
Flange Diameter—Inches
Per ANSI B16.1, B16.5, and B16.24

Nominal Pipe Size	ANSI Class* 125 (Cast Iron) or Class 150 (Steel)	ANSI Class† 250 (Cast Iron) or Class 300 (Steel)	ANSI Class 600	ANSI Class 900	ANSI Class 1500	ANSI Class 2500
1	4.25	4.88	4.88	5.88	5.88	6.25
1-1/4	4.62	5.25	5.25	6.25	6.25	7.25
1-1/2	5.00	6.12	6.12	7.00	7.00	8.00
2	6.00	6.50	6.50	8.50	8.50	9.25
2-1/2	7.00	7.50	7.50	9.62	9.62	10.50
3	7.50	8.25	8.25	9.50	10.50	12.00
4	9.00	10.00	10.75	11.50	12.25	14.00
5	10.00	11.00	13.00	13.75	14.75	16.50
6	11.00	12.50	14.00	15.00	15.50	19.00
8	13.50	15.00	16.50	18.50	19.00	21.75
10	16.00	17.50	20.00	21.50	23.00	26.50
12	19.00	20.50	22.00	24.00	26.50	30.00
14	21.00	23.00	23.75	25.25	29.50	...
16	23.50	25.50	27.00	27.75	32.50	...
18	25.00	28.00	29.25	31.00	36.00	...
20	27.50	30.50	32.00	33.75	38.75	...
24	32.00	36.00	37.00	41.00	46.00	...
30	38.75	43.00	...	...	...	...
36	46.00	50.00	...	...	...	...
42	53.00	57.00	...	...	...	...
48	59.50	65.00	...	...	...	...

*Sizes 1-inch through 12-inch also apply to ANSI Class 150 bronze flanges.
† Sizes 1-inch through 8-inch also apply to ANSI Class 300 bronze flanges.

American Pipe Flange Dimensions

Flange Thickness—Inches

Per ANSI B16.1, B16.5, and B16.24

NOMINAL PIPE SIZE	ANSI CLASS 125 CAST IRON (FF) CLASS 150 STEEL (RF)	ANSI CLASS 150 STEEL (RTJ)	ANSI CLASS 150 BRONZE	ANSI CLASS 250 CAST IRON AND CLASS 300 STEEL	ANSI CLASS 300 STEEL	ANSI CLASS 300 BRONZE	ANSI CLASS 600		ANSI CLASS 900		ANSI CLASS 1500		ANSI CLASS 2500	
				RF	RTJ		RF	RTJ	RF	RTJ	RF	RTJ	RF	RTJ
1	0.44	0.69	0.38	0.69	0.94	0.59	0.94	0.94	1.38	1.38	1.38	1.38	1.62	1.62
1-1/4	0.50	0.75	0.41	0.75	1.00	0.62	1.06	1.06	1.38	1.38	1.38	1.38	1.75	1.81
1-1/2	0.56	0.81	0.44	0.81	1.06	0.69	1.12	1.12	1.50	1.50	1.50	1.50	2.00	2.06
2	0.62	0.88	0.50	0.88	1.19	0.75	1.25	1.31	1.75	1.81	1.75	1.81	2.25	2.31
2-1/2	0.69	0.94	0.56	1.00	1.31	0.81	1.38	1.44	1.88	1.94	1.88	1.94	2.50	2.62
3	0.75	1.00	0.62	1.12	1.44	0.91	1.50	1.56	1.75	1.81	2.12	2.19	2.88	3.00
4	0.94	1.19	0.69	1.25	1.56	1.06	1.75	1.81	2.00	2.06	2.38	2.44	3.25	3.44
5	0.94	1.19	0.75	1.38	1.69	1.12	2.00	2.06	2.25	2.31	3.12	3.19	3.88	4.12
6	1.00	1.25	0.81	1.44	1.75	1.19	2.12	2.19	2.44	2.50	3.50	3.62	4.50	4.75
8	1.12	1.38	0.94	1.62	1.94	1.38	2.44	2.50	2.75	2.81	3.88	4.06	5.25	5.56
10	1.19	1.44	1.00	1.88	2.19	...	2.75	2.81	3.00	3.06	4.50	4.69	6.75	7.19
12	1.25	1.50	1.06	2.00	2.31	...	2.88	2.94	3.38	3.44	5.12	5.44	7.50	7.94
14	1.38	1.62	...	2.12	2.44	...	3.00	3.06	3.62	3.81	5.50	5.88	...	...
16	1.44	1.69	...	2.25	2.56	...	3.25	3.31	3.75	3.94	6.00	6.44	...	...
18	1.56	1.81	...	2.38	2.69	...	3.50	3.56	4.25	4.50	6.62	7.06	...	...
20	1.69	1.94	...	2.50	2.88	...	3.75	3.88	4.50	4.75	7.25	7.69	...	...
24	1.88	2.12	...	2.75	3.19	...	4.25	4.44	5.75	6.12	8.25	8.81	...	...
30	2.12	...	...	3.00	...	...	...	...	...	...	...	...	...	...
36	2.38	...	...	3.38	...	...	...	...	...	...	...	...	...	...
42	2.62	...	...	3.69	...	...	...	...	...	...	...	...	...	...
48	2.75	...	...	4.00	...	...	...	...	...	...	...	...	...	...

DIN Standards

DIN Cast Steel Valve Ratings*

NOMINAL PRESSURE (BAR)	PERMISSIBLE WORKING PRESSURE (BAR) AT TEMP. SHOWN					
	−10°C to 120°C	200°C	250°C	300°C	350°C	400°C
16	16	14	13	11	10	8
25	25	22	20	17	16	13
40	40	35	32	28	24	21
64	64	50	45	40	36	32
100	100	80	70	60	56	50
160	160	130	112	96	90	80
250	250	200	175	150	140	125
320	320	[illegible]	[illegible]	[illegible]	[illegible]	[illegible]
400	400	320	280	240	225	200

* Hydrostatic test pressure: 1.5 times rating at 20°C.

DIN Cast Steel Flange Standard

Nenndruck 16 (Nominal Pressure 16 Bar)

NOMINAL BORE	PIPE THICKNESS	FLANGE			BOLTING		
		Outside Diameter	Thickness	Bolt Circle Diameter	Number of Bolts	Thread	Bolt Hole Diameter
10	6	90	16	60	4	M12	14
15	6	95	16	65	4	M12	14
20	6.5	105	18	75	4	M12	14
25	7	115	18	85	4	M12	14
32	7	140	18	100	4	M16	18
40	7.5	150	18	110	4	M16	18
50	8	165	20	125	4	M16	18
65	8	185	18	145	4	M16	18
80	8.5	200	20	160	8	M16	18
100	9.5	220	20	180	8	M16	18
125	10	250	22	210	8	M16	18
150	11	285	22	240	8	M20	23
175	12	315	24	270	8	M20	23
200	12	340	24	295	12	M20	23
250	14	405	26	355	12	M24	27
300	15	460	28	410	12	M24	27
350	16	520	30	470	16	M24	27
400	18	580	32	525	16	M27	30
500	21	715	36	650	20	M30	33
600	23	840	40	770	20	M33	36
700	24	910	42	840	24	M33	36
800	26	1025	42	950	24	M36	39
900	27	1125	44	1050	28	M36	39
1000	29	1255	46	1170	28	M39	42
1200	32	1485	52	1390	32	M45	48
1400	34	1685	58	1590	36	M45	48
1600	36	1930	64	1820	40	M52	56
1800	39	2130	68	2020	44	M52	56
2000	41	2345	70	2230	48	M56	62
2200	43	2555	74	2440	52	M56	62

All dimensions in mm.

DIN Cast Steel Flange Standard

Nenndruck 25 (Nominal Pressure 25 Bar)

NOMINAL BORE	PIPE THICK-NESS	FLANGE			BOLTING		
		Outside Diameter	Thickness	Bolt Circle Diameter	Number of Bolts	Thread	Bolt Hole Diameter
10	6	90	16	60	4	M12	14
15	6	95	16	65	4	M12	14
20	6.5	105	18	75	4	M12	14
25	7	115	18	85	4	M12	14
32	7	140	18	100	4	M16	18
40	7.5	150	18	110	4	M16	18
50	8	165	20	125	4	M16	18
65	8.5	185	22	145	8	M16	18
80	9	200	24	160	8	M16	18
100	10	235	24	190	8	M20	23
125	11	270	26	220	8	M24	27
150	12	300	28	250	8	M24	27
175	12	330	28	280	12	M24	27
200	12	360	30	310	12	M24	27
250	14	425	32	370	12	M27	30
300	15	485	34	430	16	M27	30
350	16	555	38	490	16	M30	33
400	18	620	40	550	16	M33	36
500	21	730	44	660	20	M33	36
600	23	845	46	770	20	M36	39
700	24	960	50	875	24	M39	42
800	26	1085	54	990	24	M45	48
900	27	1185	58	1090	28	M45	48
1000	29	1320	62	1210	28	M52	56
1200	32	1530	70	1420	32	M52	56
1400	34	1755	76	1640	36	M56	62
1600	37	1975	84	1860	40	M56	62
1800	40	2195	90	2070	44	M64	70
2000	43	2425	96	2300	48	M64	70

All dimensions in mm.

DIN Cast Steel Flange Standard

Nenndruck 40 (Nominal Pressure 40 Bar)

NOMINAL BORE	PIPE THICK-NESS	FLANGE			BOLTING		
		Outside Diameter	Thickness	Bolt Circle Diameter	Number of Bolts	Thread	Bolt Hole Diameter
10	6	90	16	60	4	M12	14
15	6	95	16	65	4	M12	14
20	6.5	105	18	75	4	M12	14
25	7	115	18	85	4	M12	14
32	7	140	18	100	4	M16	18
40	7.5	150	18	110	4	M16	18
50	8	165	20	125	4	M16	18
65	8.5	185	22	145	8	M16	18
80	9	200	24	160	8	M16	18
100	10	235	24	190	8	M20	23
125	11	270	26	220	8	M24	27
150	12	300	28	250	8	M24	27
175	13	350	32	295	12	M27	30
200	14	375	34	320	12	M27	30
250	16	450	38	385	12	M30	33
300	17	515	42	450	16	M30	33
350	19	580	46	510	16	M33	36
400	21	660	50	585	16	M36	39
450	21	685	50	610	20	M36	39
500	21	755	52	670	20	M39	42
600	24	890	60	795	20	M45	48
700	27	995	64	900	24	M45	48
800	30	1140	72	1030	24	M52	56
900	33	1250	76	1140	28	M52	56
1000	36	1360	80	1250	28	M52	56
1200	42	1575	88	1460	32	M56	62
1400	47	1795	98	1680	36	M56	62
1600	54	2025	108	1900	40	M64	70

All dimensions in mm.

DIN Cast Steel Flange Standard

Nenndruck 64 (Nominal Pressure 64 Bar)

NOMINAL BORE	PIPE THICK-NESS	FLANGE			BOLTING		
		Outside Diameter	Thickness	Bolt Circle Diameter	Number of Bolts	Thread	Bolt Hole Diameter
10	10	100	20	70	4	M12	14
15	10	105	20	75	4	M12	14
25	10	140	24	100	4	M16	18
32	12	155	24	110	4	M20	23
40	10	170	28	125	4	M20	22
50	10	180	26	135	4	M20	22
65	10	205	26	160	8	M20	22
80	11	215	28	170	8	M20	22
100	12	250	30	200	8	M24	26
125	13	295	34	240	8	M27	30
150	14	345	36	280	8	M30	33
175	15	375	40	310	12	M30	33
200	16	415	42	345	12	M33	36
250	19	470	46	400	12	M33	36
300	21	530	52	460	16	M33	36
350	23	600	56	525	16	M36	39
400	26	670	60	585	16	M39	42
500	31	800	68	705	20	M45	48
600	35	930	76	820	20	M52	56
700	40	1045	84	935	24	M52	56
800	45	1165	92	1050	24	M56	62
900	50	1285	98	1170	28	M56	62
1000	55	1415	108	1290	28	M64	70
1200	64	1665	126	1530	32	M72X6	78

All dimensions in mm.

DIN Cast Steel Flange Standard

Nenndruck 100 (Nominal Pressure 100 Bar)

NOMINAL BORE	PIPE THICK-NESS	FLANGE			BOLTING		
		Outside Diameter	Thickness	Bolt Circle Diameter	Number of Bolts	Thread	Bolt Hole Diameter
10	10	100	20	70	4	M12	14
15	10	105	20	75	4	M12	14
25	10	140	24	100	4	M16	18
32	12	155	24	110	4	M20	23
40	10	170	28	125	4	M20	22
50	10	195	30	145	4	M24	26
65	11	220	34	170	8	M24	26
80	12	230	36	180	8	M24	26
100	14	265	40	210	8	M27	30
125	16	315	40	250	8	M30	33
150	18	355	44	290	12	M30	33
175	20	385	48	320	12	M30	33
200	21	430	52	360	12	M33	36
250	25	505	60	430	12	M36	39
300	29	585	68	500	16	M39	42
350	32	655	74	560	16	M45	48
400	36	715	78	620	16	M45	48
500	44	870	94	760	20	M52	56
600	51	990	104	875	20	M56	62
700	59	1145	120	1020	24	M64	70

All dimensions in mm.

DIN Cast Steel Flange Standard

Nenndruck 160 (Nominal Pressure 160 Bar)

NOMINAL BORE	PIPE THICK-NESS	FLANGE			BOLTING		
		Outside Diameter	Thickness	Bolt Circle Diameter	Number of Bolts	Thread	Bolt Hole Diameter
10	10	100	20	70	4	M12	14
15	10	105	20	75	4	M12	14
25	10	140	24	100	4	M16	18
40	10	170	28	125	4	M20	22
50	10	195	30	145	4	M24	26
65	11	220	34	170	8	M24	26
80	12	230	36	180	8	M24	26
100	14	265	40	210	8	M27	30
125	16	315	44	250	8	M30	33
150	18	355	50	290	12	M30	33
175	19	390	54	320	12	M33	36
200	21	430	60	360	12	M33	36
250	31	515	68	430	12	M39	42
300	36	585	78	500	16	M39	42

All dimensions in mm.

DIN Cast Steel Flange Standard

Nenndruck 250 (Nominal Pressure 250 Bar)

NOMINAL BORE	PIPE THICK-NESS	FLANGE			BOLTING		
		Outside Diameter	Thickness	Bolt Circle Diameter	Number of Bolts	Thread	Bolt Hole Diameter
10	10	125	24	85	4	M16	18
15	10	130	26	90	4	M16	18
25	11	150	28	105	4	M20	22
40	13	185	34	135	4	M24	26
50	13	200	38	150	8	M24	26
65	14	230	42	180	8	M24	26
80	16	255	46	200	8	M27	30
100	19	300	54	235	8	M30	33
125	22	340	60	275	12	M30	33
150	25	390	68	320	12	M33	36
175	29	430	74	355	12	M36	39
200	32	485	82	400	12	M39	42
250	38	585	100	490	16	M45	48
300	47	690	120	590	16	M48	52

All dimensions in mm.

DIN Cast Steel Flange Standard

Nenndruck 320 (Nominal Pressure 320 Bar)

NOMINAL BORE	PIPE THICK-NESS	FLANGE			BOLTING		
		Outside Diameter	Thickness	Bolt Circle Diameter	Number of Bolts	Thread	Bolt Hole Diameter
10	11	125	24	85	4	M16	18
15	11	130	26	90	4	M16	18
25	11	160	34	115	4	M20	22
40	14	195	38	145	4	M24	26
50	15	210	42	160	8	M24	26
65	18	255	51	200	8	M27	30
80	[illegible]	275	55	[illegible]	[illegible]	[illegible]	[illegible]
100	24	335	65	265	8	M33	36
125	27	380	75	310	12	M33	36
150	32	425	84	350	12	M36	39
175	35	485	95	400	12	M39	42
200	38	525	103	440	16	M39	42
250	49	640	125	540	16	M48	52

All dimensions in mm.

DIN Cast Steel Flange Standard

Nenndruck 400 (Nominal Pressure 400 Bar)

NOMINAL BORE	PIPE THICK-NESS	FLANGE			BOLTING		
		Outside Diameter	Thickness	Bolt Circle Diameter	Number of Bolts	Thread	Bolt Hole Diameter
10	11	125	28	85	4	M16	18
15	11	145	30	100	4	M20	23
25	12	180	38	130	4	M24	26
40	15	220	48	165	4	M27	30
50	18	235	52	180	8	M27	30
65	22	290	64	225	8	M30	33
80	25	305	68	240	8	M30	33
100	30	370	80	295	8	M36	39
125	36	415	92	340	12	M36	39
150	41	475	105	390	12	M39	42
175	47	545	120	450	12	M45	48
200	53	585	130	490	16	M45	48

All dimensions in mm.

Section 9

General Reference Tables

Circumferences and Areas of Circles

Diameter (In.)	Circum. (In.)	Area (Sq In.)	Diameter (In.)	Circum. (In.)	Area (Sq In.)
1/32	.0982	.00077	13/16	2.5525	.51849
1/16	.1963	.00307	27/32	2.6507	.55914
3/32	.2945	.00690	7/8	2.7489	.60132
1/8	.3927	.01228	29/32	2.8471	.64504
5/32	.4909	.01916	15/16	2.9452	.69029
3/16	.5890	.02761	31/32	3.0434	.73708
7/32	.6872	.03758	1	3.1416	.7854
1/4	.7854	.04909	1-1/16	3.3379	.8866
9/32	.8836	.06213	1-1/8	3.5343	.9940
5/16	.9817	.07670	1-3/16	3.7306	1.1075
11/32	1.0799	.09281	1-1/4	3.9270	1.2272
3/8	1.1781	.11045	1-5/16	4.1233	1.3530
13/32	1.2763	.12962	1-3/8	4.3197	1.4849
7/16	1.3744	.15033	1-7/16	4.5160	1.6230
15/32	1.4726	.17257	1-1/2	4.7124	1.7671
1/2	1.5708	.19635	1-9/16	4.9087	1.9175
17/32	1.6690	.22166	1-5/8	5.1051	2.0739
9/16	1.7671	.24850	1-11/16	5.3014	2.2365
19/32	1.8653	.27688	1-3/4	5.4978	2.4053
5/8	1.9635	.30680	1-13/16	5.6941	2.5802
21/32	2.0617	.33824	1-7/8	5.8905	2.7612
11/16	2.1598	.37122	1-15/16	6.0868	2.9483
23/32	2.2580	.40574	2	6.2832	3.1416
3/4	2.3562	.44179	2-1/16	6.4795	3.3410
25/32	2.4544	.47937	2-1/8	6.6759	3.5466

- Continued -

Circumferences and Areas of Circles (Continued)

Diameter (In.)	Circum. (In.)	Area (Sq In.)	Diameter (In.)	Circum. (In.)	Area (Sq In.)
2-3/16	6.8722	3.7583	5	15.7080	19.635
2-1/4	7.0686	3.9761	5-1/16	15.9043	20.129
2-5/16	7.2649	4.2000	5-1/8	16.1007	20.629
2-3/8	7.4613	4.4301	5-3/16	16.2970	21.135
2-7/16	7.6576	4.6664	5-1/4	16.4934	21.648
2-1/2	7.8540	4.9087	5-5/16	16.6897	22.166
2-9/16	8.0503	5.1572	5-3/8	16.8861	22.691
2-5/8	8.2467	5.4119	5-7/16	17.0824	23.221
2-11/16	8.4430	5.6727	5-1/2	17.2788	23.758
2-3/4	8.6394	5.9396	5-9/16	17.4751	24.301
2-13/16	8.8357	6.2126	5-5/8	17.6715	24.850
2-7/8	9.0321	6.4918	5-11/16	17.8678	25.406
2-15/16	9.2284	6.7771	5-3/4	18.0642	25.967
3	9.4248	7.0686	5-13/16	18.2605	26.535
3-1/16	9.6211	7.3662	5-7/8	18.4569	27.109
3-1/8	9.8175	7.6699	5-15/16	18.6532	27.688
3-3/16	10.0138	7.9798	6	18.8496	28.274
3-1/4	10.2102	8.2958	6-1/8	19.2423	29.465
3-5/16	10.4065	8.6179	6-1/4	19.6350	30.680
3-3/8	10.6029	8.9462	6-3/8	20.0277	31.919
3-7/16	10.7992	9.2806	6-1/2	20.4204	33.183
3-1/2	10.9956	9.6211	6-5/8	20.8131	34.472
3-9/16	11.1919	9.9678	6-3/4	21.2058	35.785
3-5/8	11.3883	10.321	6-7/8	21.5984	37.122
3-11/16	11.5846	10.680	7	21.9911	38.485
3-3/4	11.7810	11.045	7-1/8	22.3838	39.871
3-13/16	11.9773	11.416	7-1/4	22.7765	41.282
3-7/8	12.1737	11.793	7-3/8	23.1692	42.718
3-15/16	12.3700	12.177	7-1/2	23.5619	44.179
4	12.5664	12.566	7-5/8	23.9456	45.664
4-1/16	12.7627	12.962	7-3/4	24.3473	47.173
4-1/8	12.9591	13.364	7-7/8	24.7400	48.707
4-3/16	13.1554	13.772	8	25.1327	50.265
4-1/4	13.3518	14.186	8-1/8	25.5254	51.849
4-5/16	13.5481	14.607	8-1/4	25.9181	53.456
4-3/8	13.7445	15.033	8-3/8	26.3108	55.088
4-7/16	13.9408	15.466	8-1/2	26.7035	56.745
4-1/2	14.1372	15.904	8-5/8	27.0962	58.426
4-9/16	14.3335	16.349	8-3/4	27.4889	60.132
4-5/8	14.5299	16.800	8-7/8	27.8816	61.862
4-11/16	14.7262	17.257	9	28.2743	63.617
4-3/4	14.9226	17.721	9-1/8	28.6670	65.397
4-13/16	15.1189	18.190	9-1/4	29.0597	67.201
4-7/8	15.3153	18.665	9-3/8	29.4524	69.029
4-15/16	15.5116	19.147	9-1/2	29.8451	70.882

- Continued -

Circumferences and Areas of Circles (Continued)

Diameter (In.)	Circum. (In.)	Area (Sq In.)	Diameter (In.)	Circum. (In.)	Area (Sq In.)
9-5/8	30.2378	72.760	20-1/2	64.4026	330.06
9-3/4	30.6305	74.662	20-3/4	65.1880	338.16
9-7/8	31.0232	76.589	21	65.9734	346.36
10	31.4159	78.540	21-1/4	66.7588	354.66
10-1/4	32.2013	82.516	21-1/2	67.5442	363.05
10-1/2	32.9867	86.590	21-3/4	68.3296	371.54
10-3/4	33.7721	90.763	22	69.1150	380.13
11	34.5575	95.033	22-1/4	69.9004	388.82
11-1/4	35.3429	99.402	22-1/2	70.6858	397.61
11-1/2	36.1283	103.87	22-3/4	71.4712	406.49
11-3/4	36.9137	108.43	23	72.2566	415.48
12	37.6991	113.10	23-1/4	73.0420	424.56
12-1/4	38.4845	117.86	23-1/2	73.8274	433.74
12-1/2	39.2699	122.72	23-3/4	74.6128	443.01
12-3/4	40.0553	127.68	24	75.3982	452.39
13	40.8407	132.73	24-1/4	76.1836	461.86
13-1/4	41.6261	137.89	24-1/2	76.9690	471.44
13-1/2	42.4115	143.14	24-3/4	77.7544	481.11
13-3/4	43.1969	148.49	25	78.5398	490.87
14	43.9823	153.94	25-1/4	79.3252	500.74
14-1/4	44.7677	159.48	25-1/2	80.1106	510.71
14-1/2	45.5531	165.13	25-3/4	80.8960	520.77
14-3/4	46.3385	170.87	26	81.6814	530.93
15	47.1239	176.71	26-1/4	82.4668	541.19
15-1/4	47.9093	182.65	26-1/2	83.2522	551.55
15-1/2	48.6947	188.69	26-3/4	84.0376	562.00
15-3/4	49.4801	194.83	27	84.8230	572.56
16	50.2655	201.06	27-1/4	85.6084	583.21
16-1/4	51.0509	207.39	27-1/2	86.3938	593.96
16-1/2	51.8363	213.82	27-3/4	87.1792	604.81
16-3/4	52.6217	220.35	28	87.9646	615.75
17	53.4071	226.98	28-1/4	88.7500	626.80
17-1/4	54.1925	233.71	28-1/2	89.5354	637.94
17-1/2	54.9779	240.53	28-3/4	90.3208	649.18
17-3/4	55.7633	247.45	29	91.1062	660.52
18	56.5487	254.47	29-1/4	91.8916	671.96
18-1/4	57.3341	261.59	29-1/2	92.6770	683.49
18-1/2	58.1195	268.80	29-3/4	93.4624	695.13
18-3/4	58.9049	276.12	30	94.2478	706.86
19	59.6903	283.53	30-1/4	95.0332	718.69
19-1/4	60.4757	291.04	30-1/2	95.8186	730.62
19-1/2	61.2611	298.65	30-3/4	96.6040	742.64
19-3/4	62.0465	306.35	31	97.3894	754.77
20	62.8319	314.16	31-1/4	98.1748	766.99
20-1/4	63.6173	322.06	31-1/2	98.9602	779.31

- Continued -

Circumferences and Areas of Circles (Continued)

Diameter (In.)	Circum. (In.)	Area (Sq In.)	Diameter (In.)	Circum. (In.)	Area (Sq In.)
31-3/4	99.7456	791.73	41-3/4	131.161	1369.0
32	100.531	804.25	42	131.947	1385.4
32-1/4	101.316	816.86	42-1/4	132.732	1402.0
32-1/2	102.102	829.58	42-1/2	133.518	1418.6
32-3/4	102.887	842.39	42-3/4	134.303	1435.4
33	103.673	855.30	43	135.088	1452.2
33-1/4	104.458	868.31	43-1/4	135.874	1469.1
33-1/2	105.243	881.41	43-/12	136.659	1486.2
33-3/4	106.029	894.62	43-3/4	137.445	1503.3
34	106.814	907.92	44	138.230	1520.5
34-1/4	107.600	921.32	44-1/4	139.015	1537.9
34-1/2	108.385	934.82	44-1/2	139.801	1555.3
34-3/4	109.170	948.42	44-3/4	140.586	1572.8
35	109.956	962.11	45	141.372	1590.4
35-/14	110.741	975.91	45-1/4	142.157	1608.2
35-1/2	111.527	989.80	45-1/2	142.942	1626.0
35-3/4	112.312	1003.8	45-3/4	143.728	1643.9
36	113.097	1017.9	46	144.513	1661.9
36-1/4	113.883	1032.1	46-1/4	145.299	1680.0
36-1/2	114.668	1046.3	46-1/2	146.084	1698.2
36-3/4	115.454	1060.7	46-3/4	146.869	1716.5
37	116.239	1075.2	47	147.655	1734.9
37-1/4	117.024	1089.8	47-1/4	148.440	1753.5
37-1/2	117.810	1104.5	47-1/2	149.226	1772.1
37-3/4	118.596	1119.2	47-3/4	150.011	1790.8
38	119.381	1134.1	48	150.796	1809.6
38-1/4	120.166	1149.1	48-1/4	151.582	1828.5
38-1/2	120.951	1164.2	48-1/2	152.367	1847.5
38-3/4	121.737	1179.3	48-3/4	153.153	1866.5
39	122.522	1194.6	49	153.938	1885.7
39-1/4	123.308	1210.0	49-1/4	154.723	1905.0
39-1/2	124.093	1225.4	49-1/2	155.509	1924.4
39-3/4	124.878	1241.0	49-3/4	156.294	1943.9
40	125.664	1256.6	50	157.080	1963.5
40-1/4	126.449	1272.4			
40-1/2	127.235	1288.2			
40-3/4	128.020	1304.2			
41	128.805	1320.3			
41-1/4	129.591	1336.4			
41-1/2	130.376	1352.7			

Common Logarithms

No.	0	1	2	3	4	5	6	7	8	9
0	. . .	0000	3010	4771	6021	6990	7782	8451	9031	9542
1	0000	0414	0792	1139	1461	1761	2041	2304	2553	2788
2	3010	3222	3424	3617	3802	3979	4150	4314	4472	4624
3	4771	4914	5051	5185	5315	5441	5563	5682	5798	5911
4	6021	6128	6232	6335	6435	6532	6628	6721	6812	6902
5	6990	7076	7160	7243	7324	7404	7482	7559	7634	7709
6	7782	7853	7924	7993	8062	8129	8195	8261	8325	8388
7	8451	8513	8573	8633	8692	8751	8808	8865	8921	8976
8	9031	9085	9138	9191	9243	9294	9345	9395	9445	9494
9	9542	9590	9638	9685	9731	9777	9823	9868	9912	9956
10	0000	0043	0086	0128	0170	0212	0253	0294	0334	0374
11	0414	0453	0492	0531	0569	0607	0645	0682	0719	0755
12	0792	0828	0864	0899	0934	0969	1004	1038	1072	1106
13	1139	1173	1206	1239	1271	1303	1335	1367	1399	1430
14	1461	1492	1523	1553	1584	1614	1644	1673	1703	1732
15	1761	1790	1818	1847	1875	1903	1931	1959	1987	2014
16	2041	2068	2095	2122	2148	2175	2201	2227	2253	2279
17	2304	2330	2355	2380	2405	2430	2455	2480	2504	2529
18	2553	2577	2601	2625	2648	2672	2695	2718	2742	2765
19	2788	2810	2833	2856	2878	2900	2923	2945	2967	2989
20	3010	3032	3054	3075	3096	3118	3139	3160	3181	3201
21	3222	3243	3263	3284	3304	3324	3345	3365	3385	3404
22	3424	3444	3464	3483	3502	3522	3541	3560	3579	3598
23	3617	3636	3655	3674	3692	3711	3729	3747	3766	3784
24	3802	3820	3838	3856	3874	3892	3909	3927	3945	3962
25	3979	3997	4014	4031	4048	4065	4082	4099	4116	4133
26	4150	4166	4183	4200	4216	4232	4249	4265	4281	4298
27	4314	4330	4346	4362	4378	4393	4409	4425	4440	4456
28	4472	4487	4502	4518	4533	4548	4564	4579	4594	4609
29	4624	4639	4654	4669	4683	4698	4713	4728	4742	4757
30	4771	4786	4800	4814	4829	4843	4857	4871	4886	4900
31	4914	4928	4942	4955	4969	4983	4997	5011	5024	5038
32	5051	5065	5079	5092	5105	5119	5132	5145	5159	5172
33	5185	5198	5211	5224	5237	5250	5263	5276	5289	5302
34	5315	5328	5340	5353	5366	5378	5391	5403	5416	5428
35	5441	5453	5465	5478	5490	5502	5514	5527	5539	5551
36	5563	5575	5587	5599	5611	5623	5635	5647	5658	5670
37	5682	5694	5705	5717	5729	5740	5752	5763	5775	5786
38	5798	5809	5821	5832	5843	5855	5866	5877	5888	5899
39	5911	5922	5933	5944	5955	5966	5977	5988	5999	6010
40	6021	6031	6042	6053	6064	6075	6085	6096	6107	6117
41	6128	6138	6149	6160	6170	6180	6191	6201	6212	6222
42	6232	6243	6253	6263	6274	6284	6294	6304	6314	6325
43	6335	6345	6355	6365	6375	6385	6395	6405	6415	6425
44	6435	6444	6454	6464	6474	6484	6493	6503	6513	6522
45	6532	6542	6551	6561	6571	6580	6590	6599	6609	6618

- Continued -

Common Logarithms (Continued)

No.	0	1	2	3	4	5	6	7	8	9
46	6628	6637	6646	6656	6665	6675	6684	6693	6702	6712
47	6721	6730	6739	6749	6758	6767	6776	6785	6794	6803
48	6812	6821	6830	6839	6848	6857	6866	6875	6884	6893
49	6902	6911	6920	6928	6937	6946	6955	6964	6972	6981
50	6990	6998	7007	7016	7024	7033	7042	7050	7059	7067
51	7076	7084	7093	7101	7110	7118	7126	7135	7143	7152
52	7160	7168	7177	7185	7193	7202	7210	7218	7226	7235
53	7243	7251	7259	7267	7275	7284	7292	7300	7308	7316
54	7324	7332	7340	7348	7356	7364	7372	7380	7388	7396
55	7404	7412	7419	7427	7435	7443	7451	7459	7466	7474
56	7482	7490	7497	7505	7513	7520	7528	7536	7543	7551
57	7559	7566	7574	7582	7589	7597	7604	7612	7619	7627
58	7634	7642	7649	7657	7664	7672	7679	7686	7694	7701
59	7709	7716	7723	7731	7738	7745	7752	7760	7767	7774
60	7782	7789	7796	7803	7810	7818	7825	7832	7839	7816
61	7853	7860	7868	7875	7882	7889	7896	7903	7910	7917
62	7924	7931	7938	7945	7952	7959	7966	7973	7980	7987
63	7993	8000	8007	8014	8021	8028	8035	8041	8048	8055
64	8062	8069	8075	8082	8089	8096	8102	8109	8116	8122
65	8129	8136	8142	8149	8156	8162	8169	8176	8182	8189
66	8195	8202	8209	8215	8222	8228	8235	8241	8248	8254
67	8261	8267	8274	8280	8287	8293	8299	8306	8312	8319
68	8325	8331	8338	8344	8351	8357	8363	8370	8376	8382
69	8388	8395	8401	8407	8414	8420	8426	8432	8439	8445
70	8451	8457	8463	8470	8476	8482	8488	8494	8500	8506
71	8513	8519	8525	8531	8537	8543	8549	8555	8561	8567
72	8573	8579	8585	8591	8597	8603	8609	8615	8621	8627
73	8633	8639	8645	8651	8657	8663	8669	8675	8681	8686
74	8692	8698	8704	8710	8716	8722	8727	8733	8739	8745
75	8751	8756	8762	8768	8774	8779	8785	8791	8797	8802
76	8808	8814	8820	8825	8831	8837	8842	8848	8854	8859
77	8865	8871	8876	8882	8887	8893	8899	8904	8910	8915
78	8921	8927	8932	8938	8943	8949	8954	8960	8965	8971
79	8976	8982	8987	8993	8998	9004	9009	9015	9020	9025
80	9031	9036	9042	9047	9053	9058	9063	9069	9074	9079
81	9085	9090	9096	9101	9106	9112	9117	9122	9128	9133
82	9138	9143	9149	9154	9159	9165	9170	9175	9180	9186
83	9191	9196	9201	9206	9212	9217	9222	9227	9232	9238
84	9243	9248	9253	9258	9263	9269	9274	9279	9284	9289
85	9294	9299	9304	9309	9315	9320	9325	9330	9335	9340
86	9345	9350	9355	9360	9365	9370	9375	9380	9385	9390
87	9395	9400	9405	9410	9415	9420	9425	9430	9435	9440
88	9445	9450	9455	9460	9465	9469	9474	9479	9484	9489
89	9494	9499	9504	9509	9513	9518	9523	9528	9533	9538
90	9542	9547	9552	9557	9562	9566	9571	9576	9581	9586

- Continued -

Common Logarithms (Continued)

No.	0	1	2	3	4	5	6	7	8	9
91	9590	9595	9600	9605	9609	9614	9619	9624	9628	9633
92	9638	9643	9647	9652	9657	9661	9666	9671	9675	9680
93	9685	9689	9694	9699	9703	9708	9713	9717	9722	9727
94	9731	9736	9741	9745	9750	9754	9759	9763	9768	9773
95	9777	9782	9786	9791	9795	9800	9805	9809	9814	9818
96	9823	9827	9832	9836	9841	9845	9850	9854	9859	9863
97	9868	9872	9877	9881	9886	9890	9894	9899	9903	9908
98	9912	9917	9921	9926	9930	9934	9939	9943	9948	9952
99	9956	9961	9965	9969	9974	9978	9983	9987	9991	9996
100	0000	0004	0009	0013	0017	0022	0026	0030	0035	0039

Metric Prefixes and Symbols

Multiplication Factor	Prefix	Symbol
1 000 000 000 000 000 000 = 10^{18}	exa	E
1 000 000 000 000 000 = 10^{15}	peta	P
1 000 000 000 000 = 10^{12}	tera	T
1 000 000 000 = 10^{9}	giga	G
1 000 000 = 10^{6}	mega	M
1 000 = 10^{3}	kilo	k
100 = 10^{2}	hecto*	h
10 = 10^{1}	deka*	da
0.1 = 10^{-1}	deci*	d
0.01 = 10^{-2}	centi*	c
0.001 = 10^{-3}	milli	m
0.000 001 = 10^{-6}	micro	μ
0.000 000 001 = 10^{-9}	nano	n
0.000 000 000 001 = 10^{-12}	pico	p
0.000 000 000 000 001 = 10^{-15}	femto	f
0.000 000 000 000 000 001 = 10^{-18}	atto	a

* Avoid usage, if possible.

Greek Alphabet

Caps	Lower Case	Greek Name	Caps	Lower Case	Greek Name	Caps	Lower Case	Greek Name
A	a	Alpha	I	ι	Iota	P	ρ	Rho
B	β	Beta	K	κ	Kappa	Σ	σ	Sigma
Γ	γ	Gamma	Λ	λ	Lambda	T	τ	Tau
Δ	δ	Delta	M	μ	Mu	Y	υ	Upsilon
E	ϵ	Epsilon	N	ν	Nu	Φ	ϕ φ	Phi
Z	ζ	Zeta	Ξ	ξ	Xi	X	χ	Chi
H	η	Eta	O	o	Omicron	Ψ	ψ	Psi
θ	θ	Theta	Π	π	Pi	Ω	ω	Omega

Natural Trigonometric Functions

Deg	Function	0.0°	0.1°	0.2°	0.3°	0.4°	0.5°	0.6°	0.7°	0.8°	0.9°
0	sin	0.0000	0.0017	0.0035	0.0052	0.0070	0.0087	0.0105	0.0122	0.0140	0.0157
	cos	1.0000	1.0000	1.0000	1.0000	1.0000	1.0000	0.9999	0.9999	0.9999	0.9999
	tan	0.0000	0.0017	0.0035	0.0052	0.0070	0.0087	0.0105	0.0122	0.0140	0.0157
1	sin	0.0175	0.0192	0.0209	0.0227	0.0244	0.0262	0.0279	0.0297	0.0314	0.0332
	cos	0.9998	0.9998	0.9998	0.9997	0.9997	0.9997	0.9996	0.9996	0.9995	0.9995
	tan	0.0175	0.0192	0.0209	0.0227	0.0244	0.0262	0.0279	0.0297	0.0314	0.0332
2	sin	0.0349	0.0366	0.0384	0.0401	0.0419	0.0436	0.0454	0.0471	0.0488	0.0506
	cos	0.9994	0.9993	0.9993	0.9992	0.9991	0.9990	0.9990	0.9989	0.9988	0.9987
	tan	0.0349	0.0367	0.0384	0.0402	0.0419	0.0437	0.0454	0.0472	0.0489	0.0507
3	sin	0.0523	0.0541	0.0558	0.0576	0.0593	0.0600	0.0628	0.0645	0.0663	0.0680
	cos	0.9986	0.9985	0.9984	0.9983	0.9982	0.9981	0.9980	0.9979	0.9978	0.9977
	tan	0.0524	0.0542	0.0559	0.0577	0.0594	0.0612	0.0629	0.0647	0.0664	0.0682
4	sin	0.0698	0.0715	0.0732	0.0750	0.0767	0.0785	0.0802	0.0819	0.0837	0.0854
	cos	0.9976	0.9974	0.9973	0.9972	0.9971	0.9969	0.9968	0.9966	0.9965	0.9963
	tan	0.0699	0.0717	0.0734	0.0752	0.0769	0.0787	0.0805	0.0822	0.0840	0.0857
5	sin	0.0872	0.0889	0.0906	0.0924	0.0941	0.0958	0.0976	0.0993	0.1011	0.1028
	cos	0.9962	0.9960	0.9959	0.9957	0.9956	0.9954	0.9952	0.9951	0.9949	0.9947
	tan	0.0875	0.0892	0.0910	0.0928	0.0945	0.0963	0.0981	0.0998	0.1016	0.1033
6	sin	0.1045	0.1063	0.1080	0.1097	0.1115	0.1132	0.1149	0.1167	0.1184	0.1201
	cos	0.9945	0.9943	0.9942	0.9940	0.9938	0.9936	0.9934	0.9932	0.9930	0.9928
	tan	0.1051	0.1069	0.1086	0.1104	0.1122	0.1139	0.1157	0.1175	0.1192	0.1210
7	sin	0.1219	0.1236	0.1253	0.1271	0.1288	0.1305	0.1323	0.1340	0.1357	0.1374
	cos	0.9925	0.9923	0.9921	0.9919	0.9917	0.9914	0.9912	0.9910	0.9907	0.9905
	tan	0.1228	0.1246	0.1263	0.1281	0.1299	0.1317	0.1334	0.1352	0.1370	0.1388

8	sin cos tan	0.1392 0.9903 0.1405	0.1409 0.9900 0.1423	0.1426 0.9898 0.1441	0.1444 0.9895 0.1459	0.1461 0.9893 0.1477	0.1478 0.9890 0.1495	0.1495 0.9888 0.1512	0.1513 0.9885 0.1530	0.1530 0.9882 0.1548	0.1547 0.9880 0.1566
9	sin cos tan	0.1564 0.9877 0.1584	0.1582 0.9874 0.1602	0.1599 0.9871 0.1620	0.1616 0.9869 0.1638	0.1633 0.9866 0.1655	0.1650 0.9863 0.1673	0.1668 0.9860 0.1691	0.1685 0.9857 0.1709	0.1702 0.9854 0.1727	0.1719 0.9851 0.1745
10	sin cos tan	0.1736 0.9848 0.1763	0.1754 0.9845 0.1781	0.1771 0.9842 0.1799	0.1788 0.9839 0.1817	0.1805 0.9836 0.1835	0.1822 0.9833 0.1853	0.1840 0.9829 0.1871	0.1857 0.9826 0.1890	0.1874 0.9823 0.1908	0.1891 0.9820 0.1926
11	sin cos tan	0.1908 0.9816 0.1944	0.1925 0.9813 0.1962	0.1942 0.9810 0.1980	0.1959 0.9806 0.1998	0.1977 0.9803 0.2016	0.1994 0.9799 0.2035	0.2011 0.9796 0.2053	0.2028 0.9792 0.2071	0.2045 0.9789 0.2089	0.2062 0.9785 0.2107
12	sin cos tan	0.2079 0.9781 0.2126	0.2096 0.9778 0.2144	0.2113 0.9774 0.2162	0.2130 0.9770 0.2180	0.2147 0.9767 0.2199	0.2164 0.9763 0.2217	0.2181 0.9759 0.2235	0.2198 0.9755 0.2254	0.2215 0.9751 0.2272	0.2232 0.9748 0.2290
13	sin cos tan	0.2250 0.9744 0.2309	0.2267 0.9740 0.2327	0.2284 0.9736 0.2345	0.2300 0.9732 0.2364	0.2318 0.9728 0.2382	0.2334 0.9724 0.2401	0.2351 0.9720 0.2419	0.2368 0.9715 0.2438	0.2385 0.9711 0.2456	0.2402 0.9707 0.2475
14	sin cos tan	0.2419 0.9703 0.2493	0.2436 0.9699 .02512	0.2453 0.9694 0.2530	0.2470 0.9690 0.2549	0.2487 0.9686 0.2568	0.2504 0.9681 0.2586	0.2521 0.9677 0.2605	0.2538 0.9673 0.2623	0.2554 0.9668 0.2642	0.2571 0.9664 0.2661
15	sin cos tan	0.2588 0.9659 0.2679	0.2605 0.9655 0.2698	0.2622 0.9650 0.2717	0.2639 0.9646 0.2736	0.2656 0.9641 0.2754	0.2672 0.9636 0.2773	0.2689 0.9632 0.2792	0.2706 0.9627 0.2811	0.2723 0.9622 0.2830	0.2740 0.9617 0.2849

- Continued -

Natural Trigonometric Functions (Continued)

Deg	Function	0.0°	0.1°	0.2°	0.3°	0.4°	0.5°	0.6°	0.7°	0.8°	0.9°
16	sin	0.2756	0.2773	0.2790	0.2807	0.2823	0.2840	0.2857	0.2874	0.2890	0.2907
	cos	0.9613	0.9608	0.9603	0.9598	0.9593	0.9588	0.9583	0.9578	0.9573	0.9568
	tan	0.2867	0.2886	0.2905	0.2924	0.2943	0.2962	0.2981	0.3000	0.3019	0.3038
17	sin	0.2924	0.2940	0.2957	0.2974	0.2990	0.3007	0.3024	0.3040	0.3057	0.3074
	cos	0.9563	0.9558	0.9553	0.9548	0.9542	0.9537	0.9532	0.9527	0.9521	0.9516
	tan	0.3057	0.3076	0.3096	0.3115	0.3134	0.3153	0.3172	0.3191	0.3211	0.3230
18	sin	0.3090	0.3107	0.3123	0.3140	0.3156	0.3173	0.3190	0.3206	0.3223	0.3239
	cos	0.9511	0.9505	0.9500	0.9494	0.9489	0.9483	0.9478	0.9472	0.9466	0.9461
	tan	0.3249	0.3269	0.3288	0.3307	0.3327	0.3346	0.3365	0.3385	0.3404	0.3424
19	sin	0.3256	0.3272	0.3289	0.3305	0.3322	0.3338	0.3355	0.3371	0.3387	0.3404
	cos	0.9455	0.9449	0.9444	0.9438	0.9432	0.9426	0.9421	0.9415	0.9409	0.9403
	tan	0.3443	0.3463	0.3482	0.3502	0.3522	0.3541	0.3561	0.3581	0.3600	0.3620
20	sin	0.3420	0.3437	0.3453	0.3469	0.3486	0.3502	0.3518	0.3535	0.3551	0.3567
	cos	0.9397	0.9391	0.9385	0.9379	0.9373	0.9367	0.9361	0.9354	0.9348	0.9342
	tan	0.3640	0.3659	0.3679	0.3699	0.3719	0.3739	0.3759	0.3779	0.3799	0.3819
21	sin	0.3584	0.3600	0.3616	0.3633	0.3649	0.3665	0.3681	0.3697	0.3714	0.3730
	cos	0.9336	0.9330	0.9323	0.9317	0.9311	0.9304	0.9298	0.9291	0.9285	0.9278
	tan	0.3839	0.3859	0.3879	0.3899	0.3919	0.3939	0.3959	0.3979	0.4000	0.4020
22	sin	0.3746	0.3762	0.3778	0.3795	0.3811	0.3827	0.3843	0.3859	0.3875	0.3891
	cos	0.9272	0.9265	0.9259	0.9252	0.9245	0.9239	0.9232	0.9225	0.9219	0.9212
	tan	0.4040	0.4061	0.4081	0.4101	0.4122	0.4142	0.4163	0.4183	0.4204	0.4224
23	sin	0.3907	0.3923	0.3939	0.3955	0.3971	0.3987	0.4003	0.4019	0.4035	0.4051
	cos	0.9205	0.9198	0.9191	0.9184	0.9178	0.9171	0.9164	0.9157	0.9150	0.9143
	tan	0.4245	0.4265	0.4286	0.4307	0.4327	0.4348	0.4369	0.4390	0.4411	0.4431

24	sin	0.4067	0.4083	0.4099	0.4115	0.4131	0.4147	0.4163	0.4179	0.4195	0.4210
	cos	0.9135	0.9128	0.9121	0.9114	0.9107	0.9100	0.9092	0.9085	0.9078	0.9070
	tan	0.4452	0.4473	0.4494	0.4515	0.4536	0.4557	0.4578	0.4599	0.4621	0.4642
25	sin	0.4226	0.4242	0.4258	0.4274	0.4289	0.4305	0.4321	0.4337	0.4352	0.4368
	cos	0.9063	0.9056	0.9048	0.9041	0.9033	0.9026	0.9018	0.9011	0.9003	0.8996
	tan	0.4663	0.4684	0.4706	0.4727	0.4748	0.4770	0.4791	0.4813	0.4834	0.4856
26	sin	0.4384	0.4399	0.4415	0.4431	0.4446	0.4462	0.4478	0.4493	0.4509	0.4524
	cos	0.8988	0.8980	0.8973	0.8965	0.8957	0.8949	0.8942	0.8934	0.8926	0.8918
	tan	0.4877	0.4899	0.4921	0.4942	0.4964	0.4986	0.5008	0.5029	0.5051	0.5073
27	sin	0.4540	0.4555	0.4571	0.4586	0.4602	0.4617	0.4633	0.4648	0.4664	0.4679
	cos	0.8910	0.8902	0.8894	0.8886	0.8878	0.8870	0.8862	0.8854	0.8846	0.8838
	tan	0.5095	0.5117	0.5139	0.5161	0.5184	0.5206	0.5228	0.5250	0.5272	0.5295
28	sin	0.4695	0.4710	0.4726	0.4741	0.4756	0.4772	0.4787	0.4802	0.4818	0.4833
	cos	0.8829	0.8821	0.8813	0.8805	0.8796	0.8788	0.8780	0.8771	0.8763	0.8755
	tan	0.5317	0.5340	0.5362	0.5384	0.5407	0.5430	0.5452	0.5475	0.5498	0.5520
29	sin	0.4848	0.4863	0.4879	0.4894	0.4909	0.4924	0.4939	0.4955	0.4970	0.4985
	cos	0.8746	0.8738	0.8729	0.8721	0.8712	0.8704	0.8695	0.8686	0.8678	0.8669
	tan	0.5543	0.5566	0.5589	0.5612	0.5635	0.5658	0.5681	0.5704	0.5727	0.5750
30	sin	0.5000	0.5015	0.5030	0.5045	0.5060	0.5075	0.5090	0.5105	0.5120	0.5135
	cos	0.8660	0.8652	0.8643	0.8634	0.8625	0.8616	0.8607	0.8599	0.8590	0.8581
	tan	0.5774	0.5797	0.5820	0.5844	0.5867	0.5890	0.5914	0.5938	0.5961	0.5985
31	sin	0.5150	0.5165	0.5180	0.5195	0.5210	0.5225	0.5240	0.5255	0.5270	0.5284
	cos	0.8572	0.8563	0.8554	0.8545	0.8536	0.8526	0.8517	0.8508	0.8499	0.8490
	tan	0.6009	0.6032	0.6056	0.6080	0.6104	0.6128	0.6152	0.6176	0.6200	0.6224

- Continued -

Natural Trigonometric Functions (Continued)

Deg	Function	0.0°	0.1°	0.2°	0.3°	0.4°	0.5°	0.6°	0.7°	0.8°	0.9°
32	sin	0.5299	0.5314	0.5329	0.5344	0.5358	0.5373	0.5388	0.5402	0.5417	0.5432
	cos	0.8480	0.8471	0.8462	0.8453	0.8443	0.8434	0.8425	0.8415	0.8406	0.8396
	tan	0.6249	0.6273	0.6297	0.6322	0.6346	0.6371	0.6395	0.6420	0.6445	0.6469
33	sin	0.5446	0.5461	0.5476	0.5490	0.5505	0.5519	0.5534	0.5548	0.5563	0.5577
	cos	0.8387	0.8377	0.8368	0.8358	0.8348	0.8339	0.8329	0.8320	0.8310	0.8300
	tan	0.6494	0.6519	0.6544	0.6569	0.6594	0.6619	0.6644	0.6669	0.6694	0.6720
34	sin	0.5592	0.5606	0.5621	0.5635	0.5650	0.5664	0.5678	0.5693	0.5707	0.5721
	cos	0.8290	0.8281	0.8271	0.8261	0.8251	0.8241	0.8231	0.8221	0.8211	0.8202
	tan	0.6745	0.6771	0.6796	0.6822	0.6847	0.6873	0.6899	0.6924	0.6950	0.6976
35	sin	0.5736	0.5750	0.5764	0.5779	0.5793	0.5807	0.5821	0.5835	0.5850	0.5864
	cos	0.8192	0.8181	0.8171	0.8161	0.8151	0.8141	0.8131	0.8121	0.8111	0.8100
	tan	0.7002	0.7028	0.7054	0.7080	0.7107	0.7133	0.7159	0.7186	0.7212	0.7239
36	sin	0.5878	0.5892	0.5906	0.5920	0.5934	0.5948	0.5962	0.5976	0.5990	0.6004
	cos	0.8090	0.8080	0.8070	0.8059	0.8049	0.8039	0.8028	0.8018	0.8007	0.7997
	tan	0.7265	0.7292	0.7319	0.7346	0.7373	0.7400	0.7427	0.7454	0.7481	0.7508
37	sin	0.6018	0.6032	0.6046	0.6060	0.6074	0.6088	0.6101	0.6115	0.6129	0.6143
	cos	0.7986	0.7976	0.7965	0.7955	0.7944	0.7934	0.7923	0.7912	0.7902	0.7891
	tan	0.7536	0.7563	0.7590	0.7618	0.7646	0.7673	0.7701	0.7729	0.7757	0.7785
38	sin	0.6157	0.6170	0.6184	0.6198	0.6211	0.6225	0.6239	0.6252	0.6266	0.6280
	cos	0.7880	0.7869	0.7859	0.7848	0.7837	0.7826	0.7815	0.7804	0.7793	0.7782
	tan	0.7813	0.7841	0.7869	0.7898	0.7926	0.7954	0.7983	0.8012	0.8040	0.8069
39	sin	0.6293	0.6307	0.6320	0.6334	0.6347	0.6361	0.6374	0.6388	0.6401	0.6414
	cos	0.7771	0.7760	0.7749	0.7738	0.7727	0.7716	0.7705	0.7694	0.7683	0.7672
	tan	0.8098	0.8127	0.8156	0.8185	0.8214	0.8243	0.8273	0.8302	0.8332	0.8361

40	sin	0.6428	0.6441	0.6455	0.6468	0.6481	0.6494	0.6508	0.6521	0.6534	0.6547
	cos	0.7660	0.7649	0.7638	0.7627	0.7615	0.7604	0.7593	0.7581	0.7570	0.7559
	tan	0.8391	0.8421	0.8451	0.8481	0.8511	0.8541	0.8571	0.8601	0.8632	0.8662
41	sin	0.6561	0.6574	0.6587	0.6600	0.6613	0.6626	0.6639	0.6652	0.6665	0.6678
	cos	0.7547	0.7536	0.7524	0.7513	0.7501	0.7490	0.7478	0.7466	0.7455	0.7443
	tan	0.8693	0.8724	0.8754	0.8785	0.8816	0.8847	0.8878	0.8910	0.8941	0.8972
42	sin	0.6691	0.6704	0.6717	0.6730	0.6743	0.6756	0.6769	0.6782	0.6794	0.6807
	cos	0.7431	0.7420	0.7408	0.7396	0.7385	0.7373	0.7361	0.7349	0.7337	0.7325
	tan	0.9004	0.9036	0.9067	0.9099	0.9131	0.9163	0.9195	0.9228	0.9260	0.9293
43	sin	0.6820	0.6833	0.6845	0.6858	0.6871	0.6884	0.6896	0.6909	0.6921	0.6934
	cos	0.7314	0.7302	0.7290	0.7278	0.7266	0.7254	0.7242	0.7230	0.7218	0.7206
	tan	0.9325	0.9358	0.9391	0.9424	0.9457	0.9490	0.9523	0.9556	0.9590	0.9623
44	sin	0.6947	0.6959	0.6972	0.6984	0.6997	0.7009	0.7022	0.7034	0.7046	0.7059
	cos	0.7193	0.7181	0.7169	0.7157	0.7145	0.7133	0.7120	0.7108	0.7096	0.7083
	tan	0.9657	0.9691	0.9725	0.9759	0.9793	0.9827	0.9861	0.9896	0.9930	0.9965
45	sin	0.7071	0.7083	0.7096	0.7108	0.7120	0.7133	0.7145	0.7157	0.7169	0.7181
	cos	0.7071	0.7059	0.7046	0.7034	0.7022	0.7009	0.6997	0.6984	0.6972	0.6959
	tan	1.0000	1.0035	1.0070	1.0105	1.0141	1.0176	1.0212	1.0247	1.0283	1.0319
46	sin	0.7193	0.7206	0.7218	0.7230	0.7242	0.7254	0.7266	0.7278	0.7290	0.7302
	cos	0.6947	0.6934	0.6921	0.6909	0.6896	0.6884	0.6871	0.6858	0.6845	0.6833
	tan	1.0355	1.0392	1.0428	1.0464	1.0501	1.0538	1.0575	1.0612	1.0649	1.0686
47	sin	0.7314	0.7325	0.7337	0.7349	0.7361	0.7373	0.7385	0.7396	0.7408	0.7420
	cos	0.6820	0.6807	0.6794	0.6782	0.6769	0.6756	0.6743	0.6730	0.6717	0.6704
	tan	1.0724	1.0761	1.0799	1.0837	1.0875	1.0913	1.0951	1.0990	1.1028	1.1067

- Continued -

Natural Trigonometric Functions (Continued)

Deg	Function	0.0°	0.1°	0.2°	0.3°	0.4°	0.5°	0.6°	0.7°	0.8°	0.9°
48	sin	0.7431	0.7443	0.7455	0.7466	0.7478	0.7490	0.7501	0.7513	0.7524	0.7536
	cos	0.6691	0.6678	0.6665	0.6652	0.6639	0.6626	0.6613	0.6600	0.6587	0.6574
	tan	1.1106	1.1145	1.1184	1.1224	1.1263	1.1303	1.1343	1.1383	1.1423	1.1463
49	sin	0.7547	0.7559	0.7570	0.7581	0.7593	0.7604	0.7615	0.7627	0.7638	0.7649
	cos	0.6561	0.6547	0.6534	0.6521	0.6508	0.6494	0.6481	0.6468	0.6455	0.6441
	tan	1.1504	1.1544	1.1585	1.1626	1.1667	1.1708	1.1750	1.1792	1.1833	1.1875
50	sin	0.7660	0.7672	0.7683	0.7694	0.7705	0.7716	0.7727	0.7738	0.7749	0.7760
	cos	0.6428	0.6414	0.6401	0.6388	0.6374	0.6361	0.6347	0.6334	0.6320	0.6307
	tan	1.1918	1.1960	1.2002	1.2045	1.2088	1.2131	1.2174	1.2218	1.2261	1.2305
51	sin	0.7771	0.7782	0.7793	0.7804	0.7815	0.7826	0.7837	0.7848	0.7859	0.7869
	cos	0.6293	0.6280	0.6266	0.6252	0.6239	0.6225	0.6211	0.6198	0.6184	0.6170
	tan	1.2349	1.2393	1.2437	1.2482	1.2527	1.2572	1.2617	1.2662	1.2708	1.2753
52	sin	0.7880	0.7891	0.7902	0.7912	0.7923	0.7934	0.7944	0.7955	0.7965	0.7976
	cos	0.6157	0.6143	0.6129	0.6115	0.6101	0.6088	0.6074	0.6060	0.6046	0.6032
	tan	1.2799	1.2846	1.2892	1.2938	1.2985	1.3032	1.3079	1.3127	1.3175	1.3222
53	sin	0.7986	0.7997	0.8007	0.8018	0.8028	0.8039	0.8049	0.8059	0.8070	0.8080
	cos	0.6018	0.6004	0.5990	0.5976	0.5962	0.5948	0.5934	0.5920	0.5906	0.5892
	tan	1.3270	1.3319	1.3367	1.3416	1.3465	1.3514	1.3564	1.3613	1.3663	1.3713
54	sin	0.8090	0.8100	0.8111	0.8121	0.8131	0.8141	0.8151	0.8161	0.8171	0.8181
	cos	0.5878	0.5864	0.5850	0.5835	0.5821	0.5807	0.5793	0.5779	0.5764	0.5750
	tan	1.3764	1.3814	1.3865	1.3916	1.3968	1.4019	1.4071	1.4124	1.4176	1.4229
55	sin	0.8192	0.8202	0.8211	0.8221	0.8231	0.8241	0.8251	0.8261	0.8271	0.8281
	cos	0.5736	0.5721	0.5707	0.5693	0.5678	0.5664	0.5650	0.5635	0.5621	0.5606
	tan	1.4281	1.4335	1.4388	1.4442	1.4496	1.4550	1.4605	1.4659	1.4715	1.4770

56	sin	0.8290	0.8300	0.8310	0.8320	0.8329	0.8339	0.8348	0.8358	0.8368	0.8377
	cos	0.5592	0.5577	0.5563	0.5548	0.5534	0.5519	0.5505	0.5490	0.5476	0.5461
	tan	1.4826	1.4882	1.4938	1.4994	1.5051	1.5108	1.5166	1.5224	1.5282	1.5340
57	sin	0.8387	0.8396	0.8406	0.8415	0.8425	0.8434	0.8443	0.8453	0.8462	0.8471
	cos	0.5446	0.5432	0.5417	0.5402	0.5388	0.5373	0.5358	0.5344	0.5329	0.5314
	tan	1.5399	1.5458	1.5517	1.5577	1.5637	1.5697	1.5757	1.5818	1.5880	1.5941
58	sin	0.8480	0.8490	0.8499	0.8508	0.8517	0.8526	0.8536	0.8545	0.8554	0.8563
	cos	0.5299	0.5284	0.5270	0.5255	0.5240	0.5225	0.5210	0.5195	0.5180	0.5165
	tan	1.6003	1.6066	1.6128	1.6191	1.6255	1.6319	1.6383	1.6447	1.6512	1.6577
59	sin	0.8572	0.8581	0.8590	0.8599	0.8607	0.8616	0.8625	0.8634	0.8643	0.8652
	cos	0.5150	0.5135	0.5120	0.5105	0.5090	0.5075	0.5060	0.5045	0.5030	0.5015
	tan	1.6643	1.6709	1.6775	1.6842	1.6909	1.6977	1.7045	1.7113	1.7182	1.7251
60	sin	0.8660	0.8669	0.8678	0.8686	0.8695	0.8704	0.8712	0.8721	0.8729	0.8738
	cos	0.5000	0.4985	0.4970	0.4955	0.4939	0.4924	0.4909	0.4894	0.4879	0.4863
	tan	1.7321	1.7391	1.7461	1.7532	1.7603	1.7675	1.7747	1.7820	1.7893	1.7966
61	sin	0.8746	0.8755	0.8763	0.8771	0.8780	0.8788	0.8796	0.8805	0.8813	0.8821
	cos	0.4848	0.4833	0.4818	0.4802	0.4787	0.4772	0.4756	0.4741	0.4726	0.4710
	tan	1.8040	1.8115	1.8190	1.8265	1.8341	1.8418	1.8495	1.8572	1.8650	1.8728
62	sin	0.8829	0.8838	0.8846	0.8854	0.8862	0.8870	0.8878	0.8886	0.8894	0.8902
	cos	0.4695	0.4679	0.4664	0.4648	0.4633	0.4617	0.4602	0.4586	0.4571	0.4555
	tan	1.8807	1.8887	1.8967	1.9047	1.9128	1.9210	1.9262	1.9375	1.9458	1.9542
63	sin	0.8910	0.8918	0.8926	0.8934	0.8942	0.8949	0.8957	0.8965	0.8973	0.8980
	cos	0.4540	0.4524	0.4509	0.4493	0.4478	0.4462	0.4446	0.4431	0.4415	0.4399
	tan	1.9626	1.9711	1.9797	1.9883	1.9970	2.0057	2.0145	2.0233	2.0323	2.0413

- Continued -

Natural Trigonometric Functions (Continued)

Deg	Function	0.0°	0.1°	0.2°	0.3°	0.4°	0.5°	0.6°	0.7°	0.8°	0.9°
64	sin	0.8988	0.8996	0.9003	0.9011	0.9018	0.9026	0.9033	0.9041	0.9048	0.9056
	cos	0.4384	0.4368	0.4352	0.4337	0.4321	0.4305	0.4289	0.4274	0.4258	0.4242
	tan	2.0503	2.0594	2.0686	2.0778	2.0872	2.0965	2.1060	2.1155	2.1251	2.1348
65	sin	0.9063	0.9070	0.9078	0.9085	0.9092	0.9100	0.9107	0.9114	0.9121	0.9128
	cos	0.4226	0.4210	0.4195	0.4179	0.4163	0.4147	0.4131	0.4115	0.4099	0.4083
	tan	2.1445	2.1543	2.1642	2.1742	2.1842	2.1943	2.2045	2.2148	2.2251	2.2355
66	sin	0.9135	0.9143	0.9150	0.9157	0.9164	0.9171	0.9178	0.9184	0.9191	0.9198
	cos	0.4067	0.4051	0.4035	0.4019	0.4003	0.3987	0.3971	0.3955	0.3939	0.3923
	tan	2.2460	2.2566	2.2673	2.2781	2.2889	2.2998	2.3109	2.3220	2.3332	2.3445
67	sin	0.9205	0.9212	0.9219	0.9225	0.9232	0.9239	0.9245	0.9252	0.9259	0.9265
	cos	0.3907	0.3891	0.3875	0.3859	0.3843	0.3827	0.3811	0.3795	0.3778	0.3762
	tan	2.3559	2.3673	2.3789	2.3906	2.4023	2.4142	2.4262	2.4383	2.4504	2.4627
68	sin	0.9272	0.9278	0.9285	0.9291	0.9298	0.9304	0.9311	0.9317	0.9323	0.9330
	cos	0.3746	0.3730	0.3714	0.3697	0.3681	0.3665	0.3649	0.3633	0.3616	0.3600
	tan	2.4751	2.4876	2.5002	2.5129	2.5257	2.5386	2.5517	2.5649	2.5782	2.5916
69	sin	0.9336	0.9342	0.9348	0.9354	0.9361	0.9367	0.9373	0.9379	0.9385	0.9391
	cos	0.3584	0.3567	0.3551	0.3535	0.3518	0.3502	0.3486	0.3469	0.3453	0.3437
	tan	2.6051	2.6187	2.6325	2.6464	2.6605	2.6746	2.6889	2.7034	2.7179	2.7326
70	sin	0.9397	0.9403	0.9409	0.9415	0.9421	0.9426	0.9432	0.9438	0.9444	0.9449
	cos	0.3420	0.3404	0.3387	0.3371	0.3355	0.3338	0.3322	0.3305	0.3289	0.3272
	tan	2.7475	2.7625	2.7776	2.7929	2.8083	2.8239	2.8397	2.8556	2.8716	2.8878
71	sin	0.9455	0.9461	0.9466	0.9472	0.9478	0.9483	0.9489	0.9494	0.9500	0.9505
	cos	0.3256	0.3239	0.3223	0.3206	0.3190	0.3173	0.3156	0.3140	0.3123	0.3107
	tan	2.9042	2.9208	2.9375	2.9544	2.9714	2.9887	3.0061	3.0237	3.0415	3.0595

72	sin	0.9511	0.9516	0.9521	0.9527	0.9532	0.9537	0.9542	0.9548	0.9553	0.9558
	cos	0.3090	0.3074	0.3057	0.3040	0.3024	0.3007	0.2990	0.2974	0.2957	0.2940
	tan	3.0777	3.0961	3.1146	3.1334	3.1524	3.1716	3.1910	3.2106	3.2305	3.2506
73	sin	0.9563	0.9568	0.9573	0.9578	0.9583	0.9588	0.9593	0.9598	0.9603	0.9608
	cos	0.2924	0.2907	0.2890	0.2874	0.2857	0.2840	0.2823	0.2807	0.2790	0.2773
	tan	3.2709	3.2914	3.3122	3.3332	3.3544	3.3759	3.3977	3.4197	3.4420	3.4646
74	sin	0.9613	0.9617	0.9622	0.9627	0.9632	0.9636	0.9641	0.9646	0.9650	0.9655
	cos	0.2756	0.2740	0.2723	0.2706	0.2689	0.2672	0.2656	0.2639	0.2622	0.2605
	tan	3.4874	3.5105	3.5339	.35576	3.5816	3.6059	3.6305	3.6554	3.6806	3.7062
75	sin	0.9659	0.9664	0.9668	0.9673	0.9677	0.9681	0.9686	0.9690	0.9694	0.9699
	cos	0.2588	0.2571	0.2554	0.2538	0.2521	0.2504	0.2487	0.2470	0.2453	0.2436
	tan	3.7321	3.7583	3.7848	3.8118	3.8391	3.8667	3.8947	3.9232	3.9520	3.9812
76	sin	0.9703	0.9707	0.9711	0.9715	0.9720	0.9724	0.9728	0.9732	0.9736	0.9740
	cos	0.2419	0.2402	0.2385	0.2368	0.2351	0.2334	0.2317	0.2300	0.2284	0.2267
	tan	4.0108	4.0408	4.0713	4.1022	4.1335	4.1653	4.1976	4.2303	4.2635	4.2972
77	sin	0.9774	0.9748	0.9751	0.9755	0.9759	0.9763	0.9767	0.9770	0.9774	0.9778
	cos	0.2250	0.2232	0.2215	0.2198	0.2181	0.2164	0.2147	0.2130	0.2113	0.2096
	tan	4.3315	4.3662	4.4015	4.4374	4.4737	4.5107	4.5483	4.5864	4.6252	4.6646
78	sin	0.9781	0.9785	0.9789	0.9792	0.9796	0.9799	0.9803	0.9806	0.9810	0.9813
	cos	0.2079	0.2062	0.2045	0.2028	0.2011	0.1994	0.1977	0.1959	0.1942	0.1925
	tan	4.7046	4.7453	4.7867	4.8288	4.8716	4.9152	4.9594	5.0045	5.0504	5.0970
79	sin	0.9816	0.9820	0.9823	0.9826	0.9829	0.9833	0.9836	0.9839	0.9842	0.9845
	cos	0.1908	0.1891	0.1874	0.1857	0.1840	0.1822	0.1805	0.1788	0.1771	0.1754
	tan	5.1446	5.1929	5.2422	5.2924	5.3435	5.3955	5.4486	5.5026	5.5578	5.6140

- Continued -

Natural Trigonometric Functions (Continued)

Deg	Function	0.0°	0.1°	0.2°	0.3°	0.4°	0.5°	0.6°	0.7°	0.8°	0.9°
80	sin	0.9848	0.9851	0.9854	0.9857	0.9860	0.9863	0.9866	0.9869	0.9871	0.9874
	cos	0.1736	0.1719	0.1702	0.1685	0.1668	0.1650	0.1633	0.1616	0.1599	0.1582
	tan	5.6713	5.7297	5.7894	5.8502	5.9124	5.9758	6.0405	6.1066	6.1742	6.2432
81	sin	0.9877	0.9880	0.9882	0.9885	0.9888	0.9890	0.9893	0.9895	0.9898	0.9900
	cos	0.1564	0.1547	0.1530	0.1513	0.1495	0.1478	0.1461	0.1444	0.1426	0.1409
	tan	6.3138	6.3859	6.4596	6.5350	6.6122	6.6912	6.7720	6.8548	6.9395	7.0264
82	sin	0.9903	0.9905	0.9907	0.9910	0.9912	0.9914	0.9917	0.9919	0.9921	0.9923
	cos	0.1392	0.1374	0.1357	0.1340	0.1323	0.1305	0.1288	0.1271	0.1253	0.1236
	tan	7.1154	7.2066	7.3002	7.3962	7.4947	7.5958	7.6996	7.8062	7.9158	8.0285
83	sin	0.9925	0.9928	0.9930	0.9932	0.9934	0.9936	0.9938	0.9940	0.9942	0.9943
	cos	0.1219	0.1201	0.1184	0.1167	0.1149	0.1132	0.1115	0.1097	0.1040	0.1063
	tan	8.1443	8.2636	8.3863	8.5126	8.6427	8.7769	8.9152	9.0579	9.2052	9.3572
84	sin	0.9945	0.9947	0.9949	0.9951	0.9952	0.9954	0.9956	0.9957	0.9959	0.9960
	cos	0.1045	0.1028	0.1011	0.0993	0.0976	0.0958	0.0941	0.0924	0.0906	0.0889
	tan	9.5144	9.6768	9.8448	10.02	10.20	10.39	10.58	10.78	10.99	11.20
85	sin	0.9962	0.9963	0.9965	0.9966	0.9968	0.9969	0.9971	0.9972	0.9973	0.9974
	cos	0.0872	0.0854	0.0837	0.0819	0.0802	0.0785	0.0767	0.0750	0.0732	0.0715
	tan	11.43	11.66	11.91	12.16	12.43	12.71	13.00	13.30	13.62	13.95
86	sin	0.9976	0.9977	0.9978	0.9979	0.9980	0.9981	0.9982	0.9983	0.9984	0.9985
	cos	0.0698	0.0680	0.0663	0.0645	0.0628	0.0610	0.0593	0.0576	0.0558	0.0541
	tan	14.30	14.67	15.06	15.46	15.89	16.35	16.83	17.34	17.89	18.46
87	sin	0.9986	0.9987	0.9988	0.9989	0.9990	0.9990	0.9991	0.9992	0.9993	0.9993
	cos	0.0523	0.0506	0.0488	0.0471	0.0454	0.0436	0.0419	0.0401	0.0384	0.0366
	tan	19.08	19.74	20.45	21.20	22.02	22.90	23.86	24.90	26.03	27.27

Deg	Function	0′	6′	12′	18′	24′	30′	36′	4[illegible]′	48′	54′
88	sin	0.9994	0.9995	0.9995	0.9996	0.9996	0.9997	0.9997	0.[illegible]97	0.9998	0.9998
	cos	0.0349	0.0332	0.0314	0.0297	0.0279	0.0262	0.0244	0.[illegible]227	0.0209	0.0192
	tan	28.64	30.14	31.82	33.69	35.80	38.19	40.92	44.[illegible]7	47.74	52.08
89	sin	0.9998	0.9999	0.9999	0.9999	0.9999	1.000	1.000	1.[illegible]0	1.000	1.000
	cos	0.0175	0.0157	0.0140	0.0122	0.0105	0.0087	0.0070	0.[illegible]052	0.0035	0.0017
	tan	57.29	63.66	71.62	81.85	95.49	114.6	143.2	191.[illegible]	286.5	573.0

Standard Twist Drill Sizes

Designation	Diam. (In.)	Area (Sq. In.)	Designation	Diam. (In.)	Area (Sq. In.)	Designation	Diam. (In.)	Area (Sq. In.)
1/2	0.5000	0.1963	3	0.213	0.03563	3/32	0.0938	0.00690
31/64	0.4844	0.1843	4	0.209	0.03431	42	0.0935	0.00687
15/32	0.4688	0.1726	5	0.2055	0.03317	43	0.0890	0.00622
29/64	0.4531	0.1613	6	0.204	0.03269	44	0.0860	0.00581
7/16	0.4375	0.1503	13/64	0.2031	0.03241	45	0.0820	0.00528
27/64	0.4219	0.1398	7	0.201	0.03173	46	0.0810	0.00515
Z	0.413	0.1340	8	0.199	0.03110	47	0.0785	0.00484
13/32	0.4063	0.1296	9	0.196	0.03017	5/64	0.0781	0.00479
Y	0.404	0.1282	10	0.1935	0.02940	48	0.0760	0.00454
X	0.397	0.1238	11	0.191	0.02865	49	0.0730	0.00419
25/64	0.3906	0.1198	12	0.189	0.02806	50	0.0700	0.00385
W	0.386	0.1170	3/16	0.1875	0.02761	51	0.0670	0.00353
V	0.377	0.1116	13	0.185	0.02688	52	0.0635	0.00317
3/8	0.375	0.1104	14	0.182	0.02602	1/16	0.0625	0.00307
U	0.368	0.1064	15	0.1800	0.02554	53	0.0595	0.00278
23/64	0.3594	0.1014	16	0.1770	0.02461	54	0.0550	0.00238
T	0.358	0.1006	17	0.1730	0.02351	55	0.0520	0.00212
S	0.348	0.09511	11/64	0.1719	0.02320	3/64	0.0473	0.00173
11/32	0.3438	0.09281	18	0.1695	0.02256	56	0.0465	0.001698
R	0.339	0.09026	19	0.1660	0.02164	57	0.0430	0.001452
Q	0.332	0.08657	20	0.1610	0.02036	58	0.0420	0.001385
21/64	0.3281	0.08456	21	0.1590	0.01986	59	0.0410	0.001320
P	0.323	0.08194	22	0.1570	0.01936	60	0.0400	0.001257
O	0.316	0.07843	5/32	0.1563	0.01917	61	0.039	0.001195
5/16	0.3125	0.07670	23	0.1540	0.01863	62	0.038	0.001134
N	0.302	0.07163	24	0.1520	0.01815	63	0.037	0.001075
19/64	0.2969	0.06922	25	0.1495	0.01755	64	0.036	0.001018
M	0.295	0.06835	26	0.1470	0.01697	65	0.035	0.000962
L	0.29	0.06605	27	0.1440	0.01629	66	0.033	0.000855
9/32	0.2813	0.06213	9/64	0.1406	0.01553	67	0.032	0.000804
K	0.281	0.06202	28	0.1405	0.01549	1/32	0.0313	0.000765
J	0.277	0.06026	29	0.1360	0.01453	68	0.031	0.000755
I	0.272	0.05811	30	0.1285	0.01296	69	0.0292	0.000670
H	0.266	0.05557	1/8	0.1250	0.01227	70	0.028	0.000616
17/64	0.2656	0.05542	31	0.1200	0.01131	71	0.026	0.000531
G	0.261	0.05350	32	0.1160	0.01057	72	0.025	0.000491
F	0.257	0.05187	33	0.1130	0.01003	73	0.024	0.000452
E 1/4	0.2500	0.04909	34	0.1110	0.00968	74	0.0225	0.000398
D	0.246	0.04753	35	0.1100	0.00950	75	0.021	0.000346
C	0.242	0.04600	7/64	0.1094	0.00940	76	0.020	0.000314
B	0.238	0.04449	36	0.1065	0.00891	77	0.018	0.000254
15/64	0.2344	0.04314	37	0.1040	0.00849	78	0.016	0.000201
A	0.234	0.04301	38	0.1015	0.00809	1/64	0.0156	0.000191
1	0.228	0.04083	39	0.0995	0.00778	79	0.0145	0.000165
2	0.221	0.03836	40	0.0980	0.00754	80	0.0135	0.000143
7/32	0.2188	0.03758	41	0.0960	0.00724			

Note: Designations are in fractions of an inch, in standard twist drill letters, or in standard twist drill numbers, the latter being the same as steel wire gauge numbers.

Subject Index